An Introduction to ANALYSIS

An Introduction to
ANALYSIS

WILSON M. ZARING

DEPARTMENT OF MATHEMATICS
University of Illinois

THE MACMILLAN COMPANY
NEW YORK
COLLIER-MACMILLAN LIMITED
LONDON

First printing

Library of Congress catalog card number: 67-18457

THE MACMILLAN COMPANY, NEW YORK
COLLIER-MACMILLAN CANADA, LTD., TORONTO, ONTARIO

Printed in the United States of America

To Marjorie and David and Susan

Preface

THIS TEXT was designed specifically for the prospective teacher of the calculus. Part I is basically a review of ideas from set theory and logic that are used throughout the text. The first chapter contains some material on logic not traditionally treated in an introduction.

Part II has been developed over a period of several years as a two-semester course in introductory real analysis taught to the participants in Academic Year Institutes at the University of Illinois. It offers a careful development of the mathematical foundations of the calculus. Emphasis has been placed upon the continuity of thought, the motivation of ideas, and the clarity of exposition rather than rigor per se.

The material has been selected and arranged so that the text is suitable for courses of varying levels of sophistication. The level of topics varies from a discussion of elementary arithmetic properties of the real numbers to a proof of the Schröder-Bernstein Theorem. Insofar as was practical the selection of topics and their sequencing was determined by classroom experience and student interest. Indeed one of my favorite sections, §8.7, was not included in the original outline, but evolved from the classroom.

All starred sections include material that can be brought into discussion in a natural way but that can also be omitted without loss of continuity. For example, in Chapter 5 a section is included on the axiom of choice. Throughout the remainder of the text, those theorems in the unstarred sections that are proved by use of the axiom of choice are also provided with a second proof that does not require the axiom. Indeed, although the Heine-Borel Theorem is intended as a basic result of the course, it too can be omitted if the instructor wishes to do so.

As a basic syllabus I would suggest the following:

Chapter 4 §§0–7 (omit Heine-Borel Theorem)
Chapter 5 §§0–6
Chapter 6 §§0–4
Chapter 7 §§0–5
Chapter 8 §§0–3 and §4 through Theorem 8.41.
Chapter 9 §§0–2

Other sections can be added according to the time available and the interests of students and instructor.

The book is intended to encourage active participation on the part of the student in the development of the theory. The proofs of certain theorems are left to the reader. The exercises are arranged in order of difficulty. With the exception of a few obviously intended to provide computational practice, the exercises form an important part of the theory itself.

Whatever merits this text possesses are a result of the work and thoughts of many people. Unfortunately the errors are all my own. The two major sources of ideas behind the text are *Introduction to Mathematical Logic*, Volume 1, by Alonzo Church, for the preparation of Chapter 1, and *Differential and Integral Calculus*, by Edmund Landau, for the preparation of Part II. The development of the text was undertaken with the encouragement and advice of Professor Joseph Landin. Several members of the department of mathematics taught the material in mimeographed form. Those who contributed many helpful suggestions from their experience include Professors Peter Braunfeld, Hyman Gabai, Pierce Ketchum, Anthony Peressini, Paul Weichsel, and Bing Wong. A special note of gratitude goes to Professor William Boone for his assistance with Chapter 1, to Professor John Wetzel, who read the final manuscript, for his numerous and valuable criticisms, to Professor Peter Braunfeld for his many incisive observations and suggestions for the improvement of the text, and to Professor Robert Bartle for his wise advice and counsel.

I am grateful to Mrs. Margy Osterbur and Mrs. Marjorie Beasley for their patience and care in typing the manuscript and to Miss Barbara Davis of The Macmillan Company for her excellent editorial work.

Urbana, Illinois   W. M. Z.

Contents

PART II

An Introduction to Analysis

CONTENTS

An Introduction to ANALYSIS

PART I

Logic and Set Theory

1

Intuitive Logic

1.0 Introduction

As the title of this chapter suggests, our approach to logic will be intuitive rather than formal. It is not our intention to present a detailed, methodical study of logic but rather to discuss terminology and methods of reasoning that will be used throughout this text. Our main concern will be clarity rather than rigor. If clarity is to be achieved, it is essential that we agree at the outset not only on the use of technical terms but also on certain conventions concerning the use of language in general. As a beginning point for our discussion we wish to focus attention on those words in the English language that we call *nouns*.

1.1 Names

In this section a few observations will be made about those nouns that are commonly called *proper nouns*. We are particularly interested in their use in sentences. As an example, the sentence

George Washington slept here

contains the proper noun

George Washington.

Proper grammatical usage also permits the construction of sentences in which phrases are used as nouns. For example, in the sentence

The first President of the United States slept here,

the phrase

The first President of the United States

is used as a noun, and indeed a proper noun.

A basic use of proper nouns and noun phrases is to refer to things. In the preceding examples, the noun

George Washington

3

and the phrase

The first President of the United States

are used to refer to, or mention, a particular man. In view of this usage we will refer to such nouns and noun phrases as *names*. That is to say, a name is a proper noun or a phrase that is used as a proper noun. Thus

George Washington

and

The first President of the United States

are names. As examples of names from mathematics we offer

$$2, \ \sqrt{3}, \ 1 + 1, \ \pi, \ e,$$

$$\sum_{\alpha=1}^{3} 2^{\alpha}, \qquad \int_{0}^{2} x \, dx.$$

The thing referred to by a name we shall call the *denotation* of that name. Thus, for example, the denotation of the name '1 + 1' is the number 2; the denotation of the name 'The first President of the United States' is George Washington.

To avoid ambiguity it is, of course, essential that names not have two denotations. While it is clear that there was only one man who was the first President of the United States, there have surely been many men named 'George Washington'. In ordinary English usage we attempt to remove this ambiguity by speaking of *the* George Washington. For mathematical purposes we must exercise care and accept a new symbol as a name only after it has been verified that the symbol has at most one denotation. To assist us in such verifications it is helpful to probe deeper and ask how a name names.

Note that the name

The first President of the United States,

as an English phrase, has meaning. This meaning we shall call the *sense* of the name. We postulate that every name has a sense. We take the point of view that a name names by expressing its sense as descriptive information about its denotation. For example, the name

The first President of the United States

identifies its denotation as the holder of a certain office, while the proper name

George Washington

identifies its denotation as having the family name

Washington

and the given name

George.

From historical information we know that these are two different concepts of the same person. There is, however, a wealth of concepts that are not concepts of anything. Consider, for example,

the integer which when multiplied by zero gives one

or

the Chief of the Mohicans in 1963.

These are noun phrases which express very clear concepts. But from our knowledge of arithmetic we know that there is no integer that when multiplied by zero gives one, and from Mr. James Fenimore Cooper's famous novel we infer that the Mohicans did not have a chief in 1963. However, in spite of the fact that these phrases have no denotation, we shall accept them as names. The idea of names without denotation may strike the reader as a pointless concept to introduce. We, however, urge its acceptance and illustrate our interest in the idea with a few examples.

If we define

$$\sqrt{x}$$

as the positive real number whose square is x, then we interpret this definition as assigning a meaning or sense to each of the symbols '$\sqrt{2}$', '$\sqrt{-1}$', '$\sqrt{\pi}$', as well as to many other such symbols. The question of whether or not these are names with denotation then requires a so-called existence theorem. From the defining properties of the real numbers we can deduce that there is one and only one positive real number whose square is 2; hence '$\sqrt{2}$' is a name with denotation. We can also prove that there is no real number, positive or otherwise, whose square is -1. Hence '$\sqrt{-1}$' is a name without denotation.

In Chapter 5 we define the limit of a sequence. This definition is interpreted as giving meaning to an infinite collection of symbols, each of which is a name, although possibly a name without denotation. The traditional question of whether or not a certain limit exists we interpret as the question of whether or not a certain name has a denotation. Thus, for example, when we ask if

$$\lim_{n \to \infty} \frac{1}{n}$$

exists we are asking if this name has a denotation.

Similarly, when we define infinite series and ask if

$$\sum_{n=1}^{\infty} \frac{1}{n}$$

converges, we are asking if this name has a denotation.

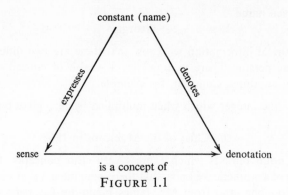

FIGURE 1.1

A name that has a denotation we shall call a *constant*. As examples of constants we offer

George Washington, the Empire State Building, Whistler's mother.

A constant whose denotation is a number we will call a *numeral*. As examples of numerals we offer

$$2, \sqrt{3}, 1 + 1, \pi, e,$$

$$\sum_{\alpha=1}^{3} 2^{\alpha}, \qquad \int_{0}^{2} x \, dx.$$

By way of summary, every name has a unique sense and at most one denotation. A constant is a name with denotation. A constant expresses its sense as a concept of its denotation. This relation between constants, senses, and denotations we emphasize by the diagram shown in Figure 1.1.

The sense and denotation of names we accept as primitive terms. We will make no effort to define them, but add the following comments. In the absence of a definition and an appropriate theory we have no means of resolving questions concerning the sense of names. However, we argue that with any reasonable definition the names

the mother of Whistler

and

Whistler's mother

have the same sense. Also, the names

$$\sum_{\alpha=1}^{3} 2^{\alpha}$$

and

$$\sum_{\beta=1}^{3} 2^{\beta}$$

have the same sense. We accept the idea of names with the same sense, and we will refer to them as *synonyms*.

To avoid ambiguity it is important that names have a unique sense. This we assume to be the case. From the assumption that the denotation of a name is determined by its sense, it follows that synonyms that have denotations must have the same denotation. It is, of course, possible for two names to have the same denotation but not the same sense. For example, the concept

the author of Tom Sawyer

is not the same as the concept

the author of Huckleberry Finn.

While these names have different senses, they have the same denotation, since the same man wrote both *Tom Sawyer* and *Huckleberry Finn.*

Names that have the same denotation we will refer to as *concurrent.* When we claim that the denotation of a name is determined by its sense we mean only that the sense of that name is a concept of at most one thing. It does not follow from this that one who understands the sense of each of two concurrent names will automatically be aware that they are concurrent. For example, it is possible that someone might know that there was a person who was the first President of the United States and also know that there was a famous American named 'George Washington' without being aware that they were one and the same person. Similarly, by a rather lengthy stretch of the imagination, we can conceive of someone who understands that there is a number $1 + 3$ and that there is a number 4 but who is unaware that they are the same number.

The fact that George Washington and the first President of the United States were the same person we could convey by the sentence

George Washington was the first President of the United States.

The sentence

$$1 + 3 \text{ is } 4$$

expresses the fact that $1 + 3$ and 4 are the same number. This usage of the verb 'is' is conveyed in mathematical writing by the use of the equality mark $(=)$, which in context is read *is equal to* or simply *equals.* Thus the so-called *equation*

$$1 + 3 = 4$$

asserts that $1 + 3$ and 4 are the same number.

Useful information concerning concurrence and hence concerning equality can be obtained by considering certain names to be derived from others by substitution. For example, the numeral

$$1 + 2$$

can be thought of as having been obtained from the numeral

$$1 + 3$$

by replacing the numeral '3' by the numeral '2'. In this particular case we
see that '2' and '3' are not concurrent and '1 + 2' and '1 + 3' are also not
concurrent. From this we conclude that substitutions involving nonconcurrent names can produce nonconcurrent names.

On the other hand, the names

Tom Sawyer

and

Huckleberry Finn

are nonconcurrent, but substitution into

the author of Tom Sawyer

produces the concurrent name

the author of Huckleberry Finn.

We conclude that substitutions involving nonconcurrent names can lead to
concurrent names.

If in

$$1 + 2$$

we replace '2' by the concurrent but not synonymous name '$(1 + 1)$', we
obtain the name

$$1 + (1 + 1),$$

which is concurrent to but not synonymous with the original. If in

$$1 + \int_0^2 x\, dx$$

we replace '$\int_0^2 x\, dx$' by the synonymous name '$\int_0^2 y\, dy$', we obtain

$$1 + \int_0^2 y\, dy,$$

which is synonymous with the original name.

The last two examples illustrate the following plausible ideas. Substitutions
involving synonymous names produce synonymous names. Substitutions involving concurrent names produce concurrent names. These two ideas are of
sufficient importance for us to state them with greater care and accept them
as basic principles:

> When a constituent name is replaced by one having the same
> sense, the sense of the entire name is not changed.

> When a constituent name is replaced by one having the same
> denotation, the denotation of the entire name is not changed.

Note that the second principle concerning the substitution of concurrent names is a justification of the property of equality commonly paraphrased

Equals substituted for equals produce equals.

As a concluding observation we point out that while names are essential for certain types of discourse, our interests are not confined exclusively to things that have names. There are surely butterflies in Africa and fishes in the depths of the sea as yet unknown to man and hence unnamed. The failure of an object to have a name would appear to be only a result of an oversight. With only a slight exercise of our imagination we can conceive of a day when all of the butterflies in Africa will be known and named; similarly all of the fishes of the seas. However, in the nineteenth century the mathematician Georg Cantor (1845–1918) discovered that when we accept the objects of mathematical discourse as things, the failure of some objects to have names can no longer be thought of as purely an oversight that time will rectify. In order to amplify this statement let us reflect a moment on the way we name things.

When we name something we frequently choose a name that is descriptive. It is surely not accidental that the fish we call 'catfish' have some resemblance to cats or that the lowly insects we call 'silverfish' are silver and fish-shaped. Thus, for example, the name '$\sqrt{2}$' is specifically chosen to convey the fact that its denotation is a number having 2 as its square. Throughout this section we have followed the convention of making names for names by including a given name in single quotation marks. Thus in the preceding sentence we use the name

$$'\sqrt{2}'$$

to indicate that the subject under discussion is the symbol '$\sqrt{2}$' and not the number $\sqrt{2}$. We are not, however, compelled to name things in any meaningful way. We may, if we choose, assign symbols to objects in a purely arbitrary way—as, for example, the choice of the symbol 'π' to denote a very important real number.

In the nineteenth century Cantor proved, by a method we will study in detail in a later chapter, that if we consider all possible symbols that can be composed from the 26 English letters—all one-letter symbols, all two-letter symbols, etc.—intent upon assigning these symbols as names of particular real numbers, then there are not enough names to go around. There are real numbers that not only do not have names at the present time but must remain forever nameless.

At first thought it might be supposed that the existence of nameless things poses a serious communications problem. This, however, is not the case. Generally there are two types of information that we wish to relate: information that is true of each individual in some collection, and information that may be true of only one particular individual. Only in the second case is a name essential. When, for example, we speak of butterflies we understand that the noun 'butterfly' is not a proper noun referring to a specific thing but a common noun referring to a collection of things. So long as the information is sufficiently general as to be true of every particular butterfly, including those as yet undiscovered, our conversation can be carried on without using names for individuals. However, when we wish to tell something that is true of one particular butterfly, then a name is essential. This again poses no problem, for when any particular butterfly is called to our attention we can always give it a name. The same is true in mathematics. Mathematics has its own special language for discussing properties that are shared by each individual in a given collection. The fact that the given collection may contain objects that must remain forever nameless poses no problem. This we will discuss in greater detail later in this chapter.

1.2 Sentences and Propositions

Continuing with our discussion of the English language, we turn to the subject of sentences and their use to communicate information. Since our main concern is with declarative sentences, we propose to use the word *sentence* to mean declarative sentence. As examples we offer

Mark Twain wrote *Tom Sawyer*

and

$$2 + 2 = 5.$$

The sense of such sentences we will call a *proposition*. As the examples illustrate, a proposition may be true or it may be false. Indeed, we take this as a basic property of propositions

> Every proposition is either true or false.
>
> No proposition is both true and false.

We are willing to accept the possibility that a declarative sentence may exist which expresses an idea that is neither true nor false. The sense of such a sentence is not a proposition.

Since there are writers who take the position that propositions are sentences, we wish to emphasize the distinction we have in mind. We can think of no better example to illustrate that propositions and sentences are not the same things than that provided by A. Church,[1] who exhorts us to ponder the results of replacing the word 'proposition' by 'declarative sentence' in the following quotation from Lincoln's Gettysburg Address:

> Fourscore and seven years ago our fathers brought forth on
> this continent a new nation conceived in liberty and dedicated
> to the proposition that all men are created equal.

---

[1] Church, A., *Introduction to Mathematical Logic, Volume* 1 (Princeton, N.J.: Princeton University Press, 1956), p. 26.

Furthermore, we point out that propositions are far more numerous than sentences. For example, the idea that a particular real number has a square root is a proposition. There are, in fact, as many such propositions as there are real numbers. However, having agreed that there exist real numbers that must remain forever nameless, there exist real numbers for which the proposition of having a square root is not the sense of a sentence in any existing language. In spite of this, the basic device by which we inform others of a particular proposition that we have in mind is the declarative sentence. A sentence that expresses a true proposition we will call a *true sentence*; a sentence that expresses a false proposition we will call a *false sentence.* Truth and falsehood we shall refer to collectively as *truth values.*

While there are propositions that are true and others that are false, it is not always necessary to specify the truth value of a proposition in order to be correctly understood in a given discussion. Let us illustrate with two statements which might occur in mathematical discourse.

> Consider the following proposition: There exists a real number whose square is two

and

> We, therefore, conclude the following: There exists a real number whose square is two.

It is clear from the context that in the first statement the sentence

> There exists a real number whose square is two

is used simply to express a proposition. However, in the second statement this sentence not only is used to express the proposition but it is expressed with the intention that it be accepted as true.

The two statements, therefore, involve different uses of the same sentence. A sentence used as in the second statement to express a proposition with the intent that it be accepted as true is called an *assertion*. As the examples illustrate, a sentence can be used assertively or nonassertively.

In addition to using sentences to express and assert propositions, we find it convenient to use them in another way. We will use them as names for truth values—a true sentence as a name for truth and a false sentence as a name for falsehood. Since sentences are names, the rules for name substitutions apply. Thus the replacement of a name in a sentence by a synonymous name produces a sentence with the same sense and denotation—i.e., truth value—as the original. The replacement of a name in a sentence by a concurrent name produces a sentence with the same truth value but not necessarily the same sense. For example, if in the sentence

> Mark Twain is the author of *Tom Sawyer*,

we replace 'the author of *Tom Sawyer*' by the concurrent name 'Mark Twain', we obtain the sentence

> Mark Twain is Mark Twain.

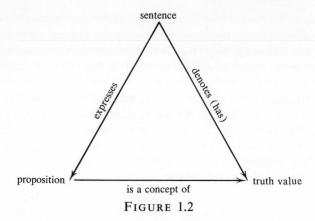

FIGURE 1.2

The two sentences express different propositions, but they are both true. If in the sentence

$$\int_0^2 x\, dx = 6,$$

we replace '$\int_0^2 x\, dx$' by the synonymous name '$\int_0^2 y\, dy$', we obtain the sentence

$$\int_0^2 y\, dy = 6.$$

These two sentences express the same false proposition.

Note the parallel between constants and sentences with denotation as illustrated by Figures 1.1 and 1.2.

1.3 Variables and Forms

For mathematical purposes we find it convenient to augment the English language by the addition of certain special symbols. Of particular importance in mathematical discourse are those special symbols we call *variables*. In the material ahead the reader will find the following symbols used as variables:

$$a,\ b,\ c,\ m,\ n,\ p,\ x,\ y,\ z,\ \alpha,\ \beta,\ \gamma.$$

This list is, however, not complete. Indeed we understand that the supply of variables is unlimited. When in a given context the discussion requires the use of many variables we will find it convenient to identify them by the use of subscripts:

$$x_1,\ x_2,\ x_3,\ \ldots.$$

We accept the notion of variable as primitive and assume that the reader's experience and the following discussion will be sufficient to enable him to decide from a given context which symbols are variables and which are not.

Variables occur in two basic contexts—in names and in *forms*. A form is an expression that contains one or more variables and can be thought of as arising in the following way. Recall that in our discussion of names we found that certain names could be thought of as having been obtained from other names by a substitution. If instead of making a name-for-name substitution we make a variable-for-name substitution the resulting expression is a form. For example, if in the numeral '$(2 \cdot 3) + 1$' we substitute the variable 'n' for the numeral '3' we obtain the form

$$(2 \cdot n) + 1.$$

Such a form we will call *a form in one variable*. If we replace two names by two different variables, the resulting expression is a form in two variables. In a similar manner we obtain forms in three variables, four variables, etc. Our main interest in variables and forms we illustrate with the following example.

Consider the form '$(2 \cdot n) + 1$'. For each replacement of 'n' by a numeral for an integer we obtain a numeral for an odd integer. If 'n' is replaced by '2' the result is '$(2 \cdot 2) + 1$'; if 'n' is replaced by '3' we obtain '$(2 \cdot 3) + 1$'. With regard to such substitutions we refer to the object whose name is substituted for the variable as a *value* of the variable and to the object named as a result of the substitution as the *corresponding value* of the form. For the example at hand, if 'n' is assigned the value 2, the corresponding value of the form is 5; if 'n' is assigned the value 3, the corresponding value of the form is 7.

For practical reasons it is clearly impossible to make all possible substitutions for 'n'. In spite of this we accept the idea that the form '$(2 \cdot n) + 1$' determines a pairing of integers, associating with each integer a particular odd integer. Conversely, each odd integer is paired with some integer, as we see from the fact that a numeral for any given odd integer can be obtained from the form by replacing 'n' by an appropriately chosen integer. For example, we obtain a numeral for 9 by replacing 'n' by '4' and a numeral for 11 by replacing 'n' by '5'. Thus if we assign the integers as a collection of values for 'n', traditionally called a *range* of values, then the odd integers will be the collection or range of values of the form.

We hasten to add that the notion of a variable having a value must not be thought of as restricted to objects that have names. Consider, for example, the form '$1/x$'. If 'x' is assigned the real numbers as its range, then each real number is a value for 'x', despite the fact that there exist real numbers that have no names. Our point of view is that each real number is namable in the sense that any particular real number we can conceive of can be named, even if we must add new symbols to the language in order to do so.

We furthermore take the point of view that if in '$1/x$' the variable 'x' is replaced by a numeral, the result is a name, although possibly a name without denotation. Since one of the defining properties of the real numbers is that every real number except 0 is the reciprocal of some real number, we conclude that the range of the form '$1/x$' is the collection of nonzero real numbers.

The use of singulary forms as previously discussed has an obvious extension to forms in more than one variable. If to each variable of such a form we assign a value, then the form either has a value or has no value according as the result of replacing every occurrence of each variable by a name for its assigned value is a name with denotation or a name without denotation. From our rules for name substitutions it follows that the value of a form is uniquely determined by the values assigned to its variables and does not depend upon the names used for these values. Thus, for example, if for the form '$1/x$' we assign 'x' the value 2, then regardless of which name for 2 we substitute—e.g., '2', '$1 + 1$', '$\sqrt{4}$', 'II'—we arrive at the same value of the form, namely, $\frac{1}{2}$.

As the foregoing discussion illustrates, forms can be used to describe collections of objects of interest. For example, the odd integers can be described as the range of the form '$(2 \cdot n) + 1$' when 'n' is assigned the integers as range. Another use of forms is illustrated by the so-called *identity problems* of elementary algebra and trigonometry. These problems are exercises in verifying that two forms are *equivalent*[1] in the following sense.

Singulary forms in the same variable are equivalent over an assigned range for that variable if and only if for each value of the variable the forms either have no value or have the same value. As a very elementary example we offer the forms '$(x + 1)^2$' and '$x^2 + 2x + 1$', which are equivalent over the real numbers. From trigonometry we know that '$\sin 2\theta$' and '$2 \sin \theta \cos \theta$' are also equivalent over the real numbers. On the other hand, the forms '$(x^2 - 2)/(x - \sqrt{2})$' and '$x + \sqrt{2}$' are not equivalent over the real numbers, since the first form has no value at $\sqrt{2}$, while the second has the value $2\sqrt{2}$. Since for all other real numbers these two forms do have the same value, it follows that they are equivalent over any collection of real numbers that does not contain $\sqrt{2}$, as, for example, the collection of rational numbers. As a final example we point out that since $\sin 0 = 0$ and $\cos 0 = 1$, the forms '$\sin \theta$' and '$\cos \theta$' are not equivalent over the real numbers or the rational numbers.

We extend the notion of equivalence to forms in more than one variable in the obvious way. Such forms are equivalent over specified ranges for the variables, provided that for each assignment of values to the variables from their respective ranges the forms either have no value or each have the same value. For example, if 'θ' and 'ϕ' are each assigned the real numbers as range, then '$\sin (\theta + \phi)$' and '$\sin \theta \cos \phi + \cos \theta \sin \phi$' are equivalent. When, as in this case, the variables are each assigned the same range, we

[1] Or *concurrent*.

say that the forms are equivalent over the common range. Thus 'sin $(\theta + \phi)$' and 'sin $\theta \cos \phi + \cos \theta \sin \phi$' are equivalent over the real numbers.

Note that the definition of equivalence does not require that two forms contain the same number of variables in order to be equivalent. For example, '$1 + x^2$' and '$1^n + x^2$' are equivalent forms with 'x' assigned the real numbers as range and 'n' assigned the integers as range. As this example illustrates, we interpret the instruction to assign values to the variables to mean only that every variable present must be assigned a value. It is not required that every variable be present in each form. By way of contrast we note that the forms '$m + n$' and 'n' are not equivalent over the integers, since the two forms have different values if 'm' and 'n' are each assigned the value 1.

We also find it convenient to extend the notion of equivalence to include constants. A form is equivalent to a constant over specified ranges for the variables if and only if for each assignment of values to the variables from their respective ranges the form has a value and that value is the denotation of the given constant. For example '$\sin^2 \theta + \cos^2 \theta$' is equivalent to '1' over the real numbers; both '1^n' and '$(-1)^{2n}$' are equivalent to '1' over the integers. Finally, to encompass the notion of concurrence, we specify that two constants are equivalent if and only if they are concurrent. Thus '1' and '$2 - 1$' are examples of equivalent constants.

As in the case of names, certain forms can be thought of as having been obtained from other forms by a substitution. For example, the form '$1 + x^2$' can be thought of as being obtained from the form '$1 + x$' by substituting 'x^2' for 'x'. We note that 'x^2' and 'x' are not equivalent over the real numbers, and neither are '$1 + x$' and '$1 + x^2$'. We conclude that substitutions involving nonequivalent forms may lead to nonequivalent forms. On the other hand, the forms '$-\theta$' and 'θ' are not equivalent over the real numbers, yet the substitution of '$-\theta$' for 'θ' in '$\cos \theta$' produces the equivalent form '$\cos (-\theta)$'. Thus substitutions involving nonequivalent forms may produce equivalent forms.

As one would expect, substitutions involving equivalent forms or constants lead to equivalent forms or constants. Indeed this is implicit in the concept of equivalence and the substitution rules for names. This idea we summarize as the following substitution principle:

> When a constituent constant or form is replaced by a constant or form that is equivalent to it, the resulting constant or form is equivalent to the original one.

For example, from the fact that '$\sin 2\theta$' is equivalent to '$2 \sin \theta \cos \theta$' over the real numbers we are assured that '$\sin 2\theta + \cos \theta$' is equivalent to '$2 \sin \theta \cos \theta + \cos \theta$'.

At this point let us pause to reflect on the use that we have made of variables. In our discussion of forms a basic idea is that of replacing a variable by a name. The variable is used as a blank or a place holder for names. A variable used in this way is called a *free variable*. Contrast this use with the use of variables in names.

In later chapters the symbols

$$\sum_{\alpha=0}^{2} 3^{\alpha}, \qquad \prod_{\beta=1}^{3} (\tfrac{1}{2})^{\beta}, \qquad \int_{0}^{2} x \, dx$$

will be defined in such a way as to establish that they are names for 13, $\frac{1}{64}$, and 2, respectively. Here the variables 'α', 'β', and 'x' occur in a role different from that of our earlier discussion. While it may seem that

$$\sum_{\alpha=0}^{2} 3^{\alpha}$$

is a very strange symbol to use as a name for 13, we will see later that it is very useful. It is intended to convey that 13 is the sum of 1, 3, and 9. We take the point of view that both the sense and denotation of this symbol are unaltered if 'α' is replaced by another variable. Thus

$$\sum_{\alpha=0}^{2} 3^{\alpha} = \sum_{\beta=0}^{2} 3^{\beta} = \sum_{x=0}^{2} 3^{x},$$

$$\int_{0}^{2} \alpha \, d\alpha = \int_{0}^{2} \beta \, d\beta = \int_{0}^{2} x \, dx.$$

Variables used in this way are called *bound variables*. A bound and a free variable may, of course, occur in the same expression, as for example

$$\sum_{\alpha=0}^{2} x^{\alpha}, \qquad \int_{0}^{x} \alpha \, d\alpha.$$

In each case 'α' occurs as a bound variable and 'x' occurs as a free variable. When referring to a form in a specified number of variables it is understood that only the free variables are counted. Thus the two preceding examples are singular forms in the variable 'x'. Of course, through all of the discussion of forms it was tacit that we assign values only to the free variables of the forms.

We conclude our discussion of forms with a few remarks concerning a special type of form that will be of particular interest to us in the material ahead, the *propositional forms*. Since we have agreed to accept sentences as names, we can obtain forms from sentences. Such forms we call *propositional forms*. As examples of propositional forms we offer

Mark Twain wrote x,

$$x + 2 = 0,$$

y wrote x,

and

$$x + y = y + x.$$

Having agreed that sentences are names for truth values it follows that the values of propositional forms are truth values. If for an assignment of values to the variables of a propositional form the form has the value truth, we will say simply that the form is true for that assignment of values to its variables. Similarly we will say that a form is false for an assignment of values to its variables if for that assignment the form has the value falsehood. For example, if 'n' is a variable on integers, then the propositional form

$$n + 1 = 4$$

is true for the value 3 and false for all other values. Similarly, since 'sin 2θ' and '$2 \sin \theta \cos \theta$' are equivalent over the real numbers, it follows that the propositional form

$$\sin 2\theta = 2 \sin \theta \cos \theta$$

is true for every real number value of 'θ'.

In summary, a singular form associates with each individual in the range of its variable at most one object in the range of the form. This provides a way of identifying interesting collections of things and inferring information about those things. For example we will find in the material ahead that it is very helpful to be able to identify the odd integers as the range of the form '$(2 \cdot n) + 1$' when 'n' is assigned the integers as a range.

Similarly propositional forms associate truth values with individuals and thereby provide a useful way of formulating and resolving interesting questions. As a simple illustration note that if 'x' is a variable on the collection of real numbers then the propositional form

$$x \text{ has a real square root}$$

associates with each real number the value truth or falsehood according to whether the form is true or false for the given value of 'x'. We are, of course, not interested in the abstract pairing of truth values with numbers but rather in the information conveyed by the propositions involved. For example, the fact that the form associates the value truth with the real number 2 is of interest because it thereby assures us that 2 has a real square root. Thus our main interest in a propositional form is in the collection of propositions that are associated with this form when the variables are assigned ranges.

Propositional forms also provide a means by which propositions may be expressed with exceptional clarity and conciseness. For this, however, we need

1.4 Quantifiers

As was pointed out, a propositional form with a range assigned to each of its free variables provides a very useful way to define a collection of propositions. In dealing with such collections we are usually concerned with one of the following questions:

Is every proposition of the collection true?

Is some proposition of the collection true?

Consider, for example, the form

x has a real square root.

If 'x' is assigned a range, a collection of propositions is defined. The statement that every proposition of the collection is true we write as

($\forall x$) x has a real square root.

The symbol '$\forall$' is called the *universal quantifier* and in context is read *for each*.[1]

We accept

($\forall x$) x has a real square root

as *a* proposition with the understanding that it is true if and only if the form

x has a real square root

is true for each value of 'x' in its assigned range. This is the case if 'x' is a variable on the positive reals. The proposition

($\forall x$) x has a real square root

is false if there exists a value of 'x' for which the form

x has a real square root

is false. This is the case if the range of 'x' is the collection of all real numbers.

If 'x' is a variable on the reals, then the form

$$x^2 = 2$$

defines a collection containing more false propositions than true. It is, however, important to know that not all of the propositions in this collection are false. This statement we write as

$$(\exists x)\ x^2 = 2.$$

The symbol '$\exists$' is called the *existential quantifier* and in context is read *for some*.[2]

We accept

$$(\exists x)\ x^2 = 2$$

as a proposition with the understanding that it is true if and only if the form

$$x^2 = 2$$

---

[1] Also, *for all* and *for every*.
[2] Also, *there exists*.

is true for some value of 'x' in its assigned range. In particular, the proposition

$$(\exists x)\ x^2 = 2$$

is false if 'x' is a variable on integers and true if 'x' is a variable on real numbers. Indeed

$$x^2 = 2$$

is true for the value $\sqrt{2}$ and also the value $-\sqrt{2}$. Variables, forms, and quantifiers enable us to express our thoughts with great clarity and conciseness.

To state that one and only one proposition of a collection is true we use the symbol '$\exists!$' which is called the *uniqueness quantifier* and in context is read *for one and only one*.[1] For example

$$(\exists! x)\ x^2 = 2$$

is a proposition that is true if and only if the form

$$x^2 = 2$$

is true for one and only one value of the variable in its assigned range. In particular,

$$(\exists! x)\ x^2 = 2$$

is false if 'x' is a variable on the integers, false if 'x' is a variable on the reals, but true if 'x' is a variable on the positive reals.

Our main interest in variables, forms, and quantifiers is in their use to make assertions. They offer important advantages over the natural languages enabling us to strip away certain nonessentials and thereby focus attention on key points of interest. These advantages include conciseness and clarity. The reader may reasonably object that the sentence

$$(\exists x)\ x \text{ has a real square root}$$

offers nothing in clarity and little in conciseness, since this proposition can be expressed with equal clarity by the simple sentence

There exists a real number which has a real square root.

Indeed this sentence has the advantage of being a more natural way of speaking. We have no quarrel with this argument. Consider, however, the associative property of addition for real numbers as expressed by

$$(\forall x)(\forall y)(\forall z)(x + y) + z = x + (y + z).$$

We urge the reader to express this proposition by an English sentence using no quantifiers or forms. We then ask the reader's judgment as to which expression is preferable from the point of view of clarity and of conciseness.

---

[1] Also, *there exists one and only one.*

To distinguish between conventional English sentences and sentences that contain forms and quantifiers we will call the latter *formal sentences*. Since we are interested in language as a means of communicating information we propose to be selective in the use of formal sentences. There are contexts in which a concise formal sentence is an aid to clarity and preferable to a conventional English sentence. There are contexts in which the reverse is the case. Indeed one of the pitfalls of formalism is that the brevity of the sentence may obscure the meaning. It is, of course, important to develop the ability to translate formal sentences into English, and vice versa.

We conclude this section with a brief remark concerning a convention for omitting universal quantifiers. We will occasionally find it convenient to drop universal quantifiers that precede a form and accept the resulting form as an assertion, with the convention that it is to be understood as though each free variable is universally quantified by quantifiers which occur to the left of the form. For example, in an appropriate context we might assert that

$$x + y = y + x$$

with the intention that this be understood as though we had asserted that

$$(\forall x)(\forall y)\; x + y = y + x.$$

Care must be exercised in using this convention, particularly with statements that contain existential quantifiers. For example, the assertion that every real number has a negative we might formalize as

$$(\forall x)(\exists y)\; x + y = 0.$$

From our knowledge of the real numbers we know that this statement is true. If, however, we reverse the quantifiers in this sentence we obtain

$$(\exists y)(\forall x)\; x + y = 0$$

which asserts that there exists a number that is the negative of every real number. This is of course false. We, therefore, cannot drop the universal quantifier from

$$(\exists y)(\forall x)\; x + y = 0$$

without changing its meaning, for by our convention we must interpret

$$(\exists y)\; x + y = 0$$

to mean

$$(\forall x)(\exists y)\; x + y = 0.$$

EXERCISES

Identify the expressions in Exercises 1–10 as names, forms, or propositional forms and the variables as free or bound.

1. $2x + 1$.
2. $\sqrt{\pi}$.
3. $\int_1^2 x \, dx$.
4. $2x + 1 = 0$.
5. $\int_1^2 x \, dx = \sqrt{\pi}$.
6. $(\forall x) \, 2x + 1 = 0$.
7. $(\exists x) \int_1^2 \alpha \, d\alpha = x$.
8. 2^n.
9. $(\forall x) \, x + y = y + x$.
10. $(\exists x)(\exists y) \, x + y \neq y + x$.

11. In the preceding material find five sentences that are used assertively and five sentences that are used nonassertively.

In Exercises 12–21 decide which sentences are true and which are false. For each false sentence obtain, if possible, a true sentence by inserting or deleting quotation marks.

12. George Washington lived in Virginia.
13. '1' + '1' = '2'.
14. '2' is a square root of 4.
15. $\sqrt{4} - 2 = 0$.
16. Abraham Lincoln was called Honest Abe.
17. 'Samuel Clemens' is a pseudonym for Mark Twain.
18. The tens digit of 211 is 1.
19. The form $(2 \cdot n) + 1$ is obtained from $(2 \cdot 7) + 1$ by replacing 7 by n.
20. 27 can be written as $20 + 7$.
21. '1 + 1' = '2'.

With the understanding that 'x', 'y', and 'z' are variables on real numbers, restate the assertions of Exercises 22–26 without using variables.

22. $(\forall x)(\exists y) \, x + y = 0$.
23. $(\forall x)(\forall y)(\forall z)$ if $x + z = y + z$, then $x = y$.
24. $(\exists y)(\forall x) \, xy = y$.
25. $(\forall x)(\forall y)$ if $xy = 0$, then $x = 0$ or $y = 0$.
26. $(\exists x) \, x^2 = 2$.

Introduce appropriate variables and express the assertions of Exercises 27–30 more formally.

27. Each state of the union has a governor.
28. Everything that goes up must come down.
29. Someone wins the Irish Sweepstakes every year.
30. The addition of real numbers is commutative.

1.5 Sentential Connectives and Negation

We have agreed that every proposition is either true or false; but given a particular proposition how is its truth value to be determined? We submit that in the absence of an oracle all anyone can do is to examine the facts and form an opinion. Thus, for example, when we assert that

Mark Twain wrote Tom Sawyer

we are at best only claiming that it is our judgment that this proposition is true. Confronted with evidence to the contrary we might change our mind.

If we accept the view that certainty is denied us, then it is of great importance to find methods which enable us to make truth value judgments with reasonable confidence in the outcome. For many questions we have come to accept the so-called scientific method, whereby we seek to relate our understanding of a given proposition and observed facts. Consider, for example, the proposition

Cancer is caused by a virus.

We consider it proper to reserve judgment on this proposition awaiting the results of studies presently being made at the various cancer research centers throughout the world. Even such a simple proposition as

It is raining outside

should be judged only after checking the local weather conditions.

Suppose, however, we ask for a judgment on the proposition

It is raining outside or it is not raining outside

or the proposition

It is raining outside and it is not raining outside.

We would surely agree that the first proposition is true and the second is false. Furthermore, we make this judgment without so much as a glance out of the window. Our decision is based on our understanding of English and the proper use of the words 'and', 'or', and 'not'.

Note that there is an important difference in our approach to the two propositions

It is raining outside

and

It is raining outside or it is not raining outside.

For the first proposition we feel very strongly that the meaning of the sentence[1] must be taken into account in making a decision concerning its truth value. For the second proposition, however, the meaning of the sentence is quite irrelevant. We conclude that the proposition is true because of the grammatical structure of the given sentence that expresses it.

As these examples illustrate, we sometimes judge the truth value of a sentence from its meaning, and we sometimes judge it from its construction.

---

[1] It is traditional to refer to the meaning of sentence as its *substance*.

Sometimes we do both. We tend to judge the truth value of a compound sentence from the truth values of its component parts and our understanding of the conjunctions used. Conjunctions used to compound sentences we shall call *sentential connectives*. It is important that we agree on their use.

For convenience in discussing the conventions for sentential connectives we introduce the symbols

$$p, \; q, \; r, \; s$$

as variables on truth values. It is traditional to refer to such variables as *propositional variables*.[1] We also find it useful to use the symbol '*t*' to denote truth, the symbol '*f*' to denote falsehood, and the symbol '~' to denote negation. By negation we understand that the form

$$\sim p$$

is true if '*p*' is assigned the value *f* and it is false if '*p*' is assigned the value *t*. A convenient way of expressing this information is the following *truth table*:

p	$\sim p$
t	f
f	t

in which the column below '*p*' lists the values assigned to '*p*' and the column below '~*p*' lists the corresponding values of the form.

Having agreed earlier that sentences are names for truth values we may substitute sentences for propositional variables. Thus since

$$2 + 2 = 4$$

is true

$$\sim (2 + 2 = 4)$$

is false. Since

The moon is made of Liederkranz

is false

~ The moon is made of Liederkranz

is true. Moreover '~$(2 + 2 = 4)$' and 'the moon is made of Liederkranz' are equivalent constants since they each have the same denotation.

Let us now reexamine the sentence

It is raining outside and it is not raining outside

and formulate our reasons for concluding that it is false. First, from our understanding of the proper use of the word 'not', we accept 'it is not

---

[1] While the term *propositional variable* is conventional, it is well to note that they are not variables on propositions but variables on truth values.

raining outside' and '$\sim$ it is raining outside' as equivalent. Second, from our understanding of negation, it follows that not both of the sentences 'it is raining outside' and 'it is not raining outside' can be true. Third, from our understanding of the proper use of the word 'and', we judge the conjunction of two sentences to be true if and only if each component sentence is true. Thus, for example, we judge the compound sentence

> Mark Twain wrote *Tom Sawyer*, and Mark Twain wrote *Huckleberry Finn*

to be true because each component sentence—'Mark Twain wrote *Tom Sawyer*' and 'Mark Twain wrote *Huckleberry Finn*'—is true. But the compound sentence

> Mark Twain wrote *Tom Sawyer*, and George Washington wrote *Huckleberry Finn*

we reject as false because a component sentence is false.

Let us, therefore, agree that the 'and' connective will always be used in this sense; that is, a compound sentence consisting of two sentences connected by 'and' is true if each component sentence is true and is false otherwise. We can express this more concisely by using the form in two variables

$$p \text{ and } q$$

and the truth table

p	q	p and q
t	t	t
t	f	f
f	t	f
f	f	f

Truth tables provide a very convenient method of checking the equivalence of propositional forms. Recall that two forms are equivalent if and only if for each assignment of values to the free variables the forms either have no value or both have the same value. As an elementary example, consider the truth table

p	q	p and q	q and p
t	t	t	t
t	f	f	f
f	t	f	f
f	f	f	f

From the third and fourth columns we see that the forms 'p and q' and 'q and p' are equivalent.

As a further example consider the truth table

p	q	r	(p and q) and r	p and (q and r)
t	t	t	t	t
t	t	f	f	f
t	f	t	f	f
t	f	f	f	f
f	t	t	f	f
f	t	f	f	f
f	f	t	f	f
f	f	f	f	f

From the last two columns we see that the forms '(p and q) and r' and 'p and (q and r)' are equivalent.

The compounding of sentences with the connective 'and' we shall call *conjunction*. As previously illustrated, the conjunction of sentences is both commutative and associative:

$$p \text{ and } q = q \text{ and } p \qquad \text{(Commutative law for conjunction)}$$
$$(p \text{ and } q) \text{ and } r = p \text{ and } (q \text{ and } r) \qquad \text{(Associative law for conjunction)}$$

Having reached agreement on the use of the connective 'and', let us now also agree on the use of the connective 'or'. Insofar as possible we would choose to conform to conventional English usage; however, in ordinary English the connective 'or' is used in two different ways. Let us illustrate. If I say

The weather will be nice for our trip tomorrow or we will stay home

we understand this prediction to be true if tomorrow the weather is nice and we go, or the weather is not nice and we stay home. The prediction is false if tomorrow the weather is nice and we stay home, or the weather is not nice and we go.

Thus of the two events

The weather will be nice for our trip tomorrow

and

We will stay home

one and only one is expected to happen.

On the other hand, if the weather man predicts

Tomorrow we will have rain or we will have snow

we accept this prediction as being correct if and only if on the appointed day it rains, it snows, or it does both. That is, the statement is accepted as true in all cases except when each component part is false.

The first usage, which excludes the possibility of each component sentence being true, is called the *exclusive* 'or'; the second, which allows each component sentence to be true, is called the *inclusive* 'or'. For mathematical purposes we find the inclusive 'or' more useful. Let us, therefore, agree that a compound sentence consisting of two sentences connected by 'or' is false if each component sentence is false and is true otherwise.

The compounding of sentences with the connective 'or' we shall call *disjunction*. The truth table for disjunction is the following:

p	q	p or q
t	t	t
t	f	t
f	t	t
f	f	f

As in the case of conjunction, the disjunction of sentences is also commutative and associative:

$$p \text{ or } q = q \text{ or } p \qquad \text{(Commutative law for disjunction)}$$
$$p \text{ or } (q \text{ or } r) = (p \text{ or } q) \text{ or } r \qquad \text{(Associative law for disjunction)}$$

We leave the verification by truth tables to the reader.

More interesting properties are the so-called *Laws of De Morgan*, which relate disjunction and conjunction. They are the following:

$$p \text{ and } (q \text{ or } r) = (p \text{ and } q) \text{ or } (p \text{ and } r)$$
$$p \text{ or } (q \text{ and } r) = (p \text{ or } q) \text{ and } (p \text{ or } r) \qquad \text{(Laws of De Morgan)}$$

For verification we again appeal to truth tables. We offer the following table as justification for the first law and leave the second as an exercise for the reader:

p	q	r	p and q	p and r	q or r	p and $(q$ or $r)$	$(p$ and $q)$ or $(p$ and $r)$
t	t	t	t	t	t	t	t
t	t	f	t	f	t	t	t
t	f	t	f	t	t	t	t
t	f	f	f	f	f	f	f
f	t	t	f	f	t	f	f
f	t	f	f	f	t	f	f
f	f	t	f	f	t	f	f
f	f	f	f	f	f	f	f

Only two other connectives are of interest to us, the so-called *conditional* and the *biconditional*. There are many ways to phrase conditional statements in English. The most common constructions use the word 'implies', as in

$$2 + 2 = 4 \text{ implies } (1 + 1) + 2 = 4$$

or the word pair 'if–then', as in

If John is older than Mary, then John is older than Bill.

For our purposes we are interested in 'implies' and 'if–then' only as sentential connectives. We wish to establish a convention for assigning truth values to sentences that are compounded with these connectives. For conditionally compounded sentences, such as the examples above, it is traditional to refer to the first component sentence as the *antecedent* and the second component sentence as the *consequent*. Thus the first of the foregoing examples has as its antecedent the sentence '$2 + 2 = 4$' and as its consequent the sentence '$(1 + 1) + 2 = 4$'.

In ordinary English usage we interpret a conditional assertion as a claim that from the antecedent the consequent can be inferred, at least in the sense that if the antecedent is true, then the consequent must also be true.[1] In view of this usage it seems reasonable to assign to a conditional the value t if both its antecedent and its consequent are true, and the value f if its antecedent is true and its consequent is false. Conventional English usage provides no guide for assigning truth values to conditional statements with false antecedents. For mathematical purposes we find it convenient to assign such statements the value t. Let us, therefore, agree to accept 'if p then q' and 'p implies q' as equivalent forms with the following truth table:[2]

p	q	if p then q
t	t	t
t	f	f
f	t	t
f	f	t

From the truth table we see that

$$t \text{ implies } f \neq f \text{ implies } t$$

and

$$(f \text{ implies } t) \text{ implies } f \neq f \text{ implies } (t \text{ implies } f).$$

Therefore the conditional is neither commutative nor associative. The conditional does, however, have the following curious property, which is known

---

[1] This use of the conditional we call *strict implication*.

[2] This use of the conditional is called *material implication*.

as the self-distributive law of implication. Its verification by a truth table we leave as an exercise for the reader.

p implies (q implies r) = (p implies q) implies (p implies r)
(Self-distributive law of [material] implication)

The last connective that we wish to discuss is the biconditional. As an example we offer

John is older than Mary if and only if John is older than Bill.

We ordinarily interpret such a statement as a claim that if either component sentence is true, then the other component sentence is also true; that is, the two component sentences are either both true or both false. Let us then agree that a biconditional statement is true if its component parts have the same truth value and is false otherwise. By abbreviating 'if and only if' as 'iff' the truth table for the biconditional is then

p	q	p iff q
t	t	t
t	f	f
f	t	f
f	f	t

We leave as an exercise for the reader the verification by truth tables of the following properties.

p iff $q = q$ iff p (Commutative law for the biconditional)
(p iff q) iff $r = p$ iff (q iff r)   (Associative law for the biconditional)
[(p iff q) and (q iff r)] implies (p iff r)   (Transitive law for the biconditional)

Good English usage of course forbids the indiscriminate compounding of sentences with unrelated subjects such as

$2 + 2 = 4$, and Mark Twain wrote *Tom Sawyer*

and

The moon is made of Liederkranz, or Old Man Mose is dead.

However, for mathematical purposes we sometimes find it necessary to compound sentences that may seem as strange as these examples. We wish to emphasize the point that the truth value of such a sentence is to be judged solely on the basis of the truth values of its component sentences and our agreement concerning the use of sentential connectives. Our tendency to interpret conditional statements as strict implications poses a problem but not a major one. With a little practice we can view with dispassion a sentence such as

If cucumbers have no seeds, then grasshoppers have wooden legs and judge that it is true, at least until such time as a seedless cucumber is developed.

We conclude this section with a brief discussion of the negation of sentences that contain quantifiers. It is intuitively clear that the assertion

Every real number has a square root

is false if and only if the assertion

There exists a real number that has no square root

is true. That is, if 'x' is a variable on real numbers, then

$$\sim [(\forall x)\ x \text{ has a square root}] = (\exists x)\ [\sim (x \text{ has a square root})].$$

Similarly the assertion

There exists a real number that is positive

is false if and only if the assertion

Every real number is not positive

is true. Thus, if 'x' is a variable on real numbers, then

$$\sim [(\exists x)\ x \text{ is positive}] = (\forall x)\ [\sim (x \text{ is positive})].$$

These examples suggest that the formal negation of a universally quantified statement is an existentially quantified statement, and the formal negation of an existentially quantified statement is a universally quantified statement.

Using 'F_x' as a variable which may be replaced by any singulary form in 'x' we summarize our observations as the following:

$$\sim (\forall x)\ F_x = (\exists x)\ \sim F_x,$$
$$\sim (\exists x)\ F_x = (\forall x)\ \sim F_x.$$

We accept these as basic principles for negation.

The negation of compound sentences is also of interest. The basic properties, however, require little explanation. We, therefore, leave them as exercises.

EXERCISES

Verify by truth tables

1. $\sim (\sim p) = p$ (Law of double negation).
2. $\sim (p \text{ and } q) = (\sim p) \text{ or } (\sim q)$.
3. $\sim (p \text{ or } q) = (\sim p) \text{ and } (\sim q)$.
4. $\sim (p \text{ implies } q) = p \text{ and } (\sim q)$.
5. $\sim (p \text{ iff } q) = (p \text{ and } \sim q) \text{ or } (q \text{ and } \sim p)$.

6. p implies $q = \sim q$ implies $\sim p$ (Law of contraposition).

7. p implies $q = (\sim p)$ or q.

8. p iff $q = (p$ implies $q)$ and $(q$ implies $p)$.

9. p iff $q = (p$ implies $q)$ and $(\sim p$ implies $\sim q)$.

10. p implies $(q$ or $r) = (p$ and $\sim q)$ implies r.

11. $(p$ or $p) = (p$ and $p) = p$.

In Exercises 12–21 'm' and 'n' are variables on integers. From your knowledge of the integers judge the truth value of each of the given propositions.

12. $(\forall n)$ (n is even or n is odd).

13. $(\forall m)(\exists n)\ m < n$.

14. $(\forall n)$ (n is even or n is odd) $= [(\forall n)\ n$ is even] or $[(\forall n)\ n$ is odd].

15. $(\exists n)$ (n is even or n is odd) $= [(\exists n)\ n$ is even] or $[(\exists n)\ n$ is odd].

16. $(\exists n)(\exists m)\ 3m + 7n = 2$.

17. $(\forall m)(\exists n)\ m = 2n + 1$.

18. $(\forall n)$ (if $n \neq 0$ then $1 \leq n^2) = (\forall n)$ ($n = 0$ or $1 \leq n^2$).

19. $(\forall n)\ [(0 < n$ implies $1 \leq n)$ and $(n < 0$ implies $n \leq -1)] = (\forall n)\ (0 < n$ implies $1 \leq n)$.

20. $(\forall n)(\exists m)\ n + m = 0$.

21. $(\exists n)(\forall m)\ nm = 1$.

In Exercises 22–30 'x' is a variable on real numbers, and 'F_x' and 'G_x' are variables which may be replaced by any singulary propositional form in 'x'. In each exercise decide whether or not the given proposition is true. In each case give reasons for your decision.

22. $(\forall x)(F_x$ or $G_x) = (\forall x)\ F_x$ or $(\forall x)\ G_x$.

23. $(\forall x)(F_x$ and $G_x) = (\forall x)\ F_x$ and $(\forall x)\ G_x$.

24. $(\forall x)(F_x$ implies $G_x) = (\forall x)\ F_x$ implies $(\forall x)\ G_x$.

25. $(\forall x)(F_x$ implies $G_x) = (\exists x)(F_x$ implies $G_x)$.

26. $(\forall x)(F_x$ iff $G_x) = (\forall x)\ F_x$ iff $(\forall x)\ G_x$.

27. $(\exists x)(F_x$ or $G_x) = (\exists x)\ F_x$ or $(\exists x)\ G_x$.

28. $(\exists x)(F_x$ and $G_x) = (\exists x)\ F_x$ and $(\exists x)\ G_x$.

29. $(\exists x)(F_x$ implies $G_x) = (\exists x)\ F_x$ implies $(\exists x)\ G_x$.

30. $(\exists x)(F_x$ iff $G_x) = (\exists x)\ F_x$ iff $(\exists x)\ G_x$.

1.6 Definitions

From time to time we will enrich our mathematical language by adding new symbols. These special symbols we introduce by means of definitions using the notion of equivalence. For example, in Chapter 2 we find the definition

Z is the set of all integers.

The purpose of the definition is to establish that hereafter the symbol 'Z' will also be used as a name for the set of all integers.

We will also use the notion of equivalence to introduce new forms. For example, the juxtaposition of symbols to indicate multiplication is introduced by means of the definition

$$xy = x \cdot y.$$

Again we understand from the material preceding the definition that '$x \cdot y$' is a form in two variables. Following the definition we accept 'xy' as a form in two variables that is equivalent to '$x \cdot y$'.

When the form to be defined is a propositional form we usually prefer to use the biconditional connective rather than equality. As an example we find in Chapter 4 the definition

$$x \leq y \text{ iff } x < y \text{ or } x = y.$$

Following this definition we accept '$x \leq y$' as a propositional form in two variables which is equivalent to '$x < y$ or $x = y$'.

From our method of defining it is apparent that any statement that we make which uses a defined term could be made without its use. We need only replace the defined terms by equivalent expressions that involve only primitive notions. However, to do so would involve us in such lengthy and cumbersome circumlocutions that the intended meaning might be obscured. Defined terms provide a conciseness which hopefully will enhance the clarity.

1.7 Proof

Using our conventions for sentential connectives we can now describe a procedure for judging the truth value of compound sentences which hopefully will increase the accuracy of our judgment. We first judge the truth value of each component simple sentence. In a purely mechanical way the truth value of the compound sentence can then be determined from the truth values of its component parts by means of the appropriate truth tables.

With this procedure there are two main sources of error: (1) from the misuse of the conventions for sentential connectives and (2) from a mistaken judgment of the truth value of the simple component sentences. Errors of the first type are of a computational nature and can be kept to a minimum by means of appropriate checks. Errors of the second type, however, are more serious in that they may arise from unknown sources and hence be difficult to identify and eliminate. One obvious way to minimize errors of judgment is to develop procedures that are as mechanical as possible, thereby minimizing the number of judgments that we must make.

With this objective in mind let us recall that there are propositional forms which have the value t regardless of the values assigned to the variables, as for example

    p implies p (Reflexive law of [material] implication)

Such a form is called a *tautology*. It then follows that any sentence that can be obtained from a tautology by substitution is true. Thus

Cancer is caused by a virus implies cancer is caused by a virus

is true no matter what the cause of cancer is. Since tautologies can be identified by means of truth tables, the truth value of sentences that result from substitutions into tautologies can be determined without judging the truth values of their component parts.

Another procedure for mechanizing the process of determining the truth value of sentences is the so-called axiomatic method. With the axiomatic method certain sentences are designated as *axioms*. From the axioms other sentences called *theorems* are identified by the use of previously agreed upon rules called *rules of inference*. More precisely, the theorems are those sentences for which there exists a *proof*.

By choosing the rules of inference in such a way that from true sentences only true sentences can be inferred, it then follows that if the axioms are true then the theorems will also be true. The axiomatic method thereby enables us to judge the truth values of a large collection of sentences with a high degree of confidence in the outcome.

For our purposes we will accept the notion of proof as a primitive term. In the material ahead we will not refer to each result that we prove as a theorem. Certain results we will call theorems, others we will call *corollaries* or *lemmas* or *exercises*. An exercise is a result whose proof is left to the reader. A lemma is a result proved only as a steppingstone to a more important result. A corollary is, of course, always a corollary to a theorem and is a result that follows easily from that theorem.

If a result to be proved is an implication, then its antecedent will be called its *hypothesis* and its consequent we will call its *conclusion*. For example, Theorem 4.11 on page 77 asserts about real numbers that

$$\text{if } x + y = x, \text{ then } y = 0.$$

Here '$x + y = x$' is the hypothesis and '$y = 0$' is the conclusion. Since any implication with a false antecedent is true, it follows that to prove an implication it is sufficient to prove that if its antecedent is true then its consequent is also true. For the example at hand, it is sufficient to prove that if for some x and y it is true that

$$x + y = x$$

then it is also true that

$$y = 0.$$

In the construction of a proof of a theorem we may use the axioms, the definitions, any previously proved result, and the hypothesis of the theorem to be proved. From these we draw conclusions using only accepted principles of reasoning. For example, if among the axioms or theorems or the hypothesis of the theorem to be proved there is a sentence compounded with the 'and' connective, then since such sentences are true only if each component sentence is true, we may infer from a conjunction either of its component sentences. Since sentences compounded with the 'or' conjunction are true only if at least one component sentence is true, we may infer from a disjunction and the falseness of one component sentence the truth of the other component sentence. Similarly from the properties of implication we understand that from an implication and its antecedent we may infer its consequent. These observations we summarize as the following rules of inference.

From 'p and q' we may infer 'p' and we may infer 'q'.

From 'p or q' and '$\sim p$' we may infer 'q'.

From 'p implies q' and 'p' we may infer 'q'. (Rule of modus ponens)

This list of rules of inference is not intended to be complete but only suggestive of what a rule of inference is. By means of such rules we prove theorems by making inferences from axioms, theorems, definitions, and the hypothesis of the theorem to be proved. We make inferences from inferences until at last we have a chain of inferences connecting the hypothesis of a theorem to its conclusion in such a way as to make clear that the conclusion is true whenever the hypothesis is true.

Such a chain of inferences, however, is not unique; that is to say, a given theorem may have several different proofs. Furthermore if we begin with the hypothesis of a theorem and construct a chain of inferences we have no guarantee that this chain will lead to the desired conclusion. A proof is, therefore, not an accidental thing. Success in proving a given result frequently depends upon a well-thought-out plan of attack or *proof strategem*.

One such strategem is *proof by contradiction*. For this method of proof we use the axioms, the definitions, previously proved results, the hypothesis of the theorem, and in addition the negation of the conclusion of the theorem. We then attempt to infer a contradiction of a previously established result. If successful we then reason that the conclusion of our theorem is true because the assumption that it is false leads us to a contradiction.

A commonly used strategem is *proof by cases*. Suppose that we are required to prove that a certain property is true for each real number. On examining the problem we see a method by which we can prove the result is true for negative numbers and another method that we can use for nonnegative numbers. Since every real number is either negative or nonnegative the two arguments cover all possible situations, and we have a proof that requires us to consider two cases.

One reason for our interest in tautologies is that they sometimes suggest a proof strategem. For example, from the law of contraposition

$$p \text{ implies } q \text{ iff } \sim q \text{ implies } \sim p$$

we have a method of *proof by contraposition*. We refer to '$\sim q$ implies $\sim p$' as the contrapositive of 'p implies q'. The equivalence of an implication and its contrapositive assures us that in order to prove an implication it is sufficient to prove its contrapositive. For certain results the contrapositive may be easier to prove.

As a final example let us recall the tautology

$$p \text{ implies } (q \text{ or } r) \text{ iff } (p \text{ and } \sim q) \text{ implies } r.$$

In the proof of Theorem 4.13, that for real numbers x and y

$$\text{if } xy = 0 \text{ then } x = 0 \text{ or } y = 0$$

we find it convenient to prove that

$$\text{if } xy = 0 \text{ and } x \neq 0 \text{ then } y = 0.$$

The tautology assures us of the equivalence of the two implications.

In the next chapter we will provide examples of arguments that we consider to be proofs. The arguments that we offer are not intended to meet the rigid specifications of formal logic. It is hoped, however, that they do carry conviction.

CHAPTER 2

Introductory Naive Set Theory

2.0 Introduction

Most of the theorems that are proved in later chapters are concerned with properties that are common to each member of some particular collection of things. To assist us in expressing our thoughts about collections we introduce in this chapter certain concepts from *set theory*. For our purposes we will accept the word 'set' as a primitive term which is used as a synonym for 'collection'. Any collection of things we will call a set. The objects that comprise a given set we will call the *elements* of that set. Thus we will speak of the set of all integers rather than the collection of all integers, and the set of all real numbers rather than the collection of all real numbers. Each particular integer is an element of the set of all integers and each particular real number is an element of the set of all real numbers.

2.1 Set Notation

The set of all integers, the set of all rational numbers, and the set of all real numbers occur so often in later discussions that we introduce special symbols to denote them.

Definition 2.10. Z is the set of all integers.
$\qquad\qquad\qquad$ Q is the set of all rational numbers.
$\qquad\qquad\qquad$ R is the set of all real numbers.

The symbol '$\in$' will be used to indicate that a given object is an element of a given set. For example, to assert that 2 is an element of Z we write

$$2 \in Z,$$

which is read 2 *is an element of* Z or simply 2 *is in* Z. The assertion that $\frac{1}{2}$ is not an element of Z we express as

$$\tfrac{1}{2} \notin Z,$$

which is read $\frac{1}{2}$ *is not an element of* Z or simply $\frac{1}{2}$ *is not in* Z.

From our earlier discussions and the preceding examples it appears that a very natural way to describe a set of interest is to specify some property that is shared by its elements but not by any other objects. For example, when we speak of the set of all integers we have in mind a set characterized by the fact that each element of the set is an integer, and each object not in the set is not an integer. We find it very convenient to identify a characteristic property of a set by means of a propositional form. For example, the set of all positive integers is the set of objects for which the form

$$n \in Z \text{ and } n > 0$$

is true. We will denote this set by

$$\{n \mid n \in Z \text{ and } n > 0\},$$

which is read *the set of all n such that n is an element of Z and n is greater than* 0. The set of odd integers we denote as

$$\{m \mid (\exists n)(n \in Z \text{ and } m = 2n + 1)\}.$$

Having introduced a very useful notation we herewith declare our intention of taking liberties with it. The modifications that we have in mind are such that the context will make clear the intended meaning. We illustrate with a few examples.

The essential information expressed by the symbol

$$\{n \mid n \in Z \text{ and } n > 0\}$$

is conveyed with equal clarity by

$$\{n \in Z \mid n > 0\},$$

which we will read *the set of all n in Z such that n is greater than* 0. Similarly we will use

$$\{2n + 1 \mid n \in Z\},$$

which is read *the set of all 2n + 1 such that n is in Z,* as an abbreviation for

$$\{m \mid (\exists n)(n \in Z \text{ and } m = 2n + 1)\}.$$

As a final example note that

$$\{n \mid n \in Z \text{ and } 1 \le n \le 2\}$$

is a rather involved name for a very simple set. This set has only the two elements 1 and 2, a fact more readily conveyed by the notation

$$\{1, 2\}.$$

If a set contains few elements we will denote it by listing names of its elements between braces. Indeed in an appropriate context we may not even name all of the elements. We might write

$$\{1, 2, \ldots, 10\}$$

to denote the set of integers between 1 and 10 inclusively and we might write

$$\{1, 3, \ldots\}$$

to denote the set of positive odd integers. We hasten to point out that the ellipsis (...) indicates an omission and should only be used when the context makes clear what has been omitted.

For the discussion of set properties we will use capital letters

$$A, B, C, \ldots$$

as variables on sets. We will also wish to discuss collections of sets and we will use script letters

$$\mathscr{S}, \mathscr{T}, \ldots$$

as variables on sets of sets.

We will also use

$$\forall x \in A, \ldots$$

as an abbreviation for

$$(\forall x)(\text{if } x \in A, \text{ then } \ldots).$$

Thus, for example, the assertion

$$\forall x \in Z, \quad x \in Q$$

is to be understood as meaning that

$$(\forall x)(\text{if } x \in Z, \text{ then } x \in Q).$$

Similarly, we will use

$$\exists x \in A, \ldots$$

as an abbreviation for

$$(\exists x)(x \in A \text{ and } \ldots).$$

Thus

$$\exists n \in Z, \quad 5 = 2n + 1$$

means

$$(\exists n)(n \in Z \text{ and } 5 = 2n + 1).$$

Care must be taken with these abbreviations, particularly when they are negated. For example, the negation of the assertion that every integer is a rational number is the assertion that some integer is not a rational number; that is,

$$\sim(\forall x \in Z, \ x \in Q) = \exists x \in Z, \ x \notin Q.$$

Similarly, the negation of the assertion that

$$\exists n \in Z, \ 5 = 2n + 1$$

is the assertion that

$$\forall n \in Z, \ 5 \neq 2n + 1;$$

that is,

$$\sim(\exists n \in Z, 5 = 2n + 1) = \forall n \in Z, \ 5 \neq 2n + 1.$$

Using 'F_x' as a variable that may be replaced by any singulary form in 'x', we summarize these observations as

Theorem 2.11. 1) $\sim(\forall x \in A, F_x) = \exists x \in A, \sim F_x$.
  2) $\sim(\exists x \in A, F_x) = \forall x \in A, \sim F_x$.

Proof. 1) From the principles for the formal negation of sentences that contain quantifiers (see page 29) we have that

$$\sim(\forall x \in A, F_x) = \ \sim[(\forall x) \text{ if } x \in A, \text{ then } F_x] = (\exists x) \sim (\text{if } x \in A, \text{ then } F_x)$$
$$= (\exists x)(x \in A \text{ and } \sim F_x) = \exists x \in A, \sim F_x.$$

2) The proof is left to the reader.

EXERCISES

In Exercises 1–10 decide whether the given statement is true or false.

  1. $4 \in Z$.   **2.** $\pi \in Z$.   **3.** $\pi \notin Q$.
  4. $2 \in Q$.   **5.** $4 \in \{2n + 1 \mid n \in Z\}$.   **6.** $10 \in \{2n \mid n \in Z\}$.
  7. $-1 \in \{x \in R \mid x \geq 0\}$.
  8. $3 \in \{x \in R \mid x^4 + 3x^3 - 2x + 1 = 0\}$.
  9. $-1 \in \{x \in R \mid x^2 > 0\}$.
  10. $5 \notin \{p \mid \exists n \in Z, \exists m \in Z, n^2 + m^2 = p\}$.

In Exercises 11–19 decide whether the given statement is true or false. In each exercise $A = \{1, 2\}$, $B = \{1, 2, 3, 4\}$, $C = \{1, 3, 5\}$, $D = \{3, 4\}$.

  11. $\forall x \in A, x \in B$.   **12.** $\forall x \in A, x \in C$.   **13.** $\forall x \in A, x \notin D$.
  14. $\exists x \in B, x \notin C$.   **15.** $\exists x \in B, x \in C$.   **16.** $\exists x \in A, x \notin B$.
  17. $\sim(\forall x \in D, x \notin A)$.
  18. $\sim(\forall x \in B, x \in A)$.
  19. $\sim(\exists x \in C, x \notin D)$.

2.2 The Empty Set

While we have agreed to accept the word 'set' as an undefined term, which is intended to convey the notion of a collection, we find it convenient to make a slight modification of our intuitive idea. Our intuitive notion of a collection does not include a collection with nothing in it. However, just as in arithmetic it is convenient to extend our concept of number to include the number of apples in an empty basket, so also in set theory it is convenient to extend our concept of set to include a set having no elements. This set we call the *empty set*. We introduce a special symbol '∅' to denote it.

Definition 2.20. $A = ∅$ iff $(∀x)\, x ∉ A$.

The empty set has some very interesting and indeed curious properties. It is so defined that

$$(∀x)\, x ∉ ∅.$$

Indeed, this is true regardless of the range assigned to 'x'.
   Consider the ridiculous sounding assertion

$$(∀x) \text{ if } x ∈ ∅, \text{ then } x \text{ is a purple cow.}$$

From the truth table for the conditional it follows that since the form '$x ∈ ∅$' is false for every value of 'x', the form 'if $x ∈ ∅$, then x is a purple cow' is true for every value of 'x'. Consequently the proposition

$$(∀x) \text{ if } x ∈ ∅, \text{ then } x \text{ is a purple cow}$$

is true.
   For those who may entertain doubts about the truth of this proposition we point out that its negation

$$(∃x)\, x ∈ ∅ \text{ and } x \text{ is not a purple cow}$$

is certainly false because it asserts that ∅ contains an element.
   One reason for our interest in these propositions is that their truth values are immediate consequences of the properties of sentential connectives and the empty set and do not depend upon the truth values of the form

$$x \text{ is a purple cow.}$$

Consequently, the form

$$(∀x) \text{ if } x ∈ ∅, \text{ then } F_x$$

is true for each replacement of 'F_x' by a singular form in 'x'. This conclusion is of sufficient importance that we restate it as

Theorem 2.21. $∀x ∈ ∅,\, F_x$.

We sometimes paraphrase Theorem 2.21 by saying that the elements of the empty set have all properties. They even have "contradictory" properties in the sense that

$$(∀x) \text{ if } x ∈ ∅, \text{ then } x \text{ is a purple cow}$$

and

$$(∀x) \text{ if } x ∈ ∅, \text{ then } x \text{ is not a purple cow}$$

are both true.

2.3 Subsets

The fact that a given object is an element of a given set does not preclude the possibility of that same object also being an element of another set. Thus, for example, 1 is an element of $\{1, 2\}$, and it is also an element of Z. When each element of one set is also an element of a second set we say that the first set is a *subset* of the second. Thus $\{1, 2\}$ is a subset of Z. We write

$$\{1, 2\} \subseteq Z,$$

which is read $\{1, 2\}$ *is a subset of* Z.

Definition 2.30. $A \subseteq B$ iff $\forall x \in A,\ x \in B$.

Example. $\{1, 2\} \subseteq \{1, 2, 3, 4\},\ Z \subseteq Q,\ \{2n \mid n \in Z\} \subseteq Z,$
$\{1, 2\} \nsubseteq \{1, 3, 4\},\ Q \nsubseteq Z.$

From Definition 2.30 and Theorem 2.21 it follows that the empty set is a subset of every set. Indeed substituting '$x \in A$' for 'F_x' in Theorem 2.21 we have that

$$\forall x \in \varnothing,\quad x \in A.$$

From Definition 2.30 we then conclude that

$$\varnothing \subseteq A.$$

We have then proved

Theorem 2.31. $(\forall A)\ \varnothing \subseteq A$.

Another interesting proof of Theorem 2.31 can be obtained by asking how a given set can fail to be a subset of another. Negating Definition 2.30 we have that

$$A \nsubseteq B \text{ iff } \exists x \in A,\ x \notin B.$$

In particular

$$\varnothing \nsubseteq B \text{ iff } \exists x \in \varnothing,\ x \notin B.$$

Thus the existence of a set that does not have $\varnothing$ as a subset implies that $\varnothing$ has an element. This being false we conclude that $\varnothing$ is a subset of every set.

From the reflexive property of implication we can easily deduce another property of subsets, namely,

Theorem 2.32. $(\forall A)\ A \subseteq A$.

Proof.   Since the propositional form

$$\text{if } p, \text{ then } p$$

is a tautology it follows by substituting '$x \in A$' for 'p' that the form

$$\text{if } x \in A, \text{ then } x \in A$$

is true for each assignment of values to the variables 'x' and 'A'; that is,

$$(\forall A) \, \forall x \in A, \; x \in A.$$

From Definition 2.30 we conclude that

$$(\forall A) \, A \subseteq A. \qquad\qquad \text{Q.E.D.}$$

With this brief discussion we leave the remaining properties as exercises and conclude this section with two definitions concerning subsets.

There are contexts in which it is important to know that a certain subset is not the entire set under consideration. Such a subset we call a *proper subset*. Thus, for example, $\{1, 2\}$ is a proper subset of Z. We write

$$\{1, 2\} \subset Z,$$

which is read $\{1, 2\}$ *is a proper subset of* Z.

Definition 2.33. $A \subset B$ iff $A \subseteq B$ and $A \neq B$.

Example. $\{1, 2\} \subset \{1, 2, 3, 4\}$, $Z \subset Q$, $Q \subset R$,
$\{1, 2\} \not\subset \{1, 3, 4\}$, $Z \not\subset Z$.

In later chapters certain sets of sets will play an important role. Of special importance and interest are the *power sets*. By a power set we mean the set of all subsets of a given set.

Definition 2.34. $\text{Pow } A = \{B \mid B \subseteq A\}$.

Example. $\text{Pow}\{1, 2\} = \{\varnothing, \{1\}, \{2\}, \{1, 2\}\}$.

EXERCISES

In Exercises 1–12 decide whether the statement is true or false. In each exercise, $A = \{1, 2\}$, $B = \{1, 2, 3, 4\}$, $C = \{1, 3, 5\}$, $D = \{3, 4\}$.

1. $A \subset B$.　　2. $\varnothing \subseteq A$.　　3. $\varnothing \subset A$.　　4. $\varnothing \subset \varnothing$.
5. $A \subseteq C$.　　6. $C \subseteq D$.　　7. $A \subseteq \varnothing$.　　8. $D \subseteq B$.
9. $\text{Pow } \varnothing = \varnothing$.
10. $\text{Pow } C = \{\varnothing, \{1\}, \{3\}, \{5\}, \{1, 3, 5\}\}$.
11. $\text{Pow } \varnothing = \{\varnothing\}$.　　　　12. $\text{Pow } A = \text{Pow } D$.
13. Prove: If $A = B$ then $A \subseteq B$ and $B \subseteq A$.
14. Prove: If $A \subseteq B$ and $B \subseteq C$ then $A \subseteq C$.
15. Prove: $\varnothing \in \text{Pow } A$ and $A \in \text{Pow } A$.
16. Prove: $(\forall A)[A = \varnothing \text{ or } (\exists x) \, x \in A]$.
17. Prove: If $\forall n \in Z, Z_n = \{m \in Z \mid m \geq n\}$ then $Z_m \subseteq Z_n$ iff $m \geq n$.
18. Prove: If $\text{Pow } A = \text{Pow } B$ then $A = B$.

2.4 Equality

In Chapter 1 we discussed equality from the point of view of its use and meaning. Understanding the meaning of an equality statement does not, however, assure a knowledge of its truth value. Consider, for example, the assertion

$$3883628 = 742 \cdot 5234.$$

While the meaning is clear, the truth of the assertion is not obvious. By a simple computation we can, however, easily verify that the claim is correct.

In mathematics we are frequently confronted with equality statements that we are required to verify. The verification or proof must consist of an appeal to some accepted principle. For questions concerning sets we propose as a basic principle

The Axiom of Extent. $(\forall A)(\forall B)$ if $A \subseteq B$ and $B \subseteq A$, then $A = B$.

The idea here is a very simple one; if each element in A is also in B and if each element in B is also in A, then A and B must be the same collection. The converse of the axiom of extent is easily proved from the substitution rules of logic. Indeed if $A = B$, then

$$x \in A \text{ iff } x \in B.$$

Thus $A \subseteq B$ and $B \subseteq A$. Our basic principle for set equality is therefore the following

$$A = B \text{ iff } A \subseteq B \text{ and } B \subseteq A.$$

As a very simple illustration of this principle we will use it to prove the following obvious properties of equality for sets.

Theorem 2.40. $(\forall A)(\forall B)$
  1) $A = A$.
  2) *If* $A = B$, *then* $B = A$.
  3) *If* $A = B$ *and* $B = C$, *then* $A = C$.

Proof.   1) From an earlier theorem we have that

$$(\forall A) A \subseteq A.$$

Since the conjunction of true statements is true, it follows that

$$(\forall A) A \subseteq A \text{ and } (\forall A) A \subseteq A.$$

But universal quantifiers distribute over conjunction. Therefore

$$(\forall A)(A \subseteq A \text{ and } A \subseteq A).$$

From the axiom of extent we then conclude that

$$(\forall A) A = A.$$

2) If $A = B$, then $A \subseteq B$ and $B \subseteq A$. Consequently, $B \subseteq A$ and $A \subseteq B$. We then conclude from the axiom of extent that $B = A$.

3) If $A = B$ and $B = C$, then

$$(A \subseteq B \text{ and } B \subseteq A) \text{ and } (B \subseteq C \text{ and } C \subseteq B).$$

In particular, we have that

$$A \subseteq B \text{ and } B \subseteq C$$

and

$$C \subseteq B \text{ and } B \subseteq A.$$

From the transitive property for subsets it then follows that

$$A \subseteq C \text{ and } C \subseteq A.$$

By the axiom of extent it then follows that

$$A = C. \qquad \text{Q.E.D.}$$

EXERCISES

1. Prove: If $A \subseteq B$ and $B \subset C$, then $A \subset C$.

2. Prove: If $A \subset B$ and $B \subseteq C$, then $A \subset C$.

3. Prove: If $A \subset B$ and $B \subset C$, then $A \subset C$.

4. Prove: $\{x\} = \{y\}$ iff $x = y$.

5. Prove: If $x_\alpha = y_\alpha$, $\alpha = 1, 2, \ldots, n$, then $\{x_1, x_2, \ldots, x_n\} = \{y_1, y_2, \ldots, y_n\}$.

6. Prove: $\{x\} = \{y, z\}$ iff $x = y = z$.

7. Prove: If $x \neq y$ and $\{x, y\} = \{w, z\}$, then $w \neq z$.

8. Prove: If $x \neq y$, if $x = w$ and if $\{x, y\} = \{w, z\}$, then $y = z$.

9. Prove: $Z = \{x \in Q \mid x$ is a root of a polynomial equation with integral coefficients and leading coefficient 1$\}$.

10. Prove: $Z \neq \{x \in R \mid x$ is a root of a polynomial equation with integral coefficients and leading coefficient 1$\}$.

2.5 Set Union, Set Intersection, and Relative Complement

As the term suggests, the *union* of two sets is a set that contains each element of the two given sets and no others. Thus, for example, the union of $\{1, 2\}$ and $\{3\}$ is $\{1, 2, 3\}$. Similarly, the *intersection* of two sets is the set of all elements common to each of the two given sets; the intersection of $\{1, 2, 3\}$ and $\{2, 3, 4\}$ is $\{2, 3\}$. The union of $\{1, 2\}$ and $\{3\}$ we will denote by

$$\{1, 2\} \cup \{3\};$$

that is,

$$\{1, 2\} \cup \{3\} = \{1, 2, 3\}.$$

The intersection of $\{1, 2, 3\}$ and $\{2, 3, 4\}$ we will denote by

$$\{1, 2, 3\} \cap \{2, 3, 4\}.$$

Thus,

$$\{1, 2, 3\} \cap \{2, 3, 4\} = \{2, 3\}.$$

Definition 2.50. $A \cup B = \{x \mid x \in A \text{ or } x \in B\}.$
$A \cap B = \{x \mid x \in A \text{ and } x \in B\}.$

The symbol '$A \cup B$' is read A *union* B; '$A \cap B$' is read A *intersect* B.

The elementary properties of union and intersection we will leave as exercises with the following theorems as guides to their proof.

Theorem 2.51. 1) $A \cup B = B \cup A$.   (Commutative law for set union)
2) $A \cap B = B \cap A$. (Commutative law for set intersection)

Proof. 1) (By axiom of extent.) If $x \in A \cup B$, then $x \in A$ or $x \in B$. Therefore $x \in B$ or $x \in A$; that is, $x \in B \cup A$. Thus $A \cup B \subseteq B \cup A$. Similarly we can prove that $B \cup A \subseteq A \cup B$. It then follows from the axiom of extent that $A \cup B = B \cup A$.
Second Proof. $A \cup B = \{x \mid x \in A \text{ or } x \in B\} = \{x \mid x \in B \text{ or } x \in A\} = B \cup A$.
2) The proof is left to the reader.

Theorem 2.52. 1) $(A \cup B) \cup C = A \cup (B \cup C)$.
(Associative law for set union)
2) $(A \cap B) \cap C = A \cap (B \cap C)$.
(Associative law for set intersection)

Proof. 2) If $x \in (A \cap B) \cap C$, then $x \in A \cap B$, and $x \in C$. Therefore, $(x \in A \text{ and } x \in B)$ and $x \in C$. Consequently, $x \in A$ and $(x \in B \text{ and } x \in C)$. Hence $x \in A$ and $x \in B \cap C$. We then have that $x \in A \cap (B \cap C)$. Thus $(A \cap B) \cap C \subseteq A \cap (B \cap C)$. Similarly we can prove that $A \cap (B \cap C) \subseteq (A \cap B) \cap C$. From the axiom of extent we then conclude that $(A \cap B) \cap C = A \cap (B \cap C)$.
1) The proof is left to the reader.

By a repeated application of Definition 2.50 we can have unions and intersections of three sets, four sets, and indeed any finite collection of sets. But why not a union and an intersection for infinite collections of sets? If $\mathscr{S}$ is a collection of sets, what reasonable definition would we wish to give to the 'union of all sets in $\mathscr{S}$' and the 'intersection of all sets in $\mathscr{S}$'? We propose the following:

Definition 2.53. $\bigcup\limits_{A \in \mathscr{S}} A = \{x \mid \exists A \in \mathscr{S}, x \in A\}$.

$\bigcap\limits_{A \in \mathscr{S}} A = \{x \mid \forall A \in \mathscr{S}, x \in A\}$.

These symbols, for union and intersection, are a bit unwieldly. We will occasionally find it convenient to abbreviate them, in an appropriate context, to '$\bigcup \mathscr{S}$' and '$\bigcap \mathscr{S}$' which we will read the *union of all sets in $\mathscr{S}$* and the *intersection of all sets in $\mathscr{S}$* respectively.

Example.   If for each n in Z, $Z_n = \{m \in Z \mid m \geq n\}$, and if $\mathscr{S} = \{Z_n \mid n \geq 1\}$, then

$$\bigcup\limits_{A \in \mathscr{S}} A = Z_1 \quad \text{and} \quad \bigcap\limits_{A \in \mathscr{S}} A = \varnothing .$$

Proof.   For each x in $\bigcup \mathscr{S}$ there exists a set A in $\mathscr{S}$ such that $x \in A$. But since $A \in \mathscr{S}$, there exists an integer n in Z, for which $A = Z_n$. We then have that $x \in Z_n$ and since $Z_n \subseteq Z_1$, it follows that $x \in Z_1$. Thus $\bigcup \mathscr{S} \subseteq Z_1$. But for each n in Z_1 we have that $n \in Z_n$ and $Z_n \in \mathscr{S}$; hence $Z_1 \subseteq \bigcup \mathscr{S}$. By the axiom of extent we then have $\bigcup \mathscr{S} = Z_1$.

If $x \in \bigcap \mathscr{S}$, then since $Z_1 \in \mathscr{S}$ we have that $x \in Z_1$; hence $Z_{x+1} \in \mathscr{S}$ and $x \in Z_{x+1}$. But this means that $x \geq x + 1$, which is a contradiction. We then have that for each x, $x \notin \bigcap \mathscr{S}$; hence $\bigcap \mathscr{S} = \varnothing$.

In addition to our interest in unions and intersections of sets we are sometimes concerned with the collection of elements that are in one of two given sets but not in the other. Such a set is called a *relative complement*.

Definition 2.54. $A - B = \{x \in A \mid x \notin B\}$.

Example. $\{1, 2\} - \{2, 4, 7\} = \{1\}$.
$\{2, 4, 7\} - \{1, 2\} = \{4, 7\}$.

In the study of set properties it is sometimes helpful to use pictorial representations of sets such as the so-called Venn diagrams in which we think of the elements of a set as represented by the points inside a circle. By the intersecting of circles and the shading of appropriate areas we can obtain very useful pictures of a very general nature. Thus, for example, the union, intersection, and relative complement of two sets may be represented graphically as shown in Figure 2.1. Venn diagrams can be useful in deciding

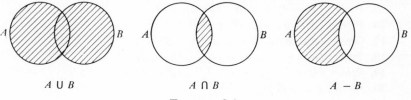

$A \cup B$ $A \cap B$ $A - B$

FIGURE 2.1

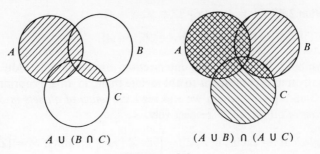

$$A \cup (B \cap C) \qquad\qquad (A \cup B) \cap (A \cup C)$$

FIGURE 2.2

the plausibility of certain statements about sets—as, for example, the claim that

$$A \cup (B \cap C) = (A \cup B) \cap (A \cup C).$$

From the Venn diagrams for $A \cup (B \cap C)$ and $(A \cup B) \cap (A \cup C)$ (Figure 2.2) it appears that the assertion is true; the claim being plausible, we then seek a proof.

EXERCISES

1. Prove: $(A \cup A) = (A \cap A) = A$.
2. Prove: $A \subseteq (A \cup B)$ and $(A \cap B) \subseteq A$.
3. Prove: $(A \cup B) = B$ iff $A \subseteq B$.
4. Prove: $(A \cap B) = A$ iff $A \subseteq B$.
5. Prove: $(\varnothing \cup A) = A$ and $(\varnothing \cap A) = \varnothing$.
6. Prove: $(A \cup B) = \varnothing$ iff $A = \varnothing$ and $B = \varnothing$.
7. Prove: i) $A \cap (B \cup C) = (A \cap B) \cup (A \cap C)$.
   ii) $A \cup (B \cap C) = (A \cup B) \cap (A \cup C)$.
   (Hint: See De Morgan's Laws, page 26.)
8. Prove: If $\mathscr{S} = \mathrm{Pow}\, B$, then $\bigcup \mathscr{S} = B$.
9. Prove: If $\mathscr{S} = \mathrm{Pow}\, B$, then $\bigcap \mathscr{S} = \varnothing$.
10. Prove: If $\mathscr{S} \subseteq \mathrm{Pow}\, B$, then $\bigcup \mathscr{S} \subseteq B$.
11. Prove: If $\mathscr{S} \subseteq \mathrm{Pow}\, B$, then $\bigcap \mathscr{S} \subseteq B$.
12. Prove: If $A = (B \cup C)$, then $(A - C) \subseteq B$.
13. Prove: $A - (A - B) = (A \cap B)$.
14. Prove: $(A \cup B) - C = (A - C) \cup (B - C)$.
15. Prove: $(A - B) = A$ iff $(A \cap B) = \varnothing$.
16. Prove: $(A - B) = \varnothing$ iff $A \subseteq B$.
17. Prove: $(A \cup B) - A = B$ iff $(A \cap B) = \varnothing$.
18. Prove: $(B - \bigcup_{A \in \mathscr{S}} A) = \bigcap_{A \in \mathscr{S}} (B - A)$.
19. Prove: $(B - \bigcap_{A \in \mathscr{S}} A) = \bigcup_{A \in \mathscr{S}} (B - A)$.
20. Prove: $x = y$ iff $\{x, y\} - \{x\} = \varnothing$.
21. Prove: $(A \cap B) = \varnothing$ iff $\forall x \in A,\ x \notin B$.

★2.6 Set Axioms

This section is intended for the reader who is interested in a deeper understanding of the theory of sets and may be omitted without loss of continuity.

Early in this chapter we found it convenient to refer to certain sets as the collection of all objects for which a given singulary form is true. We tacitly assumed that if 'F_x' is a variable that may be replaced by any singulary form in 'x', then for each such replacement in

$$\{x \mid F_x\}$$

we obtain the name of a set. This, of course, presumes that there is exactly one set having the given property; that is, we have assumed that for each F_x there is one and only one set A with the property that

$$x \in A \text{ iff '}F_x\text{' is true.}$$

That there is at most one such set follows easily from

The Axiom of Extent. If $A \subseteq B$ and $B \subseteq A$, then $A = B$.

Indeed if

$$x \in A \text{ iff '}F_x\text{' is true}$$

and

$$x \in B \text{ iff '}F_x\text{' is true}$$

it follows that

$$x \in A \text{ iff } x \in B.$$

But this implies that

$$A \subseteq B \text{ and } B \subseteq A$$

and hence from the axiom of extent

$$A = B.$$

Thus from the axiom of extent we are assured that symbols such as

$$\{x \mid x \text{ is a purple cow}\}$$

express a sense that is a concept of at most one set. On the other hand, we agreed in Chapter 1 that there are names that have no denotation. Is it possible that for some replacement of 'F_x'

$$\{x \mid F_x\}$$

is a name without denotation? Early in this century Bertrand Russell made the startling discovery that such names do indeed exist. As proof of this he gave the following example, which is known as the Russell paradox.

Consider the form

$$x \notin x.$$

Does the name

$$\{x \mid x \notin x\}$$

have a denotation? That is to say, is the assertion

$$(\exists A)\, A = \{x \mid x \notin x\}$$

true or false?

If such a set exists, then of this set Mr. Russell asks the following critical question:

Is A an element of itself?

Our intuition tells us that no set should be an element of itself. The set of all integers is not an integer; the set of all rational numbers is not a rational number. However, suppose that we are very broadminded about it all, and we consider the possibility that A might be an element of A. If so then since the form

$$x \notin x$$

is true for each element of A, it follows that it is also true for A; that is,

$$A \notin A.$$

Thus the assumption that A is an element of A leads to the contradiction that A is not an element of A.

This restores our faith in our intuition about sets. The assumption that A is an element of A leads us to a contradiction which forces us to conclude that the assumption is false; therefore, A is not an element of A. But one moment! If A is not an element of A, then A must not have the property that characterizes its elements, that is, the form

$$x \notin x$$

must be false for A and hence

$$A \in A.$$

The assumption that A is not an element of A leads to the contradiction that A is an element of A. The only escape from this dilemma is to deny that such a set exists and to accept

$$\{x \mid x \notin x\}$$

as a name without denotation. We are thereby compelled to agree that speaking of the set of all objects for which a given propositional form is true may involve us in a conversation about nothing.

In view of the Russell paradox it is reasonable to ask: Under what conditions can we speak of a set with confidence that such a set exists? Surely it is true that for any given singular propositional form there is some set, although possibly only the empty set, such that the form is true for each element of that set. The difficulty must, therefore, lie in the use of the word 'all' in such a universal sense. Suppose we confine our discussion to some less inclusive collection of objects. For illustrative purposes we take the set of all real numbers. Does the existence of the set of all real numbers for which a given propositional form is true involve us in a contradiction? Let us test for the Russell type paradox using the form

$$x \notin x.$$

Is it true that

$$(\exists A)\, A = \{x \mid x \in R \text{ and } x \notin x\}?$$

If so, we ask again

Is A an element of itself?

If A is an element of A, then the form

$$x \in R \text{ and } x \notin x$$

is true for A, which is to say that

$$A \in R \text{ and } A \notin A.$$

Again the hypothesis that A is an element of A leads to the contradiction that A is not an element of A.

On the other hand, if A is not an element of A, then the form

$$x \in R \text{ and } x \notin x$$

must be false for A, which is to say that

$$A \notin R \text{ or } A \in A.$$

Here no contradiction arises, for we are quite happy to conclude that $A \notin A$ and $A \notin R$.

From this example, we see that the Russell paradox can be resolved by speaking not of all objects for which a given form is true but rather of all objects in a given set for which the form is true. We will use the notation

$$\{x \in B \mid F_x\},$$

which is read the *set of all x in B such that F_x*.

We feel very strongly that the set of all objects in a given set for which a given singular form is true does exist. Since no paradox is known which would destroy our faith in this idea, we accept it as a basic principle, which we call

The Axiom of Separation. $(\forall B)(\forall F_x)(\exists A)\, A = \{x \in B \mid F_x\}.$

From the Russell paradox we might feel compelled to take a very skeptical point of view and question the existence of all sets. To do so would be to put the cart before the horse. The integers, for example, are a cornerstone of mathematics. If our theory of sets should bring us to the conclusion that the collection of all integers is a meaningless subject for discourse, then our next step is obvious. We would reject set theory. We, therefore, rephrase our question and ask: On what assumptions is our faith in sets founded? We have stated the axiom of extent and the axiom of separation as two such assumptions. Are they sufficient? Can we infer the existence of any particular set from them? The axiom of extent gives information only about existing sets. From the axiom of separation we can infer the existence of sets, but only from the knowledge that other sets exist. For example, if we accept the existence of the empty set, then from the empty set alone we cannot infer, from the axiom of separation, the existence of any other set. If we accept the existence of the set of all integers, Z, then we can infer the existence of any subset of Z that we can conceive of, but we cannot infer from Z alone the existence of any set that is not a subset of Z.

It would then seem that the proper solution is to hypothesize the existence of a universal set that contains everything we wish to talk about. The existence of such a set, however, brings us back to the Russell paradox, for since we wish to talk about sets, this universal set must contain all sets. Let us for the moment accept the idea and christen this universal set U. From the axiom of separation it then follows that

$$(\exists A)\, A = \{B \in U \mid B \notin B\};$$

that is, A is the set of all sets that are not elements of themselves. We then ask Mr. Russell's question:

Is A an element of itself?

As before, the answer is that A is an element of A if and only if A is not an element of A. The idea of a universal set must then be rejected.

Curiously, it has been found that the best place to begin is not at the top but at the bottom. We postulate the existence of an empty set.

The Empty Set Axiom. $(\exists A)(\forall x)\, x \notin A$.

From the axiom of extent it is immediately apparent that only one such set exists. This set we denote by '$\varnothing$', which is read the *empty set*.

As we pointed out earlier, our intuitive notion of a collection does not include a collection with nothing in it. Nor do we intuitively distinguish between an object and a collection consisting of just that object. For mathematical purposes, however, it is important to make such a distinction. We, therefore, take the point of view that to be given an object is not the same thing as to be given a set that contains only that object; to be given a pair of objects is not the same thing as to be given a set consisting of just those two objects. Must we then postulate the existence of all one-element sets, two-element sets, three-element sets, etc.? Fortunately the answer is no. It is only necessary to make the assumption that all singleton and doubleton sets exist. This idea we express as

The Axiom of Pairing. $(\forall x)(\forall y)(\exists A)\, x \in A$ and $y \in A$.

Note that the axiom of pairing does not assert uniqueness. It asserts that A contains x and y. It does not assert that A is the only such set, and it does not assert that A contains only x and y. The existence of a set whose only elements are x and y follows from the axiom of separation, which assures us that

$$(\exists B)\, B = \{z \in A \mid z = x \text{ or } z = y\}.$$

B then has the property that

$$z \in B \text{ iff } z = x \text{ or } z = y.$$

That there is only one such set follows from the axiom of extent.

In the axiom of pairing the assignment of the same value to 'x' and to 'y' is not excluded. We have, therefore, just established that for each object there is one and only one set having that object as its only element, and given any pair of objects there is one and only one set that contains those two objects and only those two objects as elements. We can then obtain sets with any specified number of elements as the union of an appropriate collection of singleton sets. But there is an assumption tacit in this statement—namely, that the union of a given collection of sets exists. This is our next article of faith which we state as

The Axiom of Unions. $(\forall \mathscr{S})(\exists B)\, B = \bigcup\limits_{A \in \mathscr{S}} A$.

It is interesting to observe that the axiom of unions alone does not insure the existence of the union of two given sets, for the axiom of unions is a property of sets of sets. To prove the existence of $A \cup B$ we appeal to the axiom of pairing to establish the existence of $\{A, B\}$. Then if $\mathscr{S} = \{A, B\}$ we use the axiom of extent to prove that $A \cup B = \bigcup \mathscr{S}$.

A new axiom is not required to establish the existence of the intersection of two sets, for from the axiom of separation we have the existence of

$$\{x \in A \mid x \in B\}.$$

From the axiom of extent it can then be easily proved that

$$A \cap B = \{x \in A \mid x \in B\}.$$

Another set building notion is the idea of a power set. Does the power set of any given set exist? We choose to believe that it does. Unable to prove a theorem to this effect, we must state a postulate:

The Power Set Axiom. $(\forall A)(\exists B)\, B = \text{Pow } A$.

We have now postulated the existence of the empty set, $\varnothing$. From the axiom of pairing we can infer the existence of the singleton set $\{\varnothing\}$. Since $\varnothing \in \{\varnothing\}$, it follows that $\varnothing \neq \{\varnothing\}$. Again, from the axiom of pairing, using the distinct objects $\varnothing$ and $\{\varnothing\}$, we can infer the existence of the doubleton set $\{\varnothing, \{\varnothing\}\}$. From this in turn we can infer the existence of the singleton set $\{\{\varnothing, \{\varnothing\}\}\}$ and hence the three-element set

$$\{\varnothing, \{\varnothing\}, \{\varnothing, \{\varnothing\}\}\} = \{\varnothing, \{\varnothing\}\} \cup \{\{\varnothing, \{\varnothing\}\}\}.$$

In general, for any set B the axiom of pairing assures the existence of $\{B\}$ and the axiom of unions assures the existence of $B \cup \{B\}$. Since $B \cup \{B\}$ contains every element of B and one additional element that is not in B—namely, B itself—we then have a process by which we can generate sets with any specified number of elements; from a set with no elements it produces a set with one element, from a set with one element it produces a set with two elements, etc. Note, however, that by this process we obtain only finite sets. Indeed each axiom stated thus far only enables us to infer from finite sets the existence of other finite sets. To obtain an infinite set we must, therefore, hypothesize the existence of at least one such set. Hence,

The Axiom of Infinity. $(\exists A)\ \varnothing \in A$ and $(\forall B)$ if $B \in A$, then $B \cup \{B\} \in A$.

Our confidence that the axiom of infinity asserts the existence of an infinite set centers around the defining property for A and the fact that the sets B_n defined inductively by

$$B_0 = \varnothing,$$
$$B_{n+1} = (B_n \cup \{B_n\})$$

are each elements of A and they are all different—that is,

$$B_m = B_n \text{ iff } m = n.$$

To prove this it is sufficient to show that

$$(\forall n)\ B_n \neq B_m, \qquad m = 0, 1, \ldots, n - 1.$$

Let us for the moment entertain the possibility that

$$(\exists m)(\exists n)\ B_n = B_m \text{ and } m < n.$$

If $m = n - 1$, then we would have

$$B_n = (B_{n-1} \cup \{B_{n-1}\}) = B_{n-1}.$$

Hence

$$B_{n-1} \in B_{n-1}.$$

Intuitively we are happy to reject this on the grounds that no set should be an element of itself. If $m = n - 2$, we then have

$$B_n = (B_{n-1} \cup \{B_{n-1}\}) = B_{n-2},$$
$$B_{n-1} = (B_{n-2} \cup \{B_{n-2}\}).$$

Hence

$$B_{n-1} \in B_{n-2} \text{ and } B_{n-2} \in B_{n-1}.$$

Similarly we can deduce that if $m < n$, then

$$B_m \in B_{m+1} \in \cdots \in B_{n-1} \in B_m.$$

We must, therefore, reject the existence of not only sets that contain themselves as elements but all chains of sets with the above property. All such possibilities are excluded by the following axiom due to Zermelo:

The Axiom of Regularity. $(\forall A)$ if $A \neq \varnothing$, then $\exists x \in A, \forall y \in x, y \notin A$.

We illustrate the role of the axiom of regularity by proving that no set is an element of itself. Indeed since $\{A\} \neq \varnothing$ it follows from the axiom of regularity that

$$\exists x \in \{A\}, \quad \forall y \in x, \quad y \notin \{A\}.$$

But $x \in \{A\}$ iff $x = A$ and $y \notin \{A\}$ iff $y \neq A$. We, therefore, conclude that

$$\text{if } y \in A, \text{ then } y \neq A,$$

the contrapositive of which is

$$\text{if } y = A, \text{ then } y \notin A.$$

We then conclude that $A \notin A$.

It is an interesting fact that using only the notion of set and element as primitive terms it is possible to define all other concepts presently in use in mathematics, including such basic notions as those of number, relation, and function. The construction of the real numbers as a part of set theory is a project that is well beyond the scope of this text. We must therefore refer the interested reader to those texts that are devoted to this subject. The definition of functions and relations as specific types of sets we will take up in the next chapter.

CHAPTER 3

Functions and Relations

3.0 Introduction

Functions and relations we choose to define in terms of ordered pairs. This makes the concept of ordered pair a rather fundamental one. We could, of course, accept this concept as primitive and simply discuss the basic properties of ordered pairs that concern us. For example, we will be interested in the fact that for distinct objects such as 1 and 2 there are two such pairs denoted by '(1, 2)' and '(2, 1)' respectively. The basic property of ordered pairs is, of course, that

$$(a, b) = (c, d) \text{ iff } a = c \text{ and } b = d.$$

However, to avoid the continued proliferation of primitive notions we choose instead to provide a definition from set theory.

Definition 3.00. $(a, b) = \{\{a\}, \{a, b\}\}$.

The symbol '(a, b)' is read the *ordered pair a, b*; a is the *first entry* of the pair and b is the *second entry*.

The acceptability of this definition rests upon establishing that ordered pairs do have the basic property that we expect of ordered pairs. This we prove as

Theorem 3.01. $(a, b) = (c, d)$ *iff* $a = c$ *and* $b = d$.

Proof. If $a = c$ and $b = d$, then $\{a\} = \{c\}$ and $\{a, b\} = \{c, d\}$. It then follows that

$$(a, b) = \{\{a\}, \{a, b\}\} = \{\{c\}, \{c, d\}\} = (c, d).$$

Conversely, if $(a, b) = (c, d)$ then $a = b$ or $a \neq b$. If $a = b$, then $\{a\} = \{a, b\}$ and consequently

$$(a, b) = \{\{a\}\}.$$

54

Since $(a, b) = (c, d)$, we then have that

$$\{\{a\}\} = \{\{c\}, \{c, d\}\},$$

from which it follows that $a = b = c = d$.

If $a \neq b$, then from the preceding argument it follows that $c \neq d$. Since $(a, b) = (c, d)$, it follows that

$$\{a\} \in \{\{c\}, \{c, d\}\}.$$

Since $\{a\} \neq \{c, d\}$ (why?), it follows that $\{a\} = \{c\}$ and hence $a = c$. But

$$\{a, b\} \in \{\{c\}, \{c, d\}\}$$

and since $\{a, b\} \neq \{c\}$ we must have $\{a, b\} = \{c, d\}$. From this we conclude that $b = d$. (Why?)

Q.E.D.

In the material ahead we will be interested in certain sets of ordered pairs. Of special interest are those sets consisting of all ordered pairs whose first entries are in a given set A and whose second entries are in a given set B. Such a set we will denote by '$A \times B$' and call the *cross product* of A with B.

Definition 3.02. $A \times B = \{(x, y) \mid x \in A \text{ and } y \in B\}$.

Example. $\{1, 2\} \times \{3, 4, 5\} = \{(1, 3), (1, 4), (1, 5), (2, 3), (2, 4), (2, 5)\}$.

3.1 Relations

As is the case with many mathematical terms, the word 'relation' has a meaning for the mathematician that differs from the usual nonmathematical usage. Fortunately there is a connection.

We frequently make statements such as

John is older than Mary,

John is heavier than Bill,

or

The Empire State Building is taller than the Washington Monument.

These statements describe relationships between the objects named. We recognize that these relationships exist between other pairs of objects. Thus, in a given collection of people, the concept *older than* defines in a very natural way a set of ordered pairs of people having the property that the first person is older than the second. We have the relation *older than* and a set of ordered pairs determined by that relation. The notion of being *older than* is not particularly useful in mathematics. On the other hand, sets of ordered pairs are very useful. For mathematical purposes we, therefore, transfer the word 'relation' from the concept *older than* to the set of ordered pairs determined by that concept,[1] thus

Definition 3.10. C is a *relation* iff C is a set of ordered pairs.

Example. $\{(1, 2), (1, 3), (2, 3)\}$ and $\{(1, 3), (3, 2), (2, 3)\}$ are relations.

The reader is cautioned not to read into Definition 3.10 anything that is not there. The idea stated is a very simple one and should not be complicated by preconceived notions of what a relation *ought* to be. By definition a relation is simply a set of ordered pairs. It is that and nothing more. The definition does not require that things be paired in any intelligent or meaningful way. Consider, for example, $\{(1, 2), (1, 3), (2, 3)\}$. This relation may be thought of as having been obtained from $\{1, 2, 3\}$ by pairing in such a way that the first entry is smaller than the second. It would, therefore, seem natural to refer to this relation as the *relation less than*.

On the other hand, $\{(1, 3), (3, 2), (2, 3)\}$ is a relation that does not call to mind any idea of importance. We must grant, of course, that our thinking is prejudiced by our knowledge that the ordering of integers is a very useful idea. By a considerable stretch of the imagination we can conceive of the existence of a context in which $\{(1, 3), (3, 2), (2, 3)\}$ is of such importance that it, too, would merit a special name.

With each relation we associate three sets called the *domain*, *range*, and *field* of that relation. The domain is the set of all first entries of the ordered pairs in the relation. The range is the set of all second entries. The field is the union of the domain and the range. More formally stated we have

Definition 3.11.   Dom $C = \{x \mid (\exists y)(x, y) \in C\}$.
        Ran $C = \{y \mid (\exists x)(x, y) \in C\}$.
        Fld $C = (\text{Dom } C \cup \text{Ran } C)$.

Thus, for example,

Dom $\{(1, 2), (1, 3), (2, 3)\} = \{1, 2\}$,   Ran $\{(1, 2), (1, 3), (2, 3)\} = \{2, 3\}$.
Dom $\{(1, 3), (3, 2), (2, 3)\} = \{1, 2, 3\}$, Ran $\{(1, 3), (3, 2), (2, 3)\} = \{2, 3\}$.
Fld $\{(1, 2), (1, 3), (2, 3)\} = \{1, 2, 3\} = $ Fld $\{(1, 3), (3, 2), (2, 3)\}$.

A relation is said to be a relation *between* its domain and its range. It is also a relation *on* its field.

Definition 3.12.   A relation C is a relation *between* A and B iff $A = \text{Dom } C$ and $B = \text{Ran } C$. A relation C is a relation *on* A iff $A = \text{Fld } C$.

Example. $\{(1, 2), (1, 3), (2, 3)\}$ is a relation between $\{1, 2\}$ and $\{2, 3\}$ and a relation on $\{1, 2, 3\}$.

---

[1] Logicians refer to concepts such as *older than* as *relations* and refer to the sets of ordered pairs determined by such concepts as *relations in extension*.

If C is a relation, then

$$\{(y, x) \mid (x, y) \in C\}$$

is also a relation. This relation we give a special name.

Definition 3.13. If C is a relation, then

$$\{(y, x) \mid (x, y) \in C\}$$

is the *converse* of C.

3.2 Equivalence Relations and Order Relations

As was pointed out in our earlier discussion, the concept of a relation is a very general one. We turn now to special kinds of relations that are of interest. The first that we wish to consider are the so-called *equivalence relations*.

Definition 3.20. A relation C is an *equivalence relation* iff it has the following properties.

    1) If $(x, y) \in C$, then $(y, x) \in C$.   (Symmetry property)

    2) If $(x, y) \in C$ and $(y, z) \in C$, then $(x, z) \in C$. (Transitivity property)

C is an equivalence relation *on* A iff C is an equivalence relation and C is a relation on A.

As an example we will prove that if $C = \{(m, n) \in Z \times Z \mid m - n \text{ is even}\}$, then C is an equivalence relation on Z.

Proof. If $(m, n) \in C$, then $m - n$ is even; consequently $n - m$ is even. Therefore $(n, m) \in C$. If $(m, n) \in C$ and $(n, p) \in C$, then $m - n$ and $n - p$ are each even; consequently, their sum $m - p$ is even. Thus $m - p \in C$ and C is an equivalence relation. Clearly Fld $C = Z$, for if $n \in Z$, then $n - n$ is even. Therefore, $(n, n) \in C$ and $n \in$ Fld C. Thus $Z \subseteq$ Fld C. Conversely, if $n \in$ Fld $C = ($Dom $C \cup$ Ran $C)$, then for some integer m, $(m, n) \in C$ or $(n, m) \in C$. In either case, $n \in Z$ and Fld $C \subseteq Z$.

                                                  Q.E.D.

As additional examples of equivalence relations we suggest for the reader's consideration parallelism and the set of all lines in the plane, and equality of area with the set of all triangles in the plane. For the first example it is, of course, necessary that we require a line to be parallel to itself.

Another class of relations of interest are the *order relations*.

Definition 3.21. A relation C is an *order relation* iff it has the following properties:

1) For each x and y in Fld C one and only one of the following is true:

$$(x, y) \in C \text{ or } x = y \text{ or } (y, x) \in C \quad \text{(Trichotomy property)}$$

2) If $(x, y) \in C$ and $(y, z) \in C$, then $(x, z) \in C$ (Transitivity property)

C is an order relation *on* A iff C is an order relation and $A = $ Fld C.

The order relation of greatest interest to us is the usual order relation on the real numbers, which traditionally is denoted by '$<$'. Its definition is beyond the scope of this text. We will assume that the reader is familiar with the elementary order properties of the real numbers, although they will be reviewed in the next chapter. For the moment we will be content with the following, rather unimpressive,

Example. $\{(1, 2), (1, 3), (2, 3)\}$ is an order relation.

We can, however, suggest some interesting geometric examples. Consider for instance the set of all line segments in the plane and the idea of one line segment being shorter than another or the set of all triangles in the plane and the idea of one triangle having less area than another.

For discussing the properties of equivalence relations and order relations it is customary to introduce a symbol such as '$\sim$' as a variable on such relations and to write '$x \sim y$' instead of '$(x, y) \in \sim$'. The basic properties then assume a more familiar form:

$$\text{if } x \sim y, \text{ then } y \sim x,$$
$$\text{if } x \sim y \text{ and } y \sim z, \text{ then } x \sim z,$$
$$x \sim y \text{ or } x = y \text{ or } y \sim x.$$

EXERCISES

1. Prove: $A \times B = \varnothing$ iff $A = \varnothing$ or $B = \varnothing$.
2. Prove: $A \times B = B \times A$ iff $A = \varnothing$ or $B = \varnothing$ or $A = B$.
3. Prove: Dom $(A \times B) = A$ iff $B \neq \varnothing$.
4. Prove: Ran $(A \times B) = B$ iff $A \neq \varnothing$.
5. Prove: Fld $(A \times B) = (A \cup B)$ iff $A \times B \neq \varnothing$.
6. Prove: If C is a relation between A and B, then the converse of C is a relation between B and A.
7. Prove: $(\forall A)(\forall B)$ if $A \times B \neq \varnothing$, then $A \times B$ is a relation between A and B.
8. Prove: $(\forall A)$ $A \times A$ is an equivalence relation on A.
9. Prove: $\{(n, n) \mid n \in Z\}$ is an equivalence relation on Z.
10. Prove: $\{(m, n) \in Z \times Z \mid m - n \text{ is a multiple of } 3\}$ is an equivalence relation on Z.

11. Prove: If C is an equivalence relation, then Dom $C =$ Ran $C =$ Fld C.

12. Prove: An equivalence relation is its own converse.

13. Prove: If C is an equivalence relation, then $\forall x \in$ Fld C, $(x, x) \in C$.

14. Prove: C is an equivalence relation on A iff $(\forall x)(\forall y)(\forall z)$ the following hold:

   1) $x \in A$ iff $(x, x) \in C$.

   2) If $(x, y) \in C$, then $(y, x) \in C$.

   3) If $(x, y) \in C$ and $(y, z) \in C$, then $(x, z) \in C$.

15. Prove: If A contains more than one element, then the set of all equivalence relations on A and the set of all order relations on A have an empty intersection.

16. Prove: The converse of an order relation is an order relation.

17. Is the union of any two equivalence relations an equivalence relation?

18. Is the intersection of any two equivalence relations an equivalence relation?

19. Is the relative complement of any two equivalence relations an equivalence relation?

20. Is the union of any two order relations an order relation?

21. Is the intersection of any two order relations an order relation?

22. Is the relative complement of any two order relations an order relation?

23. List all equivalence relations on $\{1, 2, 3\}$. (Hint: There are five.)

24. List all order relations on $\{1, 2, 3\}$.

25. Define relations on $\{1, 2, 3\}$ with each of the following properties:

   1) Symmetric but not transitive.

   2) Transitive but not symmetric.

   3) Neither symmetric nor transitive.

26. If E is an equivalence relation, what is a necessary and sufficient condition for $E - S$ to be an equivalence relation?

3.3 Functions

A very important and interesting class of relations consists of those having the property of being single valued. A relation is single valued if and only if it contains no two ordered pairs with the same first entry. For example,

$$\{(1, 2), (3, 1), (4, 2)\}$$

is a single valued relation as we see by checking the first entries and finding no duplications. The relation

$$\{(1, 2), (1, 1), (4, 2)\}$$

is not a function, since it contains two (different) pairs, $(1, 2)$ and $(1, 1)$, with the same first entry. As one might expect, a relation that is not single valued is called *multiple valued*.

Definition 3.30. C is a *function* iff C is a single valued relation—i.e., iff C is a relation with the property that

$$\text{if } (x, y) \in C \text{ and } (x, z) \in C, \text{ then } y = z.$$

We will use symbols such as

$$f, g, h, \phi, \psi, \eta$$

as variables on functions.

The importance of the single valuedness property lies in the fact that for each element of the domain of a function there is one and only one element of the range that is paired with it. Thus a function associates with each element of its domain a unique element of its range. This justifies the special and traditional notation of

Definition 3.31. $y = f(x)$ iff $(x, y) \in f$.

Example. If $f = \{(1, 2),\ (3, 1),\ (4, 2)\}$, then $f(1) = 2$, $f(3) = 1$ and $f(4) = 2$.

A function that has few elements can be described by listing its ordered pairs—as, for example, $\{(1, 2), (3, 3), (5, 7)\}$ and $\{(1, 2), (3, 7), (4, 6)\}$. We may find it more convenient to list the pairs in a tabular form such as

1	2		1	2
3	3		3	7
5	7		4	6

The first column lists the first entries, and the second column lists the corresponding second entries. Such a table is impracticable for functions with a large number of pairs and impossible for functions with infinitely many pairs. A useful way of describing a function of interest is to specify a singular form from which the second entries can be determined.

Recall that in Chapter 1 we pointed out that a singular form either has no value or has exactly one value for each value assigned to its free variable. Consequently, for each singular form 'F_x' and for each range of values A assigned to 'x'

$$\{(x, F_x) \mid x \in A\}$$

is a single valued relation; hence a function.

For example, '$x^2 + 1$' is a form which has a value for each value of 'x' in the real numbers. Consequently

$$\{(x, x^2 + 1) \mid x \in R\}$$

is a single valued relation. If $f = \{(x, x^2 + 1) \mid x \in R\}$, then for each x in $R, f(x) = x^2 + 1$.

When using a form to define a function in the manner illustrated above we will not require that the form have a value for each value of its free variable. Thus we accept

$$\left\{\left(x, \frac{1}{x}\right) \mid x \in R\right\}$$

as a function with the understanding that since '1/0' is a name without denotation, this set contains no ordered pair with first entry 0.

Set notation is, however, not the most natural and convenient notation for describing a function. In an appropriate context we will introduce functions by a more conventional means—as, for example, a statement beginning

$$\text{If } f(x) = \frac{1}{x}, \ x \neq 0, \text{ then } \dots .$$

The reader is then expected to understand from the context that

$$f = \left\{\left(x, \frac{1}{x}\right) \mid x \in R\right\}.$$

The requirement that $x \neq 0$ is a reminder that $\operatorname{Dom} f = R - \{0\}$.

Since functions are sets, the basic device for proving the equality of functions is the axiom of extent. However, because functions are a particular kind of set, equality can be established by means of the following useful result, which is a consequence of the axiom of extent.

Theorem 3.32. $f = g$ *iff* $\operatorname{Dom} f = \operatorname{Dom} g$ *and* $\forall x \in \operatorname{Dom} f, f(x) = g(x)$.

Proof. If $\operatorname{Dom} f = \operatorname{Dom} g$, if $x \in \operatorname{Dom} f$, if $f(x) = g(x)$, and if $(x, y) \in f$, then $y = f(x) = g(x)$; hence $(x, y) \in g$. Similarly, if $(x, y) \in g$, then $y = g(x) = f(x)$ and $(x, y) \in f$. We then have that $f \subseteq g$ and $g \subseteq f$, from which we conclude that $f = g$.

The converse is obvious.

Q.E.D.

Since functions are relations, they of course have converses. It is interesting to note that the converse of a function need not be a function. For example, $\{(1, 2), (3, 1), (4, 2)\}$ is a function, but its converse $\{(2, 1), (1, 3), (2, 4)\}$ is not a function. On the other hand, both $\{(1, 2), (3, 1), (4, 3)\}$ and its converse $\{(2, 1), (1, 3), (3, 4)\}$ are functions.

In order for the converse of a function to be a function it must be single valued. The requirement that the converse have no two ordered pairs with the same first entry is simply the requirement that the original function have no two ordered pairs with the same second entry. A function having this property is said to be *one-to-one*.

Definition 3.33. f is *one-to-one* iff f has the property that

$$\text{if } (x, z) \in f \text{ and } (y, z) \in f, \text{ then } x = y.$$

A function that is not one-to-one is *many-to-one*.

Note that if $(x, z) \in f$, then $z = f(x)$. Similarly, if $(y, z) \in f$, then $z = f(y)$. Consequently, if $(x, z) \in f$ and if $(y, z) \in f$, then $f(x) = f(y)$. Thus the basic property of one-to-oneness is that

$$\text{if } f(x) = f(y), \text{ then } x = y.$$

Example. If for each x in R, $f(x) = x + 1$ and if $f(x) = f(y)$, then $x + 1 = y + 1$. Consequently, $x = y$ and f is one-to-one. On the other hand, if for each x in R, $f(x) = x^2 + 1$, then since $f(1) = f(-1)$ it follows that f is not one-to-one.

As we have pointed out, the converse of f is a function if and only if f is one-to-one. When this is the case we find it convenient to denote this converse by 'f^{-1}'. However, we will speak not of the converse of f but rather of the *inverse* of f.

Definition 3.34. $g = f^{-1}$ iff g is the converse of f.

Example. If $f = \{(1, 4), (3, 6), (4, -1)\}$, then $f^{-1} = \{(4, 1), (6, 3), (-1, 4)\}$. If $f = \{(x, x^2 + 1) \mid x \in R\}$, then f^{-1} does not exist, since f is not one-to-one.

If f is a function whose domain is A and whose range is a subset of B, then we refer to f as a *mapping* of A *into* B. If $B = \operatorname{Ran} f$, then f is a mapping of A *onto* B.

Definition 3.35. $f : A \longrightarrow B$ iff $\operatorname{Dom} f = A$ and $\operatorname{Ran} f \subseteq B$.
$f : A \underset{\text{onto}}{\longrightarrow} B$ iff $\operatorname{Dom} f = A$ and $\operatorname{Ran} f = B$.
$f : A \underset{\text{onto}}{\overset{1-1}{\longrightarrow}} B$ iff $f : A \underset{\text{onto}}{\longrightarrow} B$ and f is one-to-one.

The symbol '$f : A \to B$' is read f *maps* A *into* B, '$f : A \underset{\text{onto}}{\longrightarrow} B$' is read f *maps* A *onto* B, and '$f : A \underset{\text{onto}}{\overset{1-1}{\longrightarrow}} B$' is read f *maps* A *one-to-one onto* B.

If $y = f(x)$, then y is the *image* of x under the mapping f and f maps x onto y. This very graphic terminology we also extend to sets of elements.

Definition 3.36. $f[A] = \{f(x) \mid x \in (A \cap \mathrm{Dom}\, f)\}.$

If $A \subseteq \mathrm{Dom}\, f$ and if $B = f[A]$, then B is the image of A under the mapping f.

Example.   If $f = \{(1, 4), (3, 6), (4, -1)\}$ then $f:\{1, 3, 4\} \to Z$, $f:\{1, 3, 4\} \xrightarrow[\mathrm{onto}]{1-1} \{-1, 4, 6\}$, $f[\{1, 3, 4\}] = \{-1, 4, 6\}$, $f[\{1, 3\}] = \{4, 6\}$ and $f[\{1\}] = \{4\}$.

Example.   If for each x in R, $f(x) = x^2 + 1$, then $f: R \to R$ and $f: R \xrightarrow[\mathrm{onto}]{} \{x \in R \mid x \geq 1\}.$

EXERCISES

In Exercises 1–4 decide whether or not the given relation is a function and for those that are functions whether or not they have inverses.

1. $\{(x, x) \mid x \in R\}.$ **2.** $\{(x, x^2) \mid x \in R\}.$

3. $\{(x^2, x) \mid x \in R\}.$ **4.** $\{(x, y) \in Z \times Z \mid x + y = 1\}.$

In Exercises 5–22 give a proof or a counter-example.

5. Every subset of a function is a function.

6. If $g \subseteq f$ and f is one-to-one, then g is one-to-one.

7. $\varnothing$ is a function.

8. The union of any two functions is a function.

9. The intersection of any two functions is a function.

10. The relative complement of any two functions is a function.

11. $(\forall f)(\forall g)\, \mathrm{Dom}\, (f \cup g) = (\mathrm{Dom}\, f \cup \mathrm{Dom}\, g).$

12. $(\forall f)(\forall g)\, \mathrm{Dom}\, (f \cap g) = (\mathrm{Dom}\, f \cap \mathrm{Dom}\, g).$

13. $(\forall f)(\forall g)\, \mathrm{Dom}\, (f - g) = (\mathrm{Dom}\, f - \mathrm{Dom}\, g).$

14. $(\forall f)(\forall g)\, \mathrm{Ran}\, (f \cup g) = (\mathrm{Ran}\, f \cup \mathrm{Ran}\, g).$

15. $(\forall f)(\forall g)\, \mathrm{Ran}\, (f \cap g) = (\mathrm{Ran}\, f \cap \mathrm{Ran}\, g).$

16. $(\forall f)(\forall g)\, \mathrm{Ran}\, (f - g) = (\mathrm{Ran}\, f - \mathrm{Ran}\, g).$

17. $f[A \cup B] = f[A] \cup f[B].$

18. $f[A \cap B] = f[A] \cap f[B].$

19. $f[A - B] = f[A] - f[B].$

20. $f[\varnothing] = \varnothing.$

21. If f is one-to-one, then $\mathrm{Ran}\, (f - g) = (\mathrm{Ran}\, f - \mathrm{Ran}\, g).$

22. If $g \subseteq f$, then $\mathrm{Dom}\, g \subseteq \mathrm{Dom}\, f$ and $\mathrm{Ran}\, g \subseteq \mathrm{Ran}\, f.$

In Exercises 23–26 decide which functions are one-to-one and which functions are mappings onto the set of all real numbers. In each case assume that $\mathrm{Dom}\, f = R$.

23. $f(x) = x.$ **24.** $f(x) = \dfrac{1}{x^2 + 1}.$

25. $f(x) = x^2.$ **26.** $f(x) = \dfrac{x}{x^2 + 1}.$

27. Prove: If f and g are one-to-one, then $f \cap g$ is one-to-one.

28. Prove: If f and g are one-to-one, if $(\mathrm{Dom}\, f \cap \mathrm{Dom}\, g) = \varnothing$, and $(\mathrm{Ran}\, f \cap \mathrm{Ran}\, g) = \varnothing$, then $f \cup g$ is a one-to-one function.

29. Prove: $f : A \xrightarrow[\text{onto}]{1-1} B$ iff $f^{-1} : B \xrightarrow[\text{onto}]{1-1} A$.

30. Prove: $\text{Dom} f = \varnothing$ iff $\text{Ran} f = \varnothing$ iff $f = \varnothing$.

31. Prove: $(\exists f) f : A \to \varnothing$ iff $A = \varnothing$.

32. Prove: $(\forall A)(\forall B)(\exists f) f : A \times B \xrightarrow[\text{onto}]{1-1} B \times A$.

33. Prove: If $(\exists f) f : A \xrightarrow[\text{onto}]{1-1} B$, if $x \notin A$ and if $y \notin B$, then $(\exists g)$ $g : (A \cup \{x\}) \xrightarrow[\text{onto}]{1-1} (B \cup \{y\})$.

34. Prove: If $(\exists f) f : A \xrightarrow[\text{onto}]{1-1} B$, if $x \in A$, and if $y \in B$, then $(\exists g)$ $g : A \xrightarrow[\text{onto}]{1-1} B$ and $y = g(x)$.

35. Prove: If $(\exists f) f : A \xrightarrow[\text{onto}]{1-1} B$, if $x \in A$, and if $y \in B$, then $(\exists g)$ $g : (A - \{x\}) \xrightarrow[\text{onto}]{1-1} (B - \{y\})$.

3.4 Function Composition

If g maps A into B and f maps B into C, then f and g determine, in a very natural way, a mapping of A directly into C, namely the mapping h defined by

$$h(x) = f(g(x)), \quad x \in A,$$

which we call the *composite of f with g* (see Figure 3.1).

Example. If $f = \{(1, 4), (3, 6), (4, -1)\}$ and if $g = \{(1, 1), (2, 4), (6, 3)\}$, then $g : A \to B$ and $f : B \to C$ if $A = \{1, 2, 6\}$, $B = \{1, 3, 4\}$, and $C = \{-1, 4, 6\}$. If

$$h(1) = f(g(1)) = f(1) = 4,$$
$$h(2) = f(g(2)) = f(4) = -1,$$
$$h(6) = f(g(6)) = f(3) = 6,$$

then $h = \{(1, 4), (2, -1), (6, 6)\}$ and $h : A \to C$.

Definition 3.40. $f \circ g = \{(x, f(g(x))) \mid x \in \text{Dom } g \text{ and } g(x) \in \text{Dom} f\}$.

Example. If $f = \{(1, 2), (3, 7), (7, 6)\}$ and if $g = \{(1, 2), (2, 3), (5, 7)\}$, then $f \circ g = \{(2, 7), (5, 6)\}$ and $g \circ f = \{(1, 3)\}$.

Example. If for each x in R, $f(x) = x + 1$ and $g(x) = x^2 + 1$, then $(f \circ g)(x) = x^2 + 2$ and $(g \circ f)(x) = x^2 + 2x + 2$.

From these examples we see that the composition of functions is not commutative. It is, however, associative.

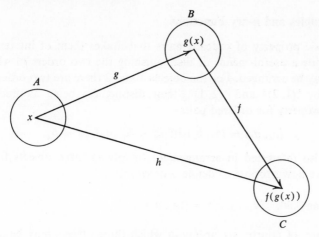

FIGURE 3.1

Theorem 3.41. $(f \circ g) \circ h = f \circ (g \circ h)$.

Proof Procedure. From Theorem 3.32 it is sufficient to prove that Dom $(f \circ g) \circ h = $ Dom $f \circ (g \circ h)$ and for each x in Dom $(f \circ g) \circ h$, $[(f \circ g) \circ h](x) = [f \circ (g \circ h)](x)$.

Proof. If $x \in$ Dom $(f \circ g) \circ h$, then $x \in$ Dom h and $h(x) \in$ Dom $f \circ g$. Since $h(x) \in$ Dom $f \circ g$, it follows that $h(x) \in$ Dom g and $g(h(x)) \in$ Dom f. But since $x \in$ Dom h and $h(x) \in$ Dom g, we have that $x \in$ Dom $g \circ h$. Furthermore, since $x \in$ Dom $g \circ h$ and $(g \circ h)(x) \in$ Dom f, it follows that $x \in$ Dom $f \circ (g \circ h)$. Therefore, Dom $(f \circ g) \circ h \subseteq$ Dom $f \circ (g \circ h)$. In a similar manner we can prove the containment in the other direction and hence prove that Dom $(f \circ g) \circ h = $ Dom $f \circ (g \circ h)$.

Finally if $x \in$ Dom $(f \circ g) \circ h$, we have that $[(f \circ g) \circ h](x) = (f \circ g)(h(x)) = f(g(h(x))) = f((g \circ h)(x)) = [f \circ (g \circ h)](x)$.

Q.E.D.

EXERCISES

1. Prove: If $g : A \to B$ and $f : B \to C$, then $f \circ g : A \to C$.

2. Prove: If $g : A \xrightarrow[\text{onto}]{} B$ and $f : B \xrightarrow[\text{onto}]{} C$, then $f \circ g : A \xrightarrow[\text{onto}]{} C$.

3. Prove: If f and g are each one-to-one, then $f \circ g$ is one-to-one and $(f \circ g)^{-1} = g^{-1} \circ f^{-1}$.

4. Prove: If $g : A \xrightarrow[\text{onto}]{1-1} B$ and $f : B \xrightarrow[\text{onto}]{1-1} C$, then $f \circ g : A \xrightarrow[\text{onto}]{1-1} C$ and $(f \circ g)^{-1} : C \xrightarrow[\text{onto}]{1-1} A$.

3.5 n-tuples and n-ary Functions

The basic property of ordered pairs that makes them of interest is that they provide a useful means of distinguishing the two orders in which two objects may be arranged. For the objects 1 and 2 there are two ordered pairs denoted by '$(1, 2)$' and '$(2, 1)$', their distinctness being assured by the equality property for ordered pairs:

$$(a_1, a_2) = (b_1, b_2) \text{ iff } a_1 = b_1 \text{ and } a_2 = b_2.$$

We are also interested in arrangements involving three objects for which purpose we now propose to define *ordered triples*.

Definition 3.50. $(a_1, a_2, a_3) = ((a_1, a_2), a_3)$.

There are, of course, six orders in which three objects may be arranged. For the objects 1, 2, and 3 the ordered triples $(1, 2, 3)$, $(1, 3, 2)$, $(2, 1, 3)$, $(2, 3, 1)$, $(3, 1, 2)$, and $(3, 2, 1)$ are distinct. Their distinctness is an immediate consequence of the following equality property for ordered triples.

Theorem 3.51. $(a_1, a_2, a_3) = (b_1, b_2, b_3)$ iff $a_1 = b_1, a_2 = b_2,$ and $a_3 = b_3$.

Proof. $(a_1, a_2, a_3) = (b_1, b_2, b_3)$ iff $((a_1, a_2), a_3) = ((b_1, b_2), b_3)$.
         $((a_1, a_2), a_3) = ((b_1, b_2), b_3)$ iff $(a_1, a_2) = (b_1, b_2)$ and $a_3 = b_3$.
         $(a_1, a_2) = (b_1, b_2)$ and $a_3 = b_3$ iff $a_1 = b_1, a_2 = b_2,$ and $a_3 = b_3$.
                                                          Q.E.D.

Defining ordered triples as ordered pairs whose first entries are ordered pairs suggests that we define *ordered quadruples* as ordered pairs whose first entries are ordered triples.

Definition 3.52. $(a_1, a_2, a_3, a_4) = ((a_1, a_2, a_3), a_4)$.

The equality property for ordered quadruples follows easily from the equality properties of ordered pairs and ordered triples. We leave the proof to the reader.

Theorem 3.53. $(a_1, a_2, a_3, a_4) = (b_1, b_2, b_3, b_4)$ *iff* $a_1 = b_1$, $a_2 = b_2$, $a_3 = b_3,$ *and* $a_4 = b_4$.

It is now clear that we can define ordered quintuples as ordered pairs whose first entries are ordered quadruples, and ordered sextuples as ordered pairs whose first entries are ordered quintuples. To define the notion of an ordered *n-tuple* for every n would, however, require infinitely many definitions. Since we clearly cannot make an infinite number of definitions we will be content to describe the pattern for defining ordered n-tuple by means of the following so-called *recursive definition*.

Definition 3.54. $(a_1, a_2, \ldots, a_{n+1}) = ((a_1, a_2, \ldots, a_n), a_{n+1})$, $n = 2, 3, \ldots$. a_i is the *i*th *entry* in $(a_1, a_2, \ldots, a_{n+1})$.

From Definition 3.54 anyone who knows what ordered pairs (2-tuples) are can find out what ordered triples (3-tuples) are. From this he can find out what ordered 4-tuples are. With a sufficient number of applications of the definition he can decide what ordered *n*-tuples are for any given *n*. It is also clear from the definition that *n*-tuples have the basic equality property:

$$(a_1, a_2, \ldots, a_n) = (b_1, b_2, \ldots, b_n) \text{ iff } a_1 = b_1, \ a_2 = b_2, \ \ldots, \ a_n = b_n.$$

The cross-product notation introduced earlier provides a useful way of denoting certain sets of ordered *n*-tuples. Thus, for sets A, B, C, and D, $A \times B$ is a set of ordered pairs, $(A \times B) \times C$ is a set of ordered triples, and $((A \times B) \times C) \times D$ is a set of ordered quadruples. When all entries of a given collection of ordered *n*-tuples are elements of the same set A we will find the following notation convenient.

Definition 3.55. $A^1 = A$
$$A^{n+1} = A^n \times A, \qquad n = 1, 2, \ldots.$$

Thus, for example, Z^2 is the set of all ordered pairs of integers, and Z^3 is the set of all ordered triples of integers.

Definition 3.56. f is an *n-ary function* iff each element of Dom f is an ordered *n*-tuple. f is an *n-ary function on A* iff Dom $f \subseteq A^n$.

$$y = f(x_1, x_2, \ldots, x_n) \text{ iff } ((x_1, x_2, \ldots, x_n), y) \in f.$$

Example.   If $A = \{1, 2\}$ and if $f = \{((1, 1), 1), \ ((1, 2), 2), \ ((2, 1), 1), ((2, 2), 2)\}$, then f is a binary function on A which maps A^2 onto A; $f(1, 1) = 1$, $f(1, 2) = 2$, $f(2, 1) = 1$, and $f(2, 2) = 2$.

Example.   If for each x and y in R, $f(x, y) = x^2 + y^2$, then f is a binary function on R which maps R^2 into R.

It should be noted that Definition 3.56 does not modify our notion of function; it only enriches the language for discussing functions. Indeed if f is an *n*-ary function on A, then f is a (singulary) function on A^n. It is also of interest to note that *n*-ary functions encompass the so-called binary operations—as, for example, the addition and multiplication of integers. For certain purposes it is convenient to think of, say, the addition of integers as a function which associates with each ordered pair of integers an integer, e.g., $f(1, 2) = 3$, $f(2, 3) = 5$, etc.

Definition 3.57. f is a *binary operation on A* iff $f : A^2 \to A$.

Definition 3.58. If f is a binary operation on A and if $B \subseteq A$, then f is *closed on B* iff for each (x, y) in $B \times B$, $f(x, y) \in B$.

Two basic properties of interest for binary operations are, of course, the commutative property

$$f(x, y) = f(y, x)$$

and the associative property

$$f(f(x, y), z) = f(x, f(y, z)).$$

For a discussion of the properties of binary operations it is customary to use a symbol such as '$*$' as a variable on binary operations and to write $x * y$ rather than $* (x, y)$. With this notation the commutative and associative properties assume a more familiar form:

$$x * y = y * x,$$
$$(x * y) * z = x * (y * z).$$

Addition and multiplication of real numbers are each binary operations on R, each operation is associative and commutative, each is closed on the set of rational numbers, and each is closed on the set of integers. From addition and multiplication for real numbers we can define other binary operations on R—as, for example, averaging:

$$x * y = \frac{x + y}{2}.$$

This operation is commutative but not associative. It is closed on the set of rational numbers but not closed on the integers. The composition of functions that map the real numbers onto the real numbers is a binary operation that is associative but not commutative.

EXERCISES

In Exercises 1–3, $*$ is a binary operation on R. Which of these operations are associative and which are commutative?
  1. $x * y = x$.   **2.** $x * y = x + y - 1$.   **3.** $x * y = x + y - xy$.
  4. Prove: If for each A and B in Pow R, $A * B = A \cup B$, then $*$ is an associative and commutative binary operation on Pow R that is closed on the power set of each subset of R.

★3.6 Existence Questions

This section may be omitted without loss of continuity. Our main objective is to point out to the interested reader that the axioms for set theory given in Section 2.6 are sufficient to establish the existence of functions and relations and to justify the theorems of this chapter. No additional axioms are needed.

Functions and relations are by definition sets of ordered pairs. The existence of ordered pairs is assured by the axiom of pairing. Indeed, for each x and y both $\{x\}$ and $\{x, y\}$ exist and hence $\{\{x\}, \{x, y\}\}$ exists. Since by definition $(x, y) = \{\{x\}, \{x, y\}\}$, it follows that (x, y) exists.

From the existence of ordered pairs and the set-building axioms—the axiom of pairing and the axiom of unions—it is clear that sets of ordered pairs, i.e., relations, do exist. A question of greater interest concerns our practice of describing functions and relations as sets of ordered pairs for which certain propositional forms are true. If '$F_{x,y}$' is a propositional form in two variables, then the Russell paradox suggests that it may not be safe to speak of

$$\{(x, y) \mid F_{x,y}\}.$$

Suppose, however, that the only ordered pairs that interest us have their first entries in a set A and their second entries in a set B; then we are assured by the axiom of separation that

$$\{(x, y) \in A \times B \mid F_{x,y}\}$$

exists provided $A \times B$ exists.

The existence of $A \times B$ follows from the axiom of pairing, the axiom of unions, the axiom of powers, and the axiom of separation in the following way. If

$$S = \mathrm{Pow}\,(A \cup B),$$

then for each x in A and for each y in B we have that $\{x\} \in S$ and $\{x, y\} \in S$. Consequently,

$$(x, y) \in \mathrm{Pow}\,S.$$

We then have that

$$A \times B = \{z \in \mathrm{Pow}\,S \mid \exists x \in A, \exists y \in B, z = (x, y)\}.$$

In particular, we are assured that $R \times R$ exists, and consequently so does every relation on R that we can conceive of.

Having established that there exist relations having specified domains and ranges, let us examine the converse; given a relation, is the existence if its domain and range inferrable from the axioms that we stated? The answer is yes and the proof is easy.

If C is a relation, then by definition

$$\mathrm{Dom}\,C = \{x \mid (\exists y)(x, y) \in C\},$$
$$\mathrm{Ran}\,C = \{y \mid (\exists x)(x, y) \in C\}.$$

The existence of $\mathrm{Dom}\,C$ and $\mathrm{Ran}\,C$ can be established by the axiom of separation, provided we can prove the existence of a set that contains all of the first entries of the pairs in C and a set that contains all of the second entries of the pairs of C. This we will do by proving the existence of a set that contains both the first and second entries of each pair in C.

Since C is a relation, C is a set of ordered pairs. But ordered pairs are sets; therefore, C is a set of sets. From the axiom of unions the union of all sets in C exists—that is, $(\exists S)\ S = \bigcup C$. It then follows that the elements of S are elements of the ordered pairs in C. But the elements of ordered pairs are also sets. Therefore, S is a set of sets whose union exists by the axiom of unions—that is, $(\exists T)\ T = \bigcup S$.

Since by definition $(x, y) = \{\{x\}, \{x, y\}\}$, it follows that if $(x, y) \in C$, then $\{x, y\} \in S$. But

$$T = \bigcup_{A \in S} A;$$

therefore, $x \in T$ and $y \in T$. We then conclude that

$$\operatorname{Dom} C = \{x \in T \mid (\exists y)(x, y) \in C\},$$
$$\operatorname{Ran} C = \{y \in T \mid (\exists x)(x, y) \in C\}.$$

Part I References

CHRISTIAN, R. R. *Introduction to Logic and Sets*. New York: Ginn and Company, 1958.

CHURCH, A. *Introduction to Mathematical Logic*. Vol. I. Princeton, N.J.: Princeton University Press, 1956.

EXNER, R. M., and M. F. ROSSKOPF. *Logic in Elementary Mathematics*. New York: McGraw-Hill Book Company, 1959.

HALMOS, P. R. *Naive Set Theory*. Princeton, N.J.: D. Van Nostrand Company, Inc., 1960.

HAMILTON, N., and J. LANDIN. *Set Theory: The Structure of Arithmetic*. Boston: Allyn and Bacon, 1961.

KLEENE, S. C. *Introduction to Metamathematics*. Princeton, N.J.: D. Van Nostrand Company, Inc., 1962.

MENDELSON, E. *Introduction to Mathematical Logic*. Princeton, N.J.: D. Van Nostrand Company, Inc., 1964.

STOLL, R. R. *Introduction to Set Theory and Logic*. San Francisco: W. H. Freeman and Company, 1963.

STOLL, R. R. *Sets, Logic, and Axiomatic Theories*. San Francisco: W. H. Freeman and Company, 1961.

SUPPES, P. *Axiomatic Set Theory*. Princeton, N.J.: D. Van Nostrand Company, Inc., 1960.

SUPPES, P., and S. HILL. *First Course in Mathematical Logic*. New York: Blaisdell Publishing Company, 1964.

PART II

An Introduction to Analysis

CHAPTER 4

The Real Number System

4.0 Introduction

The purpose of this chapter is to clarify the basic assumptions that we will make concerning the real numbers and to deduce certain elementary properties of the real numbers that are implicit in these assumptions.

The real number system consists of a set, denoted by 'R', whose elements we call *real numbers*, two binary operations on R called *addition* and *multiplication*, which we will denote by '$+$' and '$\cdot$', respectively, and an order relation called *less than*, which we will denote by '$<$'.

There are fifteen basic properties of addition, multiplication, and order which we will assume without proof and discuss in this chapter. By virtue of these fifteen properties the real number system is a *complete ordered field*. For discussion purposes we will divide these properties into three categories. The first category includes the *algebraic properties*—that is, the properties of addition and multiplication. These will be discussed in Section 4.1. The second category includes the *order properties*, which we will discuss in Section 4.2, and the third category consists of the *completeness property*, which we will discuss in Section 4.5.

Throughout this and the remaining chapters we will use lowercase letters

$$a, b, c, \ldots, \qquad x, y, z, \ldots, \qquad \alpha, \beta, \gamma, \ldots$$

as variables on R. We will use the juxtaposition of appropriate symbols to indicate multiplication, e.g., xy, $2x$. An understanding of the conventions concerning the use of grouping symbols is assumed.

4.1 The Field Postulates

The set of real numbers, R, contains two special numbers which we denote by '0' and '1'. The properties of 0 and 1 and the properties of addition and multiplication that we assume to be true are the following:

A_1. $(\forall x)(\forall y)(\forall z)\, (x + y) + z = x + (y + z)$.
A_2. $(\forall x)(\forall y)\, x + y = y + x$.
A_3. $(\forall x)\, x + 0 = x$.
A_4. $(\forall x)(\exists y)\, x + y = 0$.

M_1. $(\forall x)(\forall y)(\forall z)(xy)z = x(yz)$.

M_2. $(\forall x)(\forall y) xy = yx$.

M_3. $(\forall x) x \cdot 1 = x$.

M_4. $(\forall x)$ if $x \neq 0$, then $(\exists y) xy = 1$.

D. $(\forall x)(\forall y)(\forall z) x(y + z) = xy + xz$.

E. $0 \neq 1$.

These ten properties together with all properties that can be inferred from them constitute the *algebraic properties* of the real number system. The algebraic properties are not, however, sufficient to completely characterize the real number system. As we will see later the rational numbers, Q, under addition and multiplication share with the real number system the ten properties just described. Consequently the real number system and the rational number system have the same algebraic properties. Mathematicians refer to any mathematical system that has these ten properties as a *field*.[1] Thus the real number system and the rational number system are examples of fields. It is also of interest that the integers Z under addition and multiplication have nine of the ten field properties, all except M_4. Consequently, any result in this section whose proof does not require M_4 holds in the system of integers.

It is interesting to see how elementary properties of real numbers with which we are familiar can be deduced from the field postulates. Most of these properties we will leave as exercises with the following material to serve as a guide to their proof.

The postulates A_1 and M_1 state the associative properties for addition and multiplication; A_2 and M_2 state the commutative properties; A_3, A_4, M_3, and M_4 describe the special properties of 0 and 1 including the existence of negatives and reciprocals; and D is the distributive law. Postulate E assures us that there are at least two real numbers. It is, of course, important to know that there is only one real number having the properties that we have postulated for 0 and only one real number having the properties that we have postulated for 1. The proof that this is the case is easy and interesting.

Theorem 4.10.　1) $(\exists!y)(\forall x) x + y = x$.

　　　　　　　　　2) $(\exists!y)(\forall x) xy = x$.

Proof.　1) If y_1 and y_2 have the property, that is, if $x + y_1 = x$ for each x and if $x + y_2 = x$ for each x, then in particular we have that $y_2 + y_1 = y_2$ and $y_1 + y_2 = y_1$. From the commutative property for addition, it then follows that $y_1 = y_2$. We have, therefore, proved that at most one number

---

[1] This use of the word 'field' should not be confused with its earlier use to refer to the union of the domain and range of a relation.

has the desired property. But A_3 assures us that at least one number has the property; therefore, exactly one number does.

2) The proof is similar to the foregoing argument and is left to the reader.

Theorem 4.10 is a uniqueness theorem which assures us that

$$\text{if } (\forall x)\, x + y = x, \text{ then } y = 0.$$

However, by using the fact that negatives exist we can prove the following stronger result.

Theorem 4.11. *If* $(\exists x)\, x + y = x$, *then* $y = 0$.

Proof. If $x + y = x$, then since $(\exists z)\, x + z = 0$ it follows from the associative and commutative laws that $y = y + 0 = y + (x + z) = (y + x) + z = x + z = 0$.

Q.E.D.

Theorem 4.11 also provides an elementary but interesting proof technique which we illustrate by proving

Theorem 4.12. $(\forall x)\, x \cdot 0 = 0$.

Proof. Using the distributive law and the properties of 1 and 0 we have that

$$x + x \cdot 0 = x \cdot 1 + x \cdot 0 = x(1 + 0) = x \cdot 1 = x.$$

From Theorem 4.11 it then follows that $x \cdot 0 = 0$.

Q.E.D.

From Theorem 4.12 and the existence of reciprocals we can deduce the following important result.

Theorem 4.13. $xy = 0$ *iff* $x = 0$ *or* $y = 0$.

Proof. If $x = 0$ or $y = 0$, then from Theorem 4.12 it follows that $xy = 0$. For the converse we note that if $xy = 0$ and $x \neq 0$, then there is a real number z for which $zx = 1$. We then have that

$$xy = 0,$$
$$z(xy) = z \cdot 0,$$
$$(zx)y = 0,$$
$$1 \cdot y = 0,$$
$$y = 0.$$

Q.E.D.

We are, of course, also interested in the uniqueness of negatives and reciprocals.

Theorem 4.14.   1) $(\forall x)(\exists! y)\, x + y = 0.$

                2) $(\forall x)$ *if* $x \neq 0$, *then* $(\exists! y)\, xy = 1$.

Proof.   1) If $x + y_1 = 0$ and $x + y_2 = 0$, then from the associative and commutative laws we have that $y_1 = y_1 + 0 = y_1 + (x + y_2) =$ $(y_1 + x) + y_2 = 0 + y_2 = y_2$.

2) The proof is left to the reader.

Since negatives and reciprocals are unique, we can introduce special symbols to denote them. Following a long-standing convention we will use the minus sign to indicate the additive inverse of a number, and '-1' as an exponent to indicate the multiplicative inverse. Thus the negative of 2 is -2, the negative of -3 is $-(-3)$, and the reciprocal of 2 is 2^{-1}.

Definition 4.15. $y = -x$ iff $x + y = 0$.

                    $y = x^{-1}$ iff $xy = 1$.

                    $x - y = x + (-y)$.

                    $\dfrac{x}{y} = x \cdot y^{-1}$.

Theorem 4.16.   *If* $x \neq 0$ *and* $y \neq 0$, *then* $(xy)^{-1}$ *exists and* $(xy)^{-1} = y^{-1}x^{-1}$.

Proof.   If $x \neq 0$ and $y \neq 0$, then $xy \neq 0$. Therefore, x^{-1}, y^{-1}, and $(xy)^{-1}$ exist. Since there is one and only one real number z such that $(xy)z = 1$ and since $(xy)(y^{-1}x^{-1}) = 1$, it follows that $(xy)^{-1} = y^{-1}x^{-1}$.

                                                 Q.E.D.

We have now proved results using each of the field postulates except postulate E, whose importance is illustrated by

Theorem 4.17.   *If* $1 = 0$ *then* $(\forall x)\, x = 0$.

Proof.   If $1 = 0$, then for each x we would have that $x \cdot 1 = x \cdot 0$ and hence $x = 0$.

                                                 Q.E.D.

From Theorem 4.17 we see that if postulate E were false, then the real number system would consist of a single number.

EXERCISES

1. Prove (Cancellation laws for addition):

          1) If $x + z = y + z$, then $x = y$.

          2) If $z + x = z + y$, then $x = y$.

2. Prove (Cancellation laws for multiplication):

       1) If $xz = yz$ and $z \neq 0$, then $x = y$.

       2) If $zx = zy$ and $z \neq 0$, then $x = y$.

3. Prove: If $xy = x$ and $x \neq 0$, then $y = 1$.

4. Prove: $-1 \cdot x = -x$.

5. Prove: $-(-x) = x$.

6. Prove: $x + x = x$ iff $x = 0$.

7. Prove: If $yz \neq 0$, then $\dfrac{w}{y} = \dfrac{x}{z}$ iff $wz = xy$.

8. Prove: If $yz \neq 0$, then $\dfrac{xz}{yz} = \dfrac{x}{y}$.

9. Prove: If $yz \neq 0$, then $\dfrac{w}{y} + \dfrac{x}{z} = \dfrac{wz + xy}{yz}$,

10. Prove: If $x \neq 0$, then $x^{-1} \neq 0$.

11. Prove: If $y \neq 0$, then $\dfrac{x}{y} = 0$ iff $x = 0$.

12. Prove: If $x \neq 0$, then $(x^{-1})^{-1} = x$.

13. Prove: $x \cdot x = x$ iff $x = 1$ or $x = 0$.

14. Prove: $x - 0 = x$ and $\dfrac{x}{1} = x$.

15. Prove: $-(xy) = (-x)y = x(-y)$.

16. Prove: $-x = x$ iff $x = 0$.

4.2 The Order Postulates

With respect to the order relation $<$, the real number system has the following properties.

O_1.   For each x and y one and only one of the following is true:

$$x < y \text{ or } x = y \text{ or } y < x.$$

O_2. $(\forall x)(\forall y)(\forall z)$ if $x < y$ and $y < z$, then $x < z$.

O_3. $(\forall x)(\forall y)(\forall z)$ if $x < y$, then $x + z < y + z$.

O_4. $(\forall x)(\forall y)(\forall z)$ if $x < y$ and $0 < z$, then $xz < yz$.

While the symbols '$=$' and '$<$' are adequate to denote the relations of equality and order, it is convenient to employ three additional symbols.

Definition 4.20. $x > y$ iff $y < x$.

                       $x \geq y$ iff $x > y$ or $x = y$.

                       $x \leq y$ iff $x < y$ or $x = y$.

The new symbols are read respectively x *is greater than* y, x *is greater than or equal to* y, and x *is less than or equal to* y.

With the order property we can define a very useful property of sets of real numbers—namely, the property of *boundedness*.

Definition 4.21. b is an *upper* bound for S iff $\forall x \in S$, $x \le b$.
  b is a *lower* bound for S iff $\forall x \in S$, $x \ge b$.
  b is a *bound* for S iff $\forall x \in S$, $-b \le x \le b$.
  S is bounded *above* iff S has an upper bound.
  S is bounded *below* iff S has a lower bound.
  S is *bounded* iff S has a bound.

It is clear from Definition 4.21 that if b is an upper bound for S, then every number greater than b is also an upper bound for S. A set that is bounded above, therefore, has infinitely many upper bounds. By similar reasoning, we see that a set that is bounded below has infinitely many lower bounds. A set is bounded if and only if it is bounded above and below. (Why?)

Examples. 3 is an upper bound for $\{0, 1, 2\}$.
  0 is a lower bound for $\{0, 1, 2\}$.
  2 is an upper bound for $\{x \mid x < 1\}$.
  $\{x \mid x < 1\}$ has no lower bound.
  -1 is a lower bound for $\{x \mid x \ge 0\}$.
  $\{x \mid x \ge 0\}$ has no upper bound.
  Every number is both an upper bound and a lower bound for $\varnothing$.

Note that $\{x \mid x < 1\}$ is bounded above, is not bounded below, and therefore is not bounded. $\{x \mid x \ge 0\}$ is bounded below, is not bounded above, and therefore is not bounded. $\{x \mid 0 < x < 1\}$ is bounded above and below and hence is bounded. Indeed any number greater than or equal to 1 is an upper bound, and any number less than or equal to 0 is a lower bound. The numbers 0 and 1 are then the greatest of the lower bounds and the least of the upper bounds, respectively. These particular bounds are of special interest, and we assign them special names in

Definition 4.22. $b = \sup S$ iff b is an upper bound for S and every number smaller than b is not an upper bound for S.
  $b = \inf S$ iff b is a lower bound for S and every number larger than b is not a lower bound for S.
  The symbols 'sup S' and 'inf S' are read respectively the *supremum of S* and the *infimum of S*.

Examples. inf $\{0, 1, 2\} = 0$, sup $\{0, 1, 2\} = 2$.
  inf $\{x \mid x < 1\}$ does not exist, sup $\{x \mid x < 1\} = 1$.
  inf $\{x \mid x > 0\} = 0$, sup $\{x \mid x > 0\}$ does not exist.

Theorem 4.23. 1) *If $b = \sup S$ and $a < b$, then $\exists x \in S$, $a < x \le b$.*
2) *If $b = \inf S$ and $a > b$, then $\exists x \in S$, $b \le x < a$.*

Proof. 1) If $b = \sup S$ and $a < b$, then a is not an upper bound for S. Therefore, for some x in S, $a < x$. But b is an upper bound for S. Consequently, $a < x \le b$.
2) The proof is similar and is left to the reader.

From Theorem 4.23 we can easily prove

Theorem 4.24. 1) *If $a = \sup A$, if $b = \sup B$, and if $C = \{x + y \mid x \in A$ and $y \in B\}$, then $a + b = \sup C$.*
2) *If $a = \inf A$, if $b = \inf B$, and if $C = \{x + y \mid x \in A$ and $y \in B\}$, then $a + b = \inf C$.*

Proof. 1) For each z in C there is an x in A and a y in B such that $z = x + y$. Since $x \le a$ and $y \le b$, we have that $z \le a + b$. Thus $a + b$ is an upper bound for C. We then need only prove that no number smaller than $a + b$ is an upper bound.
If $c < a + b$, then $a + b - c > 0$. Therefore, if $\epsilon = a + b - c$, then $a - (\epsilon/2) < a$ and $b - (\epsilon/2) < b$. Since $a = \sup A$ and $b = \sup B$, it follows that for some x in A, $x > a - (\epsilon/2)$ and for some y in B, $y > b - (\epsilon/2)$. Therefore $x + y > a - (\epsilon/2) + b - (\epsilon/2) = a + b - \epsilon = c$. But $x + y \in C$. Therefore c is not an upper bound for C and hence $a + b = \sup C$.
2) The proof is similar and is left to the reader.

In certain problems it is important to know whether or not the supremum of a given set is an element of the set. Indeed the property is of sufficient importance that we introduce special terms.

Definition 4.25. $a = \max S$ iff $a = \sup S$ and $a \in S$.
$a = \min S$ iff $a = \inf S$ and $a \in S$.
'$\max S$' and '$\min S$' are read respectively the *maximum of S* and the *minimum of S*.

Examples. Max $[0, 1] = 1$, min $[0, 1] = 0$.
Max $\left\{\dfrac{1}{n} \mid n = 1, 2, \ldots\right\} = 1$, $\left\{\dfrac{1}{n} \mid n = 1, 2, \ldots\right\}$ has no
minimum.
$\{x \mid 0 < x < 1\}$ has neither a maximum nor a minimum.

Among other uses the order relation provides a means of describing certain sets of special interest which are called *intervals*. These sets we will represent by the notation of

Definition 4.26. If $a \leq b$, then

$$(a, b) = \{x \in R \mid a < x < b\},$$
$$[a, b) = \{x \in R \mid a \leq x < b\},$$
$$(a, b] = \{x \in R \mid a < x \leq b\},$$
$$[a, b] = \{x \in R \mid a \leq x \leq b\},$$
$$(a, \infty) = \{x \in R \mid x > a\},$$
$$[a, \infty) = \{x \in R \mid x \geq a\},$$
$$(-\infty, a) = \{x \in R \mid x < a\},$$
$$(-\infty, a] = \{x \in R \mid x \leq a\}.$$

The sets (a, b), $[a, b)$, $(a, b]$, and $[a, b]$ are bounded and hence are called *bounded intervals*. In each case the numbers a and b are the *end points* of the interval, and the number $b - a$ is the *length* of the interval. The sets (a, ∞), $[a, \infty)$, $(-\infty, a)$, and $(-\infty, a]$ are unbounded and are called *unbounded intervals* with end point a. We shall also refer to R as an unbounded interval with no end points.

Note that the symbol '(a, b)' denotes both an interval and an ordered pair. We will rely upon the context to make the meaning clear. Note also that a parenthesis is used to indicate that an end point is not an element of the set, and a bracket is used to indicate that an end point is an element of the set. Since the symbols '∞' and '$-\infty$' do not denote real numbers we use a parenthesis in the symbols for unbounded intervals.

From Definition 4.26 we see that a bounded interval is completely defined when its end points are given, and we are told which end points are in the interval and which are not. In later chapters we will be interested in certain bounded intervals which contain neither end point. Such intervals we will call *neighborhoods*. Rather than identify these intervals by giving their end points we find it convenient to give the midpoint of the interval and the distance from the midpoint to the end points. For this purpose the following definition will be useful.

Definition 4.27.   If $x \geq 0$ then $|x| = x$.
If $x < 0$ then $|x| = -x$.

'$|x|$' is read the *absolute value of x*.

As a further convenience not only for the definition of neighborhoods but for other purposes we adopt the notational convention of using the Greek letters

$$\epsilon, \delta$$

as variables on the set of positive real numbers, $(0, \infty)$.

Definition 4.28. $N(a, \delta) = \{x \in R \mid |x - a| < \delta\}$.
$N'(a, \delta) = N(a, \delta) - \{a\}$.

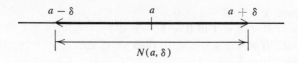

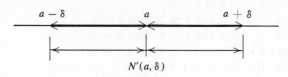

FIGURE 4.1

'$N(a, \delta)$' is read the *neighborhood of a of radius* δ. '$N'(a, \delta)$' is read the *deleted neighborhood of a of radius* δ.

That $N(a, \delta)$ is an interval we prove as

Theorem 4.29. $N(a, \delta) = (a - \delta, a + \delta)$.

Proof. (By the axiom of extent.) If $x \in N(a, \delta)$, then by Definition 4.28 we have that $|x - a| < \delta$. By the trichotomy property we have that $x - a < 0$ or $x - a \geq 0$. If $x - a < 0$, then by Definition 4.27 $|x - a| = a - x$. Then $a - x < \delta$ and from O_3 we have that $a - \delta < x < a + \delta$. (Why?) Therefore, $x \in (a - \delta, a + \delta)$. If $x - a \geq 0$, then $|x - a| = x - a$ and $x - a < \delta$. Thus $a - \delta < x < a + \delta$ and again $x \in (a - \delta, a + \delta)$. Therefore, $N(a, \delta) \subseteq (a - \delta, a + \delta)$.

The proof that $(a - \delta, a + \delta) \subseteq N(a, \delta)$ is similar to the above and is left to the reader.

As we will see in the next section, the order properties provide no means of distinguishing between the real number system and the rational number system. Indeed the properties O_1–O_4 are shared not only by the real number system and the rational number system but by the system of integers. Consequently, any result proved in this section holds in the rational number system, and any result that does not require postulate M_4 holds in the system of integers.

The order relation plays a very fundamental role in the material ahead. Success in handling certain problems will depend upon skill in manipulating inequalities. Since most of the properties that concern us at this point are not only elementary but easily proved, we leave them as exercises.

EXERCISES

1. Prove: If $x > 0$ and $y > 0$, then $xy > 0$ and $x + y > 0$.

2. Prove: $x < y$ iff $y - x > 0$.

3. Prove: $x < y$ iff $-y < -x$.

4. Prove: $x > 0$ iff $-x < 0$.

5. Prove: $0 < x < 1$ iff $0 < 1 - x < 1$.

6. Prove: If $x < y$ and $z < 0$, then $yz < xz$.

7. Prove: $0 < 1$.

8. Prove: If $xz < yz$ and $z > 0$, then $x < y$.

9. Prove: $x > -x$ iff $x > 0$.

10. Prove: If $x < y$ and $y \le z$, then $x < z$.

11. Prove: If $x \le y$ and $y < z$, then $x < z$.

12. Prove: If $x \le y$ and $y \le z$, then $x \le z$.

13. Prove: If $x + z < y + z$, then $x < y$.

14. Prove: If $w < x$ and $y < z$, then $w + y < x + z$.

15. Prove: If $0 \le w < x$ and $0 \le y < z$, then $wy < xz$.

16. Prove: $x < x + 1$.

17. Prove: $|x| \le y$ iff $-y \le x \le y$.

18. Prove: $-|x| \le x \le |x|$. (Hint: $|x| \le |x|$.)

19. Prove: $|x| = 0$ iff $x = 0$.

20. Prove: $|x| \ge 0$.

21. Prove: If $(\forall \epsilon) |x - y| < \epsilon$, then $x = y$.

22. Prove: $|xy| = |x| \, |y|$.

23. Prove: $|-x| = |x|$.

24. Prove: $|x + y| \le |x| + |y|$. (Hint: Exercises 14, 17, and 18.)

25. Prove: $|x + y| \ge |\, |x| - |y| \,|$. (Hint: $x = (x + y) + (-y)$.)

26. Prove: $|\, |x| - |y| \,| \le |x - y| \le |x| + |y|$.

27. Prove: S is bounded iff $(\exists b) \, \forall x \in S, |x| \le b$.

28. Prove: If S and T are bounded, then $S \cup T$ and $S \cap T$ are each bounded.

29. Prove: S has at most one supremum and at most one infimum.

30. Prove: If $T = \{x \mid -x \in S\}$, then
    a) $S = \varnothing$ iff $T = \varnothing$.
    b) b is an upper bound for T iff $-b$ is a lower bound for S.
    c) $b = \sup T$ iff $-b = \inf S$.

31. Prove: If $a = \sup A$, if $b = \inf A$ and if $C = \{cx \mid x \in A\}$, then
    a) $\inf C = cb$ and $\sup C = ca$ if $c \ge 0$.
    b) $\inf C = ca$ and $\sup C = cb$ if $c \le 0$.

32. Prove: If $\delta_1 \le \delta_2$, then $N(x, \delta_1) \subseteq N(x, \delta_2)$.

33. Prove: If $x \in N(x_1, \delta_1) \cap N(x_2, \delta_2)$, then $(\exists \delta) \, N(x, \delta) \subseteq N(x_1, \delta_1) \cap N(x_2, \delta_2)$.

34. Prove: If $a < b$, then $(\exists f) f : [a, b] \xrightarrow[\text{onto}]{1-1} [0, 1]$.

4.3 The Integers and Mathematical Induction

In this section we wish to show that the field postulates and the order postulates are sufficient to explain all known properties of the integers and the rational numbers. In order to do this we will define the integers and the rational numbers as subsets of the real numbers. In formulating our definition we will, of course, be guided by our knowledge of the end sought. For example, we want the integers to be defined in such a way that n is an integer if and only if $-n$ is an integer. Consequently, the set of all integers is easily defined when the set of all nonnegative integers has been defined.

We would surely agree that the set of nonnegative integers should contain 0. Furthermore, if n is in the set of nonnegative integers, then $n + 1$ should also be in the set of nonnegative integers. There are, however, many subsets of the real numbers that· have these two properties. Indeed the set of all real numbers contains 0, and for each x in R we know that $x + 1$ is also in R.

Any set that contains $x + 1$ whenever it contains x we will call a *hereditary* set. Any hereditary set that contains 0 must, of course, contain 1 and hence contain 2 and indeed contain all nonnegative integers. Thus the set of nonnegative integers must be a subset of the intersection of all hereditary sets that contain 0. But we have already agreed that the set of nonnegative integers must be hereditary and it must contain 0. Therefore the set of nonnegative integers must *be* the intersection of all hereditary sets that contain 0.

Definition 4.300. $Z_0 = \bigcap_{A \in \mathscr{S}} A$ where $\mathscr{S} = \{A \mid A \subseteq R, 0 \in A, \text{ and } A \text{ is hereditary}\}$.

From Z_0 we can then define the set of integers Z, and the set of rational numbers Q in the obvious way.

Definition 4.301. $Z = \{x \in R \mid x \in Z_0 \text{ or } -x \in Z_0\}$.
$$Q = \left\{\frac{x}{y} \mid x \in Z, y \in Z, \text{ and } y \neq 0\right\}.$$

We will use the letters

$$m, n, p, q, r, s, t$$

as variables on Z.

Let us now verify that Z_0 has the basic properties that we expect.

Theorem 4.302. *Z_0 is a hereditary set of real numbers that contains 0, and Z_0 is a subset of every hereditary set of real numbers that contains 0.*

Proof. Since Z_0 is the intersection of a collection of sets of real numbers each of which contains 0, it follows that Z_0 is a set of real numbers and $0 \in Z_0$. Furthermore, if $n \in Z_0$, then $n \in A$ for each A in $\mathscr{S}$. Since each set in $\mathscr{S}$ is hereditary, it follows that $n + 1 \in A$ for each A in $\mathscr{S}$. Therefore $n + 1 \in Z_0$, and Z_0 is hereditary.

Since every hereditary set of real numbers that contains 0 is in $\mathscr{S}$, it follows that every such set contains Z_0 as a subset.

Q.E.D.

That Z_0 is the only subset of R having the properties specified in Theorem 4.302 is also easily proved.

Theorem 4.303. *If A is a hereditary set of real numbers that contains 0 and if A is a subset of every hereditary set of real numbers that contains 0, then $A = Z_0$.*

Proof. If A is a hereditary set of real numbers that contains 0, then, by Theorem 4.302, $Z_0 \subseteq A$. If A is a subset of every hereditary set of real numbers that contains 0, then $A \subseteq Z_0$. Therefore, by the axiom of extent, $A = Z_0$.

Q.E.D.

We come now to a result of very special importance not only to a study of the integers but also to a study of the real numbers, the *principle of mathematical induction*.

Theorem 4.304. *If M is a hereditary subset of Z_0 that contains 0, then $M = Z_0$, that is, if 1) $M \subseteq Z_0$, 2) $0 \in M$, and 3) M is hereditary, then $M = Z_0$.*

Proof. If M is a hereditary set of real numbers that contains 0, then $Z_0 \subseteq M$. If in addition $M \subseteq Z_0$ then $M = Z_0$.

Q.E.D.

We now illustrate the principle of mathematical induction by using it to prove several properties of the integers. As a beginning point we will prove that the elements in Z_0 are indeed nonnegative.

Theorem 4.305. $Z_0 = \{n \in Z \mid n \geq 0\}$.

Proof. From the definition of Z we have that $n \in Z$ iff $n \in Z_0$ or $-n \in Z_0$. Since $n \leq 0$ iff $-n \geq 0$, it is therefore sufficient to prove that each element of Z_0 is greater than or equal to 0. This we do by induction. If $M = \{n \in Z_0 \mid n \geq 0\}$, then

1) $M \subseteq Z_0$.

2) $0 \in M$.

3) For each n in M we have that $n \in Z_0$ and $n \geq 0$. Since Z_0 is hereditary, it follows that $n + 1 \in Z_0$, and since $n + 1 > n$, it follows that $n + 1 \geq 0$. Therefore $n + 1 \in M$, and M is hereditary.

M is a hereditary subset of Z_0 that contains 0. Therefore, by the principle of mathematical induction, $M = Z_0$.

Q.E.D.

Theorem 4.306. *If $n \in Z_0$, then $n = 0$ or $n \geq 1$.*

Proof. If $M = \{n \in Z_0 \mid n = 0$ or $n \geq 1\}$, then
1) $M \subseteq Z_0$.
2) $0 \in M$.
3) If $n \in M$, then $n \in Z_0$, and $n = 0$ or $n \geq 1$. Since $n \in Z_0$, we have that $n + 1 \in Z_0$. Since $n = 0$ or $n \geq 1$, it follows that $n \geq 0$ and hence $n + 1 \geq 1$. Therefore $n + 1 \in M$.
From the principle of mathematical induction we conclude that $M = Z_0$.

Q.E.D.

From Theorem 4.306 we now prove that no integer lies between n and $n + 1$.

Theorem 4.307. *If $n \leq m \leq n + 1$ then $m = n$ or $m = n + 1$.*

Proof. If $n < 0$ and if there were an integer between n and $n + 1$, then it would follow that $-n - 1 \geq 0$ and there is an integer between $-n - 1$ and $-n$. It is therefore sufficient to prove the result for $n \geq 0$. This we do by induction.
If $M = \{n \in Z_0 \mid (\forall m)$ if $n \leq m \leq n + 1$ then $m = n$ or $m = n + 1\}$, then
1) $M \subseteq Z_0$.
2) If $0 \leq m \leq 1$, then from Theorems 4.305 and 4.306 it follows that $m = 0$ or $m = 1$. Therefore, $0 \in M$.
3) If $n \in M$, then we know that there are no integers between n and $n + 1$. Therefore if $n + 1 \leq m \leq (n + 1) + 1$, then $n \leq m - 1 \leq n + 1$ and hence $m = n + 1$ or $m = (n + 1) + 1$. We conclude that $n + 1 \in M$ and $M = Z_0$.

Q.E.D.

Corollary 4.308. *If $-n < mn < n$, then $m = 0$.*

Proof. If $-n < mn < n$, then $-1 < m \leq 0$ or $0 \leq m < 1$. In either case, $m = 0$.

Q.E.D.

Corollary 4.309. *$(\exists n)\ mn = 1$ iff $m = 1$ or $m = -1$.*

Proof. If $m = 1$ and $n = 1$, then $mn = 1$. If $m = -1$ and $n = -1$, then $mn = 1$. If $mn = 1$, then m and n are either both positive or both negative. If $m > 0$ and $n > 0$, then $n \geq 1$ and hence $mn \geq m$. But $mn = 1$, therefore $0 < m \leq 1$ and hence $m = 1$. If $m < 0$ and $n < 0$, then $n \leq -1$ and hence $mn \geq -m$. Therefore, since $mn = 1$, we have that $-1 \leq m < 0$ and hence $m = -1$.

Q.E.D.

A cautious reader may object to the proof of Theorem 4.307 on the grounds that it tacitly assumes that if m is an integer then $m - 1$ is an integer. This omission can be remedied by an induction argument which has a very curious twist.

Theorem 4.310. *If $m \in Z$ then $m - 1 \in Z$ and $m + 1 \in Z$.*

Proof. To prove that $m - 1 \in Z$ we note that $m \leq 0$ or $m > 0$. If $m \leq 0$, then $-m \in Z_0$ and hence $-m + 1 \in Z_0$. Therefore $m - 1 \in Z$. If $m > 0$, then $m \in Z_0$ and the proof is by induction.

If $M = \{n \in Z_0 \mid n = 0$ or $n - 1 \in Z\}$, then

1) $M \subseteq Z_0$.

2) $0 \in M$.

3) If $n \in M$, then $n \in Z_0$. Therefore, $n + 1 \in Z_0$. Thus $n + 1 \in Z_0$ and $(n + 1) - 1 \in Z_0$. From this we conclude that $n + 1 \in M$ and $M = Z_0$.

To prove that $m + 1 \in Z$ we note that if $m \in Z$ then $-m \in Z$. Therefore $-m - 1 \in Z$ and hence $m + 1 \in Z$.

Q.E.D.

We are now prepared to prove that sums and products of integers are integers.

Theorem 4.311. $(\forall m)(\forall n)(m + n) \in Z$ and $mn \in Z$.

Proof. Since $m + n$ is an integer if and only if $-m - n$ is an integer, and since $n \in Z$ if and only if $n \in Z_0$ or $-n \in Z_0$, it is sufficient to prove that the sum of any integer and any nonnegative integer is an integer. This we do by induction.

If $M = \{n \in Z_0 \mid (\forall m)\, m + n \in Z\}$, then since $m + 0 = m$ for each m in Z, we have that $0 \in M$. For each n in M we know that the sum of n and any integer is an integer—that is, $(\forall m)\, m + n \in Z$. It then follows from Theorem 4.310 that $(m + n) + 1 \in Z$. Therefore, $m + (n + 1) \in Z$. From this we conclude that $n + 1 \in M$ and $M = Z_0$.

The proof for products is similar and is left to the reader.

From Theorem 4.311 we see that addition and multiplication are closed on Z. Furthermore, since 0 and 1 are in Z and since for each n in Z, $-n \in Z$, it follows that if we consider the number system consisting of Z with addition, multiplication, and order restricted to Z, then this system has all of the field and order properties except M_3, the existence of reciprocals. Indeed from Corollary 4.309 we see that the only integers having their reciprocals among the integers are 1 and -1. The results needed to establish that the rational number system has all of the properties of an ordered field will be found in the exercises at the end of this section.

Our faith in the definition of the integers that we have given will be strengthened as we prove more and more properties of the integers. Theorem 4.311 is only the first step in establishing that the integers as defined do have the arithmetic properties that we expect. Let us digress from this objective for a moment to observe the integers and mathematical induction in another role, *counting*.

When we count a particular collection of things we point to the objects in turn and call out integer names in order beginning with 1. Counting is a process for establishing a one-to-one correspondence between the objects to be counted and a certain collection of integers. When we claim that the set A has n elements we mean that we can establish a one-to-one correspondence between $\{1, 2, \ldots, n\}$ and A. More formally stated, there exists a function f such that

$$f:\{1, 2, \ldots, n\} \xrightarrow[\text{onto}]{1-1} A.$$

We mean more than this, however. We also mean that n is the only integer for which such a one-to-one correspondence can be established; that is, if there exists an integer m and a function g such that

$$g:\{1, 2, \ldots, m\} \xrightarrow[\text{onto}]{1-1} A$$

then $m = n$.

To prove that for a given set there is at most one integer that has this property it is sufficient to prove

Theorem 4.312. *If $m \in Z_0$ and $n \in Z_0$ and if there exists a function f with the property that*

$$f:\{1, 2, \ldots, m\} \xrightarrow[\text{onto}]{1-1} \{1, 2, \ldots, n\},$$

then $m = n$.

Proof. If $M = \{n \in Z_0 \mid \forall m \in Z_0 \text{ if } (\exists f) f:\{1, 2, \ldots, m\} \xrightarrow[\text{onto}]{1-1} \{1, 2, \ldots, n\}$ then $m = n\}$, then

1) $M \subseteq Z_0$.

2) To prove that $0 \in M$ we must recall that '$\{1, 2, \ldots, n\}$' is an abbreviation for '$\{p \mid 1 \le p \le n\}$'. If $n = 0$, then $\{p \mid 1 \le p \le n\} = \varnothing$. Thus if $m \in Z_0$ and if $(\exists f) f:\{p \mid 1 \le p \le m\} \xrightarrow[\text{onto}]{1-1} \varnothing$, then $\text{Ran} f = \varnothing$. From this it follows that $\text{Dom} f = \varnothing$. But $\text{Dom} f = \{p \mid 1 \le p \le m\}$. It then follows that $m = 0$ and hence $0 \in M$.

3) If $n \in M$ and if $(\exists f) f:\{1, 2, \ldots, m\} \xrightarrow[\text{onto}]{1-1} \{1, 2, \ldots, n\}$ then $m = n$. But if $(\exists g) g:\{1, 2, \ldots, m\} \xrightarrow[\text{onto}]{1-1} \{1, 2, \ldots, n + 1\}$, then $(\exists f) f:\{1, 2, \ldots, m - 1\} \xrightarrow[\text{onto}]{1-1} \{1, 2, \ldots, n\}$. (Why?) It then follows that $n = m - 1$. Therefore $m = n + 1$, $n + 1 \in M$, and $M = Z_0$.

Q.E.D.

Corollary 4.313.   *If $m \geq 0$ and $n \geq 0$, if $(\exists f) f:\{1, 2, \ldots, m\} \xrightarrow[\text{onto}]{1-1} A$, and if $(\exists g) g:\{1, 2, \ldots, n\} \xrightarrow[\text{onto}]{1-1} A$, then $m = n$.*

Proof.   Under the given conditions $g^{-1} \circ f:\{1, 2, \ldots, m\} \xrightarrow[\text{onto}]{1-1} \{1, 2, \ldots, n\}$. Therefore, $m = n$.

Q.E.D.

Corollary 4.313 then justifies

Definition 4.314. $\#A = n$ iff $n \geq 0$ and $(\exists f) f:\{1, 2, \ldots, n\} \xrightarrow[\text{onto}]{1-1} A$. A is a *finite* set iff $\#A$ exists. A is an *infinite* set iff A is not finite.

The symbol '$\#A$' is read the *count of A* or simply *count A*.

Let us now deduce a few properties of finite sets. As exercises for the reader we suggest the following.

Theorem 4.315. $\#A = 0$ iff $A = \emptyset$.

Theorem 4.316.   1) *If $\#A = n$ and $x \in A$, then $\#(A - \{x\}) = n - 1$.*
2) *If $\#A = n$ and $x \notin A$, then $\#(A \cup \{x\}) = n + 1$.*

From these results we prove

Theorem 4.317.   *A subset of a finite set is finite.*

Proof.   (By induction.) If $M = \{n \in Z_0 \mid (\forall A)$ if $\#A = n$ and $B \subseteq A$, then B is finite$\}$, then

1) $M \subseteq Z_0$.

2) $0 \in M$ because if $\#A = 0$ and $B \subseteq A$, then $B = \emptyset$, hence B is finite by Theorem 4.315.

3) For each n in M and for each A if $\#A = n$ and $B \subseteq A$, then B is finite. Let us consider sets with count $n + 1$. If $\#A = n + 1$ and $B \subseteq A$, then A is finite. Therefore if $B = A$, then B is finite. If $B \neq A$, then there exists an x in A for which $x \notin B$ and hence $B \subseteq (A - \{x\})$. Since $\#(A - \{x\}) = n$ and since $B \subseteq (A - \{x\})$, it follows that B is finite, hence $n + 1 \in M$.

Q.E.D.

Corollary 4.318. *The intersection of two finite sets is finite.*

Corollary 4.319. *The intersection of any collection of finite sets is finite.*

The proofs are left to the reader.

Theorem 4.320. *The union of two finite sets is finite.*

The proof is by induction and is left to the reader.

Theorem 4.321. *The set of integers is infinite.*

Proof. It is sufficient to prove that Z_0 is infinite. (Why?) Our proof is by contradiction. If Z_0 is finite, then for some n, $\#Z_0 = n$, that is, $(\exists f)\, f:\{1, 2, \ldots, n\} \xrightarrow[\text{onto}]{1-1} Z_0$. If g is then defined on Z_0 by $g(n) = n + 1$, then $g:Z_0 \xrightarrow[\text{onto}]{1-1} (Z_0 - \{0\})$ and $g \circ f:\{1, 2, \ldots, n\} \xrightarrow[\text{onto}]{1-1} (Z_0 - \{0\})$. That is, $\#(Z_0 - \{0\}) = n$. Since $0 \notin (Z_0 - \{0\})$ we have from Theorem 4.316 that $\#Z_0 = n + 1$. But this is a contradiction. We are then forced to conclude that Z_0 is infinite and Z is infinite.

Q.E.D.

The theorems we have proved thus far were chosen to illustrate an interesting variety of results that can be established by induction and thereby strengthen our claim that induction is a basic tool for proofs. To emphasize further the importance of induction we turn now to results that we will prove by induction, and which themselves provide basic techniques for the proof of other things.

Let us recall that the basic idea underlying the principle of mathematical induction is that every hereditary set that contains 0 must contain all integers greater than 0. This, however, is not a property that is possessed exclusively by 0. Indeed every hereditary set that contains an integer m must contain all integers greater than m. From this fact we can easily deduce an infinite collection of induction principles, one for each integer m.

Definition 4.322. $Z_m = \{n \in Z \mid n \geq m\}$.

Example. $Z_{-10} = \{-10, -9, -8, \ldots\}$.
$\qquad\qquad\ Z_2 = \{2, 3, 4, \ldots\}$.

Theorem 4.323. *If M is a hereditary subset of Z_m that contains m, then $M = Z_m$.*

Proof.   (By induction.) If $M' = \{n \in Z_0 \mid n + m \in M\}$, then

1) $M' \subseteq Z_0$.

2) Since $m \in M$, it follows that $0 \in M'$.

3) If $n \in M'$, then $n + m \in M$. But M is hereditary; therefore, $n + 1 + m \in M$ and hence $n + 1 \in M'$.

It then follows that $M' = Z_0$. Furthermore, if $n \in Z_m$, then $n - m \geq 0$. Therefore, $n - m \in Z_0$. But $Z_0 = M'$. Consequently $n - m \in M'$, $n \in M$, and $Z_m \subseteq M$. Since by hypothesis $M \subseteq Z_m$, we conclude that $M = Z_m$.

Q.E.D.

An induction argument dealing with hereditary subsets of Z_m is referred to as an induction *beginning with m* or an induction with *base m*. Because of the similarity between an induction with base 0 and an induction with any other base we offer no special illustrative examples.

As we gain greater understanding of induction arguments we will wish to omit certain obvious details. For example, in an induction we always define the set M in such a way that M is a subset of Z_m. There is no reason to continue to repeat this fact. In proving that M is hereditary we must prove that if n is in M then $n + 1$ is in M. This requires that we prove that $n + 1$ has a certain property under the assumption that n has that property. The assumption that n has the property we call the *induction hypothesis*. When in a given problem it is clear how the set M is to be defined we will not bother to define it. We will take the point of view that a proof by induction with base m has been completed when we have established that m has the property in question and that $n + 1$ has the property whenever n does. We provide one example. To prove that if $n \geq 1$, then

$$1 + 2 + \cdots + n = \frac{n(n + 1)}{2}$$

we will be content to argue that if $n = 1$, then

$$1 = \frac{1(1 + 1)}{2}.$$

Hence the result is true for the base 1. If the result is true for n, then since

$$1 + 2 + \cdots + (n + 1) = (1 + 2 + \cdots + n) + (n + 1)$$

it follows from the induction hypothesis that

$$1 + 2 + \cdots + (n + 1) = \frac{n(n + 1)}{2} + (n + 1) = \frac{(n + 1)(n + 2)}{2}.$$

By means of an induction with base m we can prove the following very useful result which is known as the *well-ordering principle for integers*.

Theorem 4.324.   *Every nonempty subset of Z_m contains a smallest element —that is, if $A \subseteq Z_m$ and $A \neq \varnothing$, then $\exists p \in A, \forall n \in A, n \geq p$.*

Proof Procedure.   Our proof involves an interesting and rather sophisti-
cated use of induction. Since every nonempty set of integers contains an
integer, it is sufficient to prove for each n in Z_m and for each subset A that
if $n \in A$ then A has a smallest element.

Proof.   If $M = \{n \in Z_m \mid (\forall A)$ if $A \subseteq Z_m$ and $n \in A$ then A has a smallest
element$\}$, and if A is a subset of Z_m that contains m then for each n in A,
$n \geq m$; that is, m is the smallest element of A. Therefore, $m \in M$; that is,
the base of the induction has the required property.

For each n in M we have as our induction hypothesis that every subset
of Z_m that contains n has a smallest element. Therefore if A is a subset of
Z_m that contains $n + 1$, then $A \cup \{n\}$ is a subset of Z_m that contains n.
From the induction hypothesis it follows that $A \cup \{n\}$ has a smallest element.
If p is the smallest element in $A \cup \{n\}$, then $p \in A$ or $p \notin A$. If $p \in A$ then p
is the smallest element in A. If $p \notin A$ then $p = n$, and $n + 1$ is the smallest
element in A. (Why?) In either event $n + 1 \in M$ and $M = Z_0$.

Q.E.D.

We illustrate the use of the well-ordering principle by proving

Theorem 4.325   (The Division Theorem for Integers).   *For each pair of
integers m and n, if $n \neq 0$ then there exists one and only one integer q and
there exists one and only one integer r such that*

$$m = nq + r \text{ and } 0 \leq r < |n|.$$

Proof.   If $A = \{m - nq \mid q \in Z$ and $m - nq \geq 0\}$, then $A \subseteq Z_0$. Furthermore if $m \geq 0$ and if $q = 0$, we see that $m \in A$. If $m < 0$ and if $q = mn$
we see that $m(1 - n^2) \in A$. Since $A \neq \varnothing$, it follows from the well-ordering
principle that A has a smallest element. If r is the smallest element of A,
then it follows from the definition of A that there exists an integer q for
which $m = nq + r$. Furthermore, by the trichotomy property of the order
relation, we have that $r < |n|$ or $r \geq |n|$. If $r \geq |n|$, then $r - |n| \geq 0$. If
$n \geq 0$, then $r - |n| = r - n = m - n(q + 1)$. If $n < 0$, then $r - |n| =
r + n = m - n(q - 1)$. In either case $r - |n| \in A$, but since $n \neq 0$,
$r - |n| < r$. We then have that $r - |n|$ is an element of A that is smaller
than the smallest element of A. This contradiction forces us to the conclusion
that

$$m = nq + r \text{ and } 0 \leq r < |n|.$$

For the uniqueness we note that if $m = nq_1 + r_1$ and $m = nq_2 + r_2$
then $n(q_1 - q_2) = r_2 - r_1$. If in addition $0 \leq r_1 < |n|$ and $0 \leq r_2 < |n|$,
then $-|n| < r_2 - r_1 < |n|$. We then have that $-|n| < n(q_1 - q_2) < |n|$.
From Corollary 4.308 it then follows that $q_1 = q_2$ and hence $r_1 = r_2$.

Q.E.D.

In proving the hereditary property in an induction argument, we are required to prove that $n + 1$ has a certain property from the induction hypothesis that n has the property. For certain problems the hereditary property, in an induction with base m, is more easily established if we are permitted the stronger hypothesis that $m, m + 1, m + 2, \ldots, n$ each have the property in question. That this type of induction hypothesis is permissible is easily proved from the well-ordering principle. An induction argument using this induction hypothesis is called a proof by *strong induction*. We prove the principle for inductions with base 0 and leave the proof for inductions with base m to the reader.

Definition 4.326. $\bar{n} = \{m \mid 0 \leq m < n\}$.

Note that $\bar{0} = \varnothing$.

Theorem 4.327 (The Principle of Strong Induction). *If*
1) $M \subseteq Z_0$,
2) $(\forall n)$ *if* $\bar{n} \subseteq M$, *then* $n \in M$,
then $M = Z_0$.

Proof. (By contradiction.) If $M \neq Z_0$, then there is some nonnegative integer that is not in M. By the well-ordering principle there is a smallest nonnegative integer n such that $n \notin M$. Therefore if $0 \leq m < n$, then $m \in M$, hence $\bar{n} \subseteq M$. From 2) we conclude that $n \in M$. This is a contradiction that forces us to conclude that $M = Z_0$.

Q.E.D.

Note that since $\bar{0} = \varnothing$ and since the empty set is a subset of every set, the proof of 2) requires among other things the proof that $0 \in M$.

As an illustration of the use of the principle of strong induction we have chosen to prove two basic results: the existence of decimal representations for integers and the fundamental theorem of arithmetic. For each of these we will need the conventional exponential notation which we now define for all real numbers.

Definition 4.328. $x^0 = 1$.
$$x^{n+1} = x^n \cdot x \text{ for } n \geq 0.$$
$$x^{-n} = (x^{-1})^n \cdot x \text{ for } n \geq 0 \text{ and } x \neq 0.$$

Example. $\pi^0 = 1$, $(-\tfrac{1}{2})^1 = -\tfrac{1}{2}$, $5^2 = 25$, $5^{-2} = \tfrac{1}{25}$, $0^0 = 1$.

When we use decimal notation, such as '3476', to refer to an integer we are identifying that integer as being

$$3 \cdot 10^3 + 4 \cdot 10^2 + 7 \cdot 10 + 6.$$

That every integer has such a representation is easily deduced from the division theorem for integers by strong induction. We have, of course, assumed an understanding of decimal notation from the outset. We now wish to show that this notation can be justified. To be very circumspect we should, of course, define the conventional numerals.

Definition 4.329. $2 = 1 + 1$ $3 = 2 + 1$ $4 = 3 + 1$
$5 = 4 + 1$ $6 = 5 + 1$ $7 = 6 + 1$
$8 = 7 + 1$ $9 = 8 + 1$ $10 = 9 + 1.$

Theorem 4.330. *If $n \geq 0$, then there exist integers $a_0, a_1, \ldots, a_m$ such that* $0 \leq a_0 \leq 9, 0 \leq a_1 \leq 9, \ldots, 0 \leq a_m \leq 9$, *and* $n = a_m 10^m + a_{m-1} 10^{m-1} + \cdots + a_0.$

Proof. (By strong induction.) As our induction hypothesis we assume that the result is true for all integers that are greater than or equal to 0 but less than n, and we will show that the result is true for n. We consider two cases $n = 0$ and $n \neq 0$.

If $n = 0$ if $m = 0$ and if $a_0 = 0$, then we have that $0 \leq a_0 \leq 9$ and $n = a_0$. Therefore the result is true for n.

If $n \neq 0$ then from the division theorem for integers there exist integers q and r such that
$$n = 10q + r \text{ and } 0 \leq r < 10.$$

We then have that $n \geq n - r = 10q \geq q$. Since $n \neq 0$ we cannot have both q and r zero; hence $n > q$, and by the induction hypothesis there exist integers $b_0, b_1, \ldots, b_p$ such that $0 \leq b_0 \leq 9$, $0 \leq b_1 \leq 9, \ldots,$ $0 \leq b_p \leq 9$, and $q = b_p 10^p + b_{p-1} 10^{p-1} + \cdots + b_0$. Therefore

$$n = 10q + r = b_p 10^{p+1} + b_{p-1} 10^p + \cdots + b_0 10 + r.$$

Q.E.D.

Leaving the proof that decimal representation is unique as an exercise for the reader, we turn to the fundamental theorem of arithmetic which asserts that every composite integer can be factored into a product of primes. Furthermore the factorization can be done in essentially only one way. The proof requires several divisibility properties of the integers.

Definition 4.331. $m|n$ iff $(\exists p) n = mp$.
'$m|n$' is read m divides n.

Example. $2|4, -3|12, -5|10, 4|4, 1|3, 17|0.$

It is obvious that for each n, $1|n$, $-1|n$, $n|n$, and $-n|n$. We refer to 1, -1, n, and $-n$ as *trivial divisors* of n; all other divisors of n are *proper divisors* of n.

Definition 4.332. *m* is a *proper divisor of n* iff $m|n$, $|m| \neq 1$ and $|m| \neq |n|$. *m* is a *trivial divisor of n* iff $m|n$ and *m* is not a proper divisor of *n*.

Theorem 4.333. *If* $n \neq 0$ *and* $m|n$, *then* $1 \leq |m| \leq |n|$.

Proof. Since $m|n$ there exists an integer *p* for which $n = mp$. Since $n \neq 0$ we have that $m \neq 0$ and $p \neq 0$. It then follows that $1 \leq |m|$ and $1 \leq |p|$. From the fact that $|m| \geq 0$ and $1 \leq |p|$ it follows that $|m| < |m| |p|$. But $|mp| = |n|$. Therefore, $1 \leq |m| \leq |n|$.

Q.E.D.

Corollary 4.334. *If* $n \neq 0$ *and* *m* *is* *a* *proper* *divisor* *of* *n*, *then* $1 < |m| < |n|$.

Corollary 4.335. *If* $n \neq 0$, *if* *m* *is a proper divisor of n and if* $n = mp$, *then p is a proper divisor of n.*

The proofs are left to the reader.
From Corollary 4.335 we see that proper divisors occur in pairs.

Example.   2 and 3 are proper divisors of 6.
    −2 and −4 are proper divisors of 8.

We are particularly interested in those integers other than −1, 0, and 1 that have no proper divisors. These are, of course, the *primes*.

Definition 4.336.   *p* is *prime* iff $|p| > 1$ and *p* has no proper divisors.
    p is *composite* iff $|p| > 1$ and *p* has proper divisors.

Example.   2, 3, −5, 7, and −11 are prime.
    4, 6, −8, 9, and −10 are composite.

For the proof of a needed divisibility property of primes we introduce next the notion of the *greatest common divisor* of two integers. Indeed for many purposes—as, for example, computations with rational numbers—we are interested not only in the greatest common divisor but also in the *least common multiple* of pairs of integers. As the names suggest the greatest common divisor of two integers is the largest integer that divides each of them, and the least common multiple is the smallest positive integer that is a multiple of—i.e., divisible by—each. For example, the largest integer that divides both 6 and 9 is 3 and the smallest positive integer that is a multiple of 6 and 9 is 18.

Our reference to *the* greatest common divisor and *the* least common multiple tacitly assumes uniqueness. This is in fact easily proved.

Theorem 4.337. 1) $(\forall m)(\forall n)$ *there is at most one integer p with the property that $p|m$, $p|n$, and $(\forall q)$ if $q|m$ and $q|n$, then $q \leq p$.*

2) $(\forall m)(\forall n)$ *there is at most one integer p with the property that $p > 0$, $m|p$, $n|p$, and $(\forall q)$ if $q > 0$, $m|q$ and $n|q$, then $q \geq p$.*

Proof. 1) and 2) If p_1 and p_2 each have the given property, then $p_1 \leq p_2$ and $p_2 \leq p_1$, hence $p_1 = p_2$.

Q.E.D.

Theorem 4.337 then justifies

Definition 4.338. $p = (m, n)$ iff $p|m$, $p|n$, and $(\forall q)$ if $q|m$ and $q|n$, then $q \leq p$.

$p = [m, n]$ iff $m|p$, $n|p$, $p > 0$, and $(\forall q)$ if $q > 0$, $m|q$ and $n|q$, then $q \geq p$.

Example. $(6, 9) = 3$, $(-2, 6) = 2$, $(0, 1) = 1$.
$[6, 9] = 18$, $[-2, 6] = 6$, $[1, 1] = 1$.

Definition 4.339. *m and n are relatively prime iff $(m, n) = 1$.*

Example. 2 and 3 are relatively prime because $(2, 3) = 1$.
-6 and 35 are relatively prime because $(-6, 35) = 1$.
2 and 6 are not relatively prime because $(2, 6) = 2$.

Note that the symbol '$(2, 6)$' now has three possible meanings. It denotes an ordered pair, an interval, and an integer. We will rely upon the context to make the meaning clear.

It is untuitively obvious that if m and n are not both 0 then (m, n) exists. The proof that this is indeed true involves an interesting use of the well-ordering principle.

Theorem 4.340. *If $m \neq 0$ or $n \neq 0$, then there exist integers s and t such that $(m, n) = ms + nt$.*

Proof. If $M = \{ms + nt \mid s \in Z \text{ and } t \in Z \text{ and } ms + nt > 0\}$, then since $m \neq 0$ or $n \neq 0$, it follows that $m^2 + n^2 > 0$. If $s = m$ and $t = n$ it follows that $m^2 + n^2 \in M$, hence $M \neq \varnothing$. Since M is a nonempty set of nonnegative integers, it follows from the well-ordering principle that M has a smallest element. If p is the smallest element in M, then from the definition of M it follows that there are integers s and t such that $p = ms + nt$. We need only prove that p is the greatest common divisor of m and n.

To prove that $p|m$ we note that if $m = 0$ then $m = p \cdot 0$, i.e., $p|m$. If $m \neq 0$ then from the division theorem there exist integers q and r such that $m = pq + r$ and $0 \leq r < p$. Since $p = ms + nt$ it follows that $pq = msq + ntq$, and since $r = m - pq$ we have that $r = m(1 - sq) + n(-tq)$.

From this it follows that if $r > 0$ then $r \in M$. But r is smaller than the smallest element in M. It then follows that $r \notin M$, hence $r = 0$ and $p|m$. By a similar argument we can prove that $p|n$.

Finally we see that if $q|m$ and $q|n$, then since $p = ms + nt$, it follows that $q|p$. Since $q|p$ and since $p > 0$, we have that $q \leq p$ and hence $p = (m, n)$.

Q.E.D.

Theorem 4.341. *If $p|mn$ and $(p, m) = 1$, then $p|n$.*

Proof. Since $(p, m) = 1$, we have from Theorem 4.340 that there are integers s and t such that $1 = ps + mt$; then $n = nps + mnt$ and since $p|mn$, it follows that $p|n$.

Q.E.D.

Corollary 4.342. *If $p|mn$ and p is prime, then $p|m$ or $p|n$.*

Corollary 4.343. *If $p|m_1 m_2 \cdots m_n$ and p is prime, then $p|m_1$ or $p|m_2 \cdots$ or $p|m_n$.*

The proofs are left to the reader.

We are now prepared to prove that every composite integer can be factored into a product of primes, and this factorization can be done in essentially only one way. There are, of course, two questions here, and we choose to deal with them separately.

Definition 4.344. n is a *product of primes* iff n is a prime or there exist positive primes $p_1, p_2, \ldots, p_m$ with $m > 1$ such that $n = p_1 p_2 \cdots p_m$ or $n = -p_1 p_2 \cdots p_m$.

It is a matter of convenience to think of a prime as a factorization of itself into primes.

Example.   2 is a product of primes because 2 is prime.
            -5 is a product of primes because -5 is prime.
            10 is a product of primes because $10 = 2 \cdot 5$.

Lemma 1. *n is a product of primes iff $-n$ is a product of primes.*

Proof. Obvious from Definition 4.344.

Lemma 2. *If $n > 1$, then n is a product of primes.*

Proof. (By strong induction.) If $n > 1$ and if every integer greater than 1 and less than n is a product of primes, then we argue that n is prime or n is composite. If n is prime, then n is a product of primes. If n is composite, then there exist integers p and q such that $n = pq$, $1 < p < n$, and $1 < q < n$. From the induction hypothesis it follows that p and q are each a product of primes, and hence n is also a product of primes.

Q.E.D.

From Lemmas 1 and 2 we see that every composite integer can be factored into a product of primes. For the proof of uniqueness of prime factorization we need

Lemma 3. *If $p_1, p_2, \ldots, p_m$ and $q_1, q_2, \ldots, q_n$ are positive primes and if $p_1 p_2 \cdots p_m = q_1 q_2 \cdots q_n$, then $\{p_1, p_2, \ldots, p_m\} = \{q_1, q_2, \ldots, q_n\}$.*

Proof. For each p_s in $\{p_1, p_2, \ldots, p_m\}$ we have that $p_s | p_1 p_2 \cdots p_m$. Therefore $p_s | q_1 q_2 \cdots q_n$. From this it follows that there exists an integer t such that $1 \leq t \leq n$ and $p_s | q_t$. Since p_s and q_t are each positive and prime, it follows that $p_s = q_t$. Therefore, $\{p_1, p_2, \ldots, p_m\} \subseteq \{q_1, q_2, \ldots, q_n\}$. By a similar argument we can prove that $\{q_1, q_2, \ldots, q_n\} \subseteq \{p_1, p_2, \ldots, p_m\}$.

Q.E.D.

Lemma 4. *If $s \geq 1$, if $p_1, p_2, \ldots, p_s$ are distinct positive primes, if $m_1, m_2, \ldots, m_s$ and $n_1, n_2, \ldots, n_s$ are positive integers, and if*

$$p_1^{m_1} p_2^{m_2} \cdots p_s^{m_s} = p_1^{n_1} p_2^{n_2} \cdots p_s^{n_s}$$

then $m_1 = n_1, m_2 = n_2, \ldots, m_s = n_s$.

Proof. (By induction.) If in addition to the hypothesis given we add the requirement that $m_1 + m_2 + \cdots + m_s = 1$, it would then follow that $s = 1$, $m_1 = 1$, and

$$p_1 = p_1^{n_1}.$$

From this we see that $n_1 = 1$; that is, $m_1 = n_1$. We have proved that the lemma is true provided $m_1 + m_2 + \cdots + m_s = 1$. As our induction hypothesis we assume the result true provided $m_1 + m_2 + \cdots + m_s = m$ and we consider the case when $m_1 + m_2 + \cdots + m_s = m + 1$. We have that

$$p_1^{m_1} p_2^{m_2} \cdots p_s^{m_s} = p_1^{n_1} p_2^{n_2} \cdots p_s^{n_s}.$$

Dividing by p_1 we obtain

$$p_1^{m_1-1} p_2^{m_2} \cdots p_s^{m_s} = p_1^{n_1-1} p_2^{n_2} \cdots p_s^{n_s}.$$

But $(m_1 - 1) + m_2 + \cdots + m_s = m$; therefore from the induction hypothesis $m_1 - 1 = n_1 - 1$, $m_2 = n_2, \ldots, m_s = n_s$; hence $m_1 = n_1$, $m_2 = n_2$, $\ldots, m_s = n_s$.

Q.E.D.

The information of Lemmas 1–4 we summarize as

Theorem 4.345 (The Fundamental Theorem of Arithmetic). *If $|n| > 1$, then n is a product of primes. Furthermore n has essentially only one factorization into a product of primes.*

This section was intended primarily as a discussion of induction with examples of its use. While we have concentrated on properties of the integers for these examples we have not developed all of the properties that will be needed in the material ahead. We choose to assume a knowledge of these properties and encourage the interested reader to approach the material critically, supplying for himself those definitions and theorems that are necessary to make the theory complete.

EXERCISES

1. Prove: If $m < n + 1$, then $m \le n$.
2. Prove: If $m < n$, then $m + 1 \le n$.
3. Prove: If $m \le m + n$ and if $n \ne 0$, then $m < m + n$.
4. Prove: $(\exists p)\, m + p = n$.
5. Prove: $m \mid n$ iff $-m \mid n$.
6. Prove: If $m \mid n$, then $n = 0$ or $|m| \le |n|$.
7. Prove: $m \mid 1$ iff $m = 1$ or $m = -1$.
8. Prove: If $m \mid n$ and $n \mid m$, then $|m| = |n|$.
9. Prove: If $m > 0$ and $n > 0$, then $(\exists p)\, m < np$.
10. Prove: If $x \in Q$, then $(\exists m)(\exists n)\, n > 0$ and $x = m/n$.
11. Prove: If $x \in Q$ and $x \ge 0$, then $(\exists m)(\exists n)\, m \ge 0$, $n > 0$, $(m, n) = 1$, and $x = m/n$.
12. Prove: If x and y are positive rational numbers, then there exists an integer m such that $x < my$.
13. Prove: If $x \in Q$ and $x \ne 0$, then $\exists y \in Q$, $xy = 1$.
14. Prove: If $x \in Q$ and $y \in Q$, then $x + y \in Q$ and $xy \in Q$.
15. Prove: $x \in Q$ iff $-x \in Q$.
16. Prove: If $n > 0$, then $0^n = 0$, $1^n = 1$, $(-1)^{2n} = 1$ and $(-1)^{2n-1} = -1$.
17. Prove: If $n \ge 1$, then $\dfrac{1}{1 \cdot 2} + \dfrac{1}{2 \cdot 3} + \cdots + \dfrac{1}{n(n + 1)} = \dfrac{n}{n + 1}$.
18. Prove: If $n \ge 1$, then $1 + 3 + 5 + \cdots + (2n - 1) = n^2$.
19. Prove: If $n \ge 1$, then $1 + 3 + 3^2 + \cdots + 3^{n-1} = \dfrac{3^n - 1}{2}$.
20. Prove: If $n \ge 1$, then $1 - 2^2 + 3^2 - \cdots + (-1)^{n-1} n^2 = (-1)^{n-1} \dfrac{n(n + 1)}{2}$.
21. Prove: If $xy \ne 0$, then $x^m x^n = x^{m+n}$ and $(x^m y^n)^p = x^{mp} y^{np}$.
22. Prove: If $x > 0$, then $x^n > 0$.
23. Prove: If $x > 0$, if $y > 0$, and if $n > 0$, then $x^n < y^n$ iff $x < y$.
24. Prove: If $n > 0$ and $x^n = y^n$, then $|x| = |y|$.

25. Prove: If $n \geq 2$ and $x > 1$, then $x^n > x$.

26. Prove: If $n \geq 2$ and $0 < x < 1$, then $x^n < x$.

27. Prove (Bernoulli's inequality): If $x > -1$, if $x \neq 0$, and if $n \geq 2$, then $(1 + x)^n > 1 + nx$.

28. Prove: If $n \geq 0$, then n has a ternary representation; i.e., there exist integers $a_0, a_1, \ldots, a_m$ such that $0 \leq a_0 \leq 2$, $0 \leq a_1 \leq 2, \ldots$, $0 \leq a_m \leq 2$, and $n = a_m 3^m + a_{m-1} 3^{m-1} + \cdots + a_0$.

29. Prove: If A is a nonempty finite set of real numbers, then max S and min S exist.

30. Prove: If A is infinite and B is finite, then $A - B$ is infinite.

31. Prove: The set of all rational numbers in [0, 1] is infinite.

32. Prove: If $n > 0$, then $\left\{ \dfrac{p}{q} \middle| \dfrac{p}{q} \in [0, 1] \text{ and } 0 < q < n \right\}$ is finite.

33. Prove: If $(\exists \delta)\, N(a, \delta) \cap A$ is finite, then $(\exists \delta)\, N'(a, \delta) \cap A = \varnothing$.

34. Prove: If $(\forall a)\, S_a = \{x \in S \mid x \leq a\}$ and if $A = \{a \mid S_a \text{ is infinite}\}$, then

    1) if $a < b$, then $S_a \subseteq S_b$,

    2) if $a \notin A$, then a is a lower bound for A,

    3) if $a \in A$, then $[a, \infty) \subseteq A$.

4.4 Sum and Product Notation

For the study of certain properties of the real numbers, the conventional Σ and Π notation is virtually indispensable.

Definition 4.40. If $n < m$

$$\sum_{\alpha=m}^{n} x_\alpha = 0 \text{ and } \prod_{\alpha=m}^{n} x_\alpha = 1.$$

If $n \geq m - 1$

$$\sum_{\alpha=m}^{n+1} x_\alpha = \sum_{\alpha=m}^{n} x_\alpha + x_{n+1} \text{ and } \prod_{\alpha=m}^{n+1} x_\alpha = \left(\prod_{\alpha=m}^{n} x_\alpha \right) x_{n+1}.$$

Example. $\displaystyle\sum_{\alpha=1}^{0} x_\alpha = 0, \sum_{\alpha=1}^{1} x_\alpha = x_1, \sum_{\alpha=1}^{2} x_\alpha = x_1 + x_2.$

$\displaystyle\prod_{\alpha=1}^{0} x_1 = 1, \prod_{\alpha=1}^{1} x_\alpha = x_1, \prod_{\alpha=1}^{2} x_\alpha = x_1 x_2.$

The elementary properties of sums and products that interest us are for the most part intuitively clear, as, for example,

Theorem 4.41. $\displaystyle\sum_{\alpha=m}^{n} (x_\alpha + y_\alpha) = \sum_{\alpha=m}^{n} x_\alpha + \sum_{\alpha=m}^{n} y_\alpha, \sum_{\alpha=m}^{n} a x_\alpha = a \sum_{\alpha=m}^{n} x_\alpha.$

If $n < m$, the results are obvious. If $n \geq m$, then $n \in Z_m$, and the proof is by induction. The details are left to the reader.

Theorem 4.42. *If $m - 1 \leq s \leq n$, then*

$$\sum_{\alpha=m}^{n} x_\alpha = \sum_{\alpha=m}^{s} x_\alpha + \sum_{\alpha=s+1}^{n} x_\alpha.$$

Proof. (By induction on n.) If $n \leq m$ the result is obvious. If whenever $m - 1 \leq s \leq n$ we have that

$$\sum_{\alpha=m}^{n} x_\alpha = \sum_{\alpha=m}^{s} x_\alpha + \sum_{\alpha=s+1}^{n} x_\alpha,$$

then for $m - 1 \leq s \leq n + 1$ we have that $s \leq n$ or $s = n + 1$. If $s \leq n$, then

$$\sum_{\alpha=m}^{n+1} x_\alpha = \sum_{\alpha=m}^{n} x_\alpha + x_{n+1} = \sum_{\alpha=m}^{s} x_\alpha + \sum_{\alpha=s+1}^{n} x_\alpha + x_{n+1} = \sum_{\alpha=m}^{s} x_\alpha + \sum_{\alpha=s+1}^{n+1} x_\alpha.$$

If $s = n + 1$, then

$$\sum_{\alpha=s+1}^{n+1} x_\alpha = 0$$

and hence

$$\sum_{\alpha=m}^{n+1} x_\alpha = \sum_{\alpha=m}^{s} x_\alpha + \sum_{\alpha=s+1}^{n+1} x_\alpha.$$

Q.E.D.

Corollary 4.43. *If $m \leq n$, then*

$$\sum_{\alpha=m}^{n} x_\alpha = x_m + \sum_{\alpha=m+1}^{n} x_\alpha.$$

We leave the proof to the reader and turn to a result that justifies a procedure used in computations with the $\sum$ notation known as *shifting the index*.

Theorem 4.44. $\displaystyle\sum_{\alpha=m}^{n} x_\alpha = \sum_{\alpha=m+s}^{n+s} x_{\alpha-s}.$

Proof. (By induction on n.) If $n \leq m$ the result is obvious. If for $n \geq m$ we have

$$\sum_{\alpha=m}^{n} x_\alpha = \sum_{\alpha=m+s}^{n+s} x_{\alpha-s}$$

then

$$\sum_{\alpha=m}^{n+1} x_\alpha = \sum_{\alpha=m}^{n} x_\alpha + x_{n+1} = \sum_{\alpha=m+s}^{n+s} x_{\alpha-s} + x_{(n+1+s)-s} = \sum_{\alpha=m+s}^{(n+1)+s} x_{\alpha-s}.$$

Q.E.D.

Example. $\displaystyle\sum_{\alpha=1}^{3} x_\alpha = \sum_{\alpha=4}^{6} x_{\alpha-3}.$

To illustrate the use of Theorem 4.44 we will prove the binomial formula. For this we need

Definition 4.45. $0! = 1$, $(n + 1)! = n!(n + 1)$ for $n \geq 0$.

$$\binom{m}{n} = \frac{m!}{n!(m - n)!} \text{ for } 0 \leq n \leq m.$$

Example. $4! = 1 \cdot 2 \cdot 3 \cdot 4$, $\binom{5}{3} = \frac{5!}{3!2!} = \frac{1 \cdot 2 \cdot 3 \cdot 4 \cdot 5}{1 \cdot 2 \cdot 3 \cdot 1 \cdot 2} = 10$.

We also need the following result whose proof we leave to the reader.

Lemma 4.46. 1) *If* $n \geq 0$, *then* $\binom{n}{0} = \binom{n}{n} = 1$.

2) *If* $0 \leq n < m$, *then* $\binom{m}{n} + \binom{m}{n + 1} = \binom{m + 1}{n + 1}$.

Theorem 4.47 (The Binomial Formula). *If* $n \geq 0$, *then*

$$(x + y)^n = \sum_{\alpha = 0}^{n} \binom{n}{\alpha} x^{n - \alpha} y^{\alpha}.$$

Proof. (By induction on n.) If $n = 0$ the result is obvious. If for $n \geq 0$ we have that

$$(x + y)^n = \sum_{\alpha = 0}^{n} \binom{n}{\alpha} x^{n - \alpha} y^{\alpha},$$

then

$$(x + y)^{n + 1} = (x + y) \sum_{\alpha = 0}^{n} \binom{n}{\alpha} x^{n - \alpha} y^{\alpha}$$

$$= \sum_{\alpha = 0}^{n} \binom{n}{\alpha} x^{n + 1 - \alpha} y^{\alpha} + \sum_{\alpha = 0}^{n} \binom{n}{\alpha} x^{n - \alpha} y^{\alpha + 1}.$$

From Corollary 4.43 and Definition 4.40 we then have that

$$(x + y)^{n + 1} = x^{n + 1} + \sum_{\alpha = 1}^{n} \binom{n}{\alpha} x^{n + 1 - \alpha} y^{\alpha} + \sum_{\alpha = 0}^{n - 1} \binom{n}{\alpha} x^{n - \alpha} y^{\alpha + 1} + y^{n + 1}.$$

But from Theorem 4.44

$$\sum_{\alpha = 0}^{n - 1} \binom{n}{\alpha} x^{n - \alpha} y^{\alpha + 1} = \sum_{\alpha = 1}^{n} \binom{n}{\alpha - 1} x^{n + 1 - \alpha} y^{\alpha}.$$

Therefore, from Theorem 4.41 and Lemma 4.46

$$(x + y)^{n + 1} = x^{n + 1} + \sum_{\alpha = 1}^{n} \binom{n}{\alpha} x^{n + 1 - \alpha} y^{\alpha} + \sum_{\alpha = 1}^{n} \binom{n}{\alpha - 1} x^{n + 1 - \alpha} y^{\alpha} + y^{n + 1}$$

$$= x^{n + 1} + \sum_{\alpha = 1}^{n} \binom{n + 1}{\alpha} x^{n + 1 - \alpha} y^{\alpha} + y^{n + 1}$$

$$= \sum_{\alpha = 0}^{n + 1} \binom{n + 1}{\alpha} x^{n + 1 - \alpha} y^{\alpha}.$$

Q.E.D.

As a final example of the use of the $\sum$ notation we have chosen to prove the *generalized associative law for addition*. From the definition of a binary operation as given in Chapter 3 we understand that addition for real numbers, which we denote by '+', is a binary function that maps ordered pairs of real numbers onto real numbers. Since addition is a binary function it cannot be applied to ordered triples. However, a sum of three numbers can be obtained by repeated application of addition—as, for example,

$$(x_1 + x_2) + x_3 \text{ or } x_1 + (x_2 + x_3).$$

The associative law for addition assures us that these are equal. However, we wish to think of these formulas in a different way. They define functions on ordered triples which we choose to call sum functions. From this point of view the associative law asserts that there is only one such sum function for ordered triples of real numbers. For ordered quadruples there are five formulas

$$x_1 + (x_2 + (x_3 + x_4)), \quad x_1 + ((x_2 + x_3) + x_4), \quad (x_1 + x_2) + (x_3 + x_4),$$
$$((x_1 + x_2) + x_3) + x_4, \quad (x_1 + (x_2 + x_3)) + x_4,$$

each of which defines the same sum function. If we generalize to sum functions on n-tuples in the obvious way, the generalized associative law assures us that there is only one such sum function for n-tuples of real numbers. For the formal definition of sum function we find it convenient to include a singulary sum function.

Definition 4.48. f is an *n-ary sum function* iff $n = 1$ and $(\forall x)\, f(x) = x$ or $n > 1$ and there exists an m-ary sum function g and a p-ary sum function h such that $m \geq 1$, $p \geq 1$, $n = m + p$, and

$$f(x_1, \ldots, x_n) = g(x_1, \ldots, x_m) + h(x_{m+1}, \ldots, x_n).$$

Theorem 4.49 (The Generalized Associative Law for Addition). *For each n-ary sum function f we have that $f(x_1, \ldots, x_n) = \sum_{\alpha=1}^{n} x_\alpha$.*

Proof. (By contradiction.) If there is an n-ary sum function f such that $f(x_1, \ldots, x_n) \neq \sum_{\alpha=1}^{n} x_\alpha$, then there is a smallest integer n for which there exists an n-ary sum function f such that $f(x_1, \ldots, x_n) \neq \sum_{\alpha=1}^{n} x_\alpha$. Since we must have $n > 1$ (why?), there exists an m-ary sum function g and a p-ary sum function h such that $m \geq 1$, $p \geq 1$, $n = m + p$, and

$$f(x_1, \ldots, x_n) = g(x_1, \ldots, x_m) + h(x_{m+1}, \ldots, x_n).$$

Since $m < n$ and $p < n$,

$$g(x_1, \ldots, x_m) = \sum_{\alpha=1}^{m} x_\alpha \text{ and } h(x_{m+1}, \ldots, x_n) = \sum_{\alpha=m+1}^{n} x_\alpha.$$

(Why?) But from this it follows that

$$f(x_1, \ldots, x_n) = \sum_{\alpha=1}^{m} x_\alpha + \sum_{\alpha=m+1}^{n} x_\alpha = \sum_{\alpha=1}^{n} x_\alpha.$$

This is a contradiction.

Q.E.D.

In Section 4.3 we used the notation

$$1 + 2 + \cdots + n$$

in our discussion of the problem of summing the first n integers. This notation is quite natural and intuitive except when n is less than or equal to 1. It was our intention, of course, that we interpret

$$1 + 2 + \cdots + n$$

as a form, in the single variable 'n', that is equivalent to the form '$\sum_{\alpha=1}^{n} \alpha$'; consequently if $n < 1$, then

$$1 + 2 + \cdots + n = 0$$

and if $n = 1$, then

$$1 + 2 + \cdots + n = 1.$$

While the $\sum$ notation is important and must be mastered, the notation

$$x_1 + x_2 + \cdots + x_n$$

is so natural and intuitive that we will use it with the understanding that it be accepted as a form that is equivalent to

$$\sum_{\alpha=1}^{n} x_\alpha$$

and hence if $n < 1$

$$x_1 + x_2 + \cdots + x_n = 0,$$

if $n = 1$

$$x_1 + x_2 + \cdots + x_n = x_1,$$

etc.

EXERCISES

In Exercises 1–23 assume that $n \geq 0$ and $m \geq 0$ but identify those exercises for which this assumption is not required.

1. Prove: $\prod_{\alpha=m}^{n} (x_\alpha y_\alpha) = \left(\prod_{\alpha=m}^{n} x_\alpha \right) \left(\prod_{\alpha=m}^{n} y_\alpha \right).$

2. Prove: If $x_\alpha = x$, $\alpha = 1, 2, \ldots, n$, then $\prod_{\alpha=1}^{n} x_\alpha = x^n.$

3. Prove: $\prod\limits_{\alpha=1}^{n} (ax_\alpha) = a^n \left(\prod\limits_{\alpha=1}^{n} x_\alpha \right)$.

4. Prove: $\prod\limits_{\alpha=m}^{n} x_\alpha = \prod\limits_{\alpha=m+s}^{n+s} x_{\alpha-s}$.

5. Prove: If $m - 1 \le s \le n$, then $\prod\limits_{\alpha=m}^{n} x_\alpha = \left(\prod\limits_{\alpha=m}^{s} x_\alpha \right)\left(\prod\limits_{\alpha=s+1}^{n} x_\alpha \right)$.

6. Prove: If $m \le n$, then $\prod\limits_{\alpha=m}^{n} x_\alpha = x_m \left(\prod\limits_{\alpha=m+1}^{n} x_\alpha \right)$.

7. Prove: If $n \le m$, then $n! = \prod\limits_{\alpha=1}^{n} \alpha$ and $n! \left(\prod\limits_{\alpha=n+1}^{m} \alpha \right) = m!$

8. Prove: $\prod\limits_{\alpha=1}^{n} (-x_\alpha) = (-1)^n \prod\limits_{\alpha=1}^{n} x_\alpha$ and $\sum\limits_{\alpha=1}^{n} (-x_\alpha) = - \sum\limits_{\alpha=1}^{n} x_\alpha$.

9. Prove: If $x_\alpha > 0, \quad \alpha = 1, 2, \ldots, n, \quad$ then $\sum\limits_{\alpha=1}^{n} x_\alpha \ge 0$ and

$\prod\limits_{\alpha=1}^{n} x_\alpha > 0$.

10. Prove: If $x_\alpha \ge 0, \alpha = 1, 2, \ldots, n$, then $\sum\limits_{\alpha=1}^{n} x_\alpha \le \sum\limits_{\alpha=1}^{n+1} x_\alpha$.

11. Prove: If $x_\alpha \ge 1, \alpha = 1, 2, \ldots, n$, then $\prod\limits_{\alpha=1}^{n} x_\alpha \le \prod\limits_{\alpha=1}^{n+1} x_\alpha$.

12. Prove: $\left| \prod\limits_{\alpha=1}^{n} x_\alpha \right| = \prod\limits_{\alpha=1}^{n} |x_\alpha|$ and $\left| \sum\limits_{\alpha=1}^{n} x_\alpha \right| \le \sum\limits_{\alpha=1}^{n} |x_\alpha|$.

13. Prove: $x^n - y^n = (x - y) \sum\limits_{\alpha=0}^{n-1} x^{n-1-\alpha} y^\alpha$.

14. Prove: If $x \ne 1$, then $\sum\limits_{\alpha=0}^{n} x^\alpha = \dfrac{1 - x^{n+1}}{1 - x}$; if $x = 1$, then

$\sum\limits_{\alpha=0}^{n} x^\alpha = n + 1$.

15. Prove: $\sum\limits_{\alpha=0}^{n} \binom{n}{\alpha} = 2^n$.

16. Prove: $\sum\limits_{\alpha=1}^{n} (2\alpha - 1) = n^2$.

17. Prove: $\sum\limits_{\alpha=1}^{n} \alpha = \dfrac{n(n + 1)}{2}$.

18. Prove: $\sum\limits_{\alpha=1}^{n} \alpha^2 = \dfrac{n(n + 1)(2n + 1)}{6}$.

19. Prove: $\sum\limits_{\alpha=1}^{n} \dfrac{1}{(2\alpha - 1)(2\alpha + 1)} = \dfrac{n}{2n + 1}$.

20. Prove: $\sum\limits_{\alpha=1}^{n} \dfrac{1}{\alpha(\alpha + 1)} = \dfrac{n}{n + 1}$.

21. Prove: If $a \le x_\alpha \le b, \alpha = 1, 2, \ldots, n$ then $na \le \sum\limits_{\alpha=1}^{n} x_\alpha \le nb$.

22. Prove: $\sum\limits_{\alpha=2^n+1}^{2^{n+1}} \dfrac{1}{\alpha} > \dfrac{1}{2}$ and $\sum\limits_{\alpha=2^n}^{2^{n+1}-1} \dfrac{1}{\alpha^2} \le \dfrac{1}{2^n}$ (Hint: Exercise 21).

23. Prove: $\sum\limits_{\alpha=1}^{2^n} \dfrac{1}{\alpha} \ge \dfrac{n + 2}{2}$ and $\sum\limits_{\alpha=1}^{2^n-1} \dfrac{1}{\alpha^2} \le \sum\limits_{\alpha=0}^{n-1} \dfrac{1}{2^\alpha}$ (Hint: Exercise 22).

24. State and prove a generalized associative law for multiplication.

25. State and prove a generalized commutative law for addition and a generalized commutative law for multiplication.

4.5 The Completeness Property

In Sections 4.1 and 4.2 we listed the fourteen properties that characterize *ordered fields*. We have observed that these fourteen properties are properties of both the real number system and the rational number system. Indeed thirteen of them are properties of the system of integers. The failure of the set of integers to contain reciprocals is, of course, one distinguishing characteristic between the system of integers and the system of rational numbers and between the system of integers and the system of real numbers. We now consider a property that distinguishes the real number system from the rational number system. This is the property of *completeness*.

Recall that the supremum of a set is an upper bound for that set. A set, therefore, has a supremum only if it is bounded above. On the other hand, the empty set is bounded above and has no supremum because every real number is an upper bound. We conclude that in order for a set to have a supremum that set must be bounded above and nonempty. This suggests a very natural question: Does every nonempty set of real numbers that is bounded above have a supremum? The completeness property which we now postulate assures us that the answer is "yes."

C. $(\forall S)$ if $S \neq \varnothing$ and if S is bounded above, then S has a supremum.

The completeness property is of particular value in making existence arguments. Suppose that we have in mind some property and we wish to know whether or not there exists a real number having this property. If we are sufficiently ingenious, we may be able to define a set in such a way that its supremum has the desired property. We illustrate by proving the existence of nth roots for positive real numbers.

Definition 4.50. b is an nth *root* of a iff $b^n = a$.

Theorem 4.51.   *If $a > 0$ and $n \geq 2$, then $(\exists! b)\, b > 0$ and $b^n = a$.*

Analysis.   For discussion purposes let us assume that $a > 1$. The nth power of every positive number that is less than 1 is, of course, less than a. In fact the nth power of numbers a little larger than 1 are also less than a. On the other hand, the nth power of any number larger than a is larger than a, and the nth power of a is larger than a. Indeed, numbers a little smaller than a have nth power larger than a.

It is then plausible that somewhere between 1 and a is a number b with the property that positive numbers smaller than b have nth power smaller than a and numbers larger than b have nth power larger than a. If so, then b is the only positive number whose nth power could possibly be equal to a. Furthermore if

$$S = \{x \mid x \geq 0 \text{ and } x^n < a\}$$

then $b = \sup S$. Since $0 \in S$ and since a is an upper bound for S (why?) the existence of b is assured by the completeness property. At this point we suggest that the reader make a similar analysis assuming that $a < 1$.

It, of course, still remains to be proved that b is an nth root of a. For this we appeal to the trichotomy property, which assures us that $b^n < a$ or $b^n = a$ or $b^n > a$. That $b^n = a$ we can prove by showing that the other cases are impossible. This we prove by contradiction by showing that if $b^n < a$, then there is a number c such that $c > b$ and $c^n < a$. Consequently c is an element of S that is larger than $\sup S$, while if $b^n > a$, then there is a number c such that $c < b$ and $c^n > a$, from which we can show that c is an upper bound for S which is smaller than the supremum of S.

The proof of the existence of c involves an interesting use of Bernoulli's inequality (see Exercise 27, page 101) from which we have that if $0 < h < 1$ then

$$(1 - h)^n > 1 - nh.$$

Since $0 < 1 - h < 1$ it follows that if $c = b(1 - h)$ then $c < b$ and if $c = b/(1 - h)$ then $c > b$. Thus if $b^n < a$ and $c = b/(1 - h)$,

$$b < c \text{ and } b^n < c^n = \frac{b^n}{(1 - h)^n} < \frac{b^n}{1 - nh}.$$

From this we see that if

$$\frac{b^n}{1 - nh} = a$$

then we will have that $b < c$ and $b^n < c^n < a$. By a simple computation we see that in order for $b^n/(1 - nh)$ to be equal to a we must have that

$$h = \frac{1}{n}\left(1 - \frac{b^n}{a}\right).$$

Similarly, if $b^n > a$ and $c = b(1 - h)$,

$$b > c \text{ and } b^n > c^n = b^n(1 - h)^n > b^n(1 - nh).$$

Therefore if

$$b^n(1 - nh) = a$$

then $c < b$ and $a < c^n < b^n$. For this we must have that

$$h = \frac{1}{n}\left(1 - \frac{a}{b^n}\right).$$

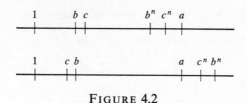

FIGURE 4.2

The remainder of the proof consists of showing in each case that if h is so defined, then the claims made are correct.

Proof. If b_1 and b_2 are each positive nth roots of a, then we have that $b_1^n = b_2^n$. This, however, is true iff $b_1 = b_2$. (See Exercise 24, page 100.) Therefore there is at most one positive nth root for each positive real number.

To prove that every positive real number has at least one positive nth root we argue that if

$$S = \{x \mid x \geq 0 \text{ and } x^n < a\}$$

then $0 \in S$. It is, however, important to know that S does not consist of the number 0 alone. That S contains at least one positive number follows from the fact that if $a < 1$ then $a^n < a$, hence $a \in S$, while if $a \geq 1$ then S contains all positive numbers less than 1. Thus S is not only nonempty, it contains at least one positive number.

To prove that S is bounded above we note that since $a > 0$ we have that $a + 1 > 1$. Therefore $(a + 1)^n > a + 1 > a$. Since for each x in S, $x^n < a$ it follows that $x < a + 1$; therefore $a + 1$ is an upper bound for S. Thus S is a nonempty set that is bounded above and hence has a supremum.

If $b = \sup S$, then since S contains at least one positive number, we have that $b > 0$. By the law of trichotomy one and only one of the following is true:

$$b^n < a \text{ or } b^n = a \text{ or } b^n > a.$$

If $b^n < a$, then since $b > 0$ we have that

$$0 < b^n < a,$$
$$0 < \frac{b^n}{a} < 1,$$
$$0 < 1 - \frac{b^n}{a} < 1,$$
$$0 < \frac{1}{n}\left(1 - \frac{b^n}{a}\right) < 1.$$

Thus if

$$h = \frac{1}{n}\left(1 - \frac{b^n}{a}\right), \text{ then } a = \frac{b^n}{1 - nh}$$

$0 < h < 1$ and $1 - nh > 0$. From Bernoulli's inequality we than have that

$$1 - nh < (1 - h)^n,$$

$$\frac{1}{(1 - h)^n} < \frac{1}{1 - nh},$$

$$\frac{b^n}{(1 - h)^n} < \frac{b^n}{1 - nh},$$

Therefore if $c = b/(1 - h)$, then $c > b$ and

$$b^n < c^n = \frac{b^n}{(1 - h)^n} < \frac{b^n}{1 - nh} = a.$$

Thus $c \in S$ and $c > b$, but $b = \sup S$. This is a contradiction that forces the conclusion that b^n is not less than a.

If $a < b^n$, then

$$0 < a < b^n,$$

$$0 < \frac{a}{b^n} < 1,$$

$$0 < 1 - \frac{a}{b^n} < 1,$$

$$0 < \frac{1}{n}\left(1 - \frac{a}{b^n}\right) < 1.$$

Therefore if

$$h = \frac{1}{n}\left(1 - \frac{a}{b^n}\right),$$

then $a = b^n(1 - nh)$, $0 < h < 1$ and

$$1 - nh < (1 - h)^n,$$
$$b^n(1 - nh) < b^n(1 - h)^n.$$

Thus if $c = b(1 - h)$, then $c < b$ and from Bernoulli's inequality

$$a = b^n(1 - nh) < b^n(1 - h)^n = c^n < b^n.$$

Since for each x in S, $x^n < a$ it follows that $x < c$. Therefore c is an upper bound for S. But $c < b$ and $b = \sup S$. This is a contradiction from which we conclude that b^n is not greater than a. It then follows that

$$b^n = a$$

Q.E.D.

Corollary 4.52. 1) *If $a > 0$ and n is even and positive, then $(\exists! b)\, b < 0$ and $b^n = a$.*

2) *If $a < 0$ and n is even and positive, then a has no nth root.*

3) *If n is odd and positive, then $(\forall a)(\exists! b)\, b^n = a$.*

The proof is left to the reader.

Since $a^1 = a$ and for positive n we have that $a^n = 0$ iff $a = 0$, it follows from Theorem 4.51 and its corollary that for positive n every positive a has exactly two nth roots for n even, that every negative a has no nth root for n even, while for n odd every real number has exactly one nth root. The fact that there are two even roots for each positive number prompts us to define a principal nth root:

Definition 4.53. $b = \sqrt[n]{a}$ iff n is odd and $b^n = a$ or n is even, $b \geq 0$ and $b^n = a$. $\sqrt{a} = \sqrt[2]{a}, a^{1/n} = \sqrt[n]{a}$.

We have now established, among other things, the existence of a positive real number, denoted by $\sqrt{2}$, with the property that its square is two. That this is a property that the rational number system does not have we prove as

Theorem 4.54. $\forall x \in Q, \quad x^2 \neq 2$.

Proof Procedure.   Since $x^2 = (-x)^2$ and since $x^2 = 0$ iff $x = 0$, it is sufficient to prove that the square of every positive rational is not 2.

Proof.   If $x \in Q$ and $x > 0$, then there are relatively prime positive integers m and n such that $x = (m/n)$. Therefore, if $x^2 = 2$ then $(m/n)^2 = 2$; hence $m^2 = 2n^2$. Thus 2 divides m^2. But 2 is a prime. Therefore since 2 divides m^2, it follows that 2 divides m. Then for some integer p we have that $m = 2p$ and hence

$$(2p)^2 = 2n^2,$$
$$4p^2 = 2n^2,$$
$$2p^2 = n^2.$$

Therefore, 2 divides n. But 2 also divides m. Since m and n are relatively prime, this is a contradiction that forces the conclusion that $x^2 \neq 2$.

Q.E.D.

From Theorem 4.54 we see that the rational number system does not have the completeness property, for if it did there would have to exist a rational number whose square is 2. Thus the real number system is richer than the rational number system in that there are problems that can be solved using real numbers that cannot be solved if we are restricted to rational numbers.

Another important consequence of the completeness property is the so-called *Archimedean order property*. In general any appropriately defined mathematical system that contains the integers as a subset is Archimedean ordered if the set of integers is unbounded in that system. The Archimedean order property for the real number system asserts that no real number is an upper bound for the set of integers. The surprising thing is not that the

integers are an unbounded subset of the reals, but rather that such a seem-
ingly obvious fact is of such depth as to require the completeness property
for its proof.

In order for the integers to be an unbounded subset of the reals, it is
necessary that for each real number there exist an integer that is larger.
That no integer is an upper bound for the set of integers follows from the
fact that for each integer n we have that $n + 1 > n$. Thus the system of
integers is Archimedean ordered. That no rational number is an upper
bound for the set of all integers follows from the fact that for each positive
rational number x there are positive integers m and n such that $x = m/n$.
From this it follows that $m + 1 > x$. Thus the system of rational numbers
is Archimedean ordered. The Archimedean order property for the real
number system follows easily from

Theorem 4.55. *Every nonempty set of integers S that is bounded above
has a maximum; i.e.,* $\exists m \in S, \forall n \in S, n \leq m$.

Proof. Since S is nonempty and bounded above, S has a supremum.
If $b = \sup S$ we need only prove that $b \in S$. Since $b - 1 < b$ it follows
from Theorem 4.23 that for some n in S we have $b - 1 < n \leq b$. Either
$n < b$ or $n = b$. If $n < b$ then again using Theorem 4.23 there is an m in
S for which $n < m \leq b$. It then follows that $0 < m - n < 1$ (why?); that is,
$m - n$ is a integer lying between 0 and 1. This is a contradiction from
which we conclude that $n = b$ and hence $b \in S$.

Q.E.D.

Theorem 4.56. *The real number system is Archimedean ordered; i.e.,*
$(\forall x)(\exists n) \, n > x$.

Proof. If $x \leq 0$, then $1 > x$. If $x > 0$ and if

$$S = \{n \in Z_0 \mid n \leq x\}$$

then $0 \in S$ and x is an upper bound for S. Thus S is a nonempty set of
integers that is bounded above. By Theorem 4.55 S must have a maximal
element m. Since m is the largest element in S and $m < m + 1$, it follows
that $m + 1$ is not in S. Hence $m + 1 > x$.

Q.E.D.

Corollary 4.57. 1) $(\forall a)(\forall b)$ *if* $b > 0$, *then* $(\exists n) \, nb > a$.
2) $(\forall a)(\exists ! n) \, n \leq a < n + 1$.

The proof is left to the reader.

The fact, established in Corollary 4.57, that every nonintegral real number
lies between two consecutive integers will be used in later chapters to define
functions with special and interesting properties. In anticipation of its
later use we introduce

Definition 4.58. $[\![x]\!] = n$ iff $n \leq x < n + 1$.
$$\{x\} = \min\{[\![x]\!] + 1 - x, x - [\![x]\!]\}.$$

'$[\![x]\!]$' is read the *largest integer that is less than or equal to x;* '$\{x\}$' is read the *distance from x to the nearest integer.*

From the Archimedean order property we can easily deduce the following valuable result.

Theorem 4.59. *If $a < b$, then*
1) *there exists a rational number x such that $a < x < b$, and*
2) *there exists an irrational number y such that $a < y < b$.*

Proof. 1) By the Archimedean order property there exists an integer n such that $n > 1/(b - a)$ and hence

$$nb - na > 1.$$

Also there exists an integer m such that $m > na$. Therefore there is a smallest integer that is greater than na. If m is the smallest such integer then $m < nb$, for if $m \geq nb$, then since $m - 1 \leq na < m$ we would have $m - 1 \leq na < nb \leq m$ and hence $nb - na < 1$. We then conclude that

$$a < \frac{m}{n} < b.$$

2) From the above we know that there is a rational number x such that

$$\frac{a}{\sqrt{2}} < x < \frac{b}{\sqrt{2}},$$

Either $x = 0$ or $x \neq 0$. If $x = 0$, then there exists a rational number x_1 such that

$$\frac{a}{\sqrt{2}} < 0 < x_1 < \frac{b}{\sqrt{2}}$$

and hence $x_1 \neq 0$. Thus there exists a rational number x such that $x \neq 0$ and

$$\frac{a}{\sqrt{2}} < x < \frac{b}{\sqrt{2}}.$$

Consequently $a < x\sqrt{2} < b$. Since $\sqrt{2}$ is irrational it follows that $x\sqrt{2}$ is irrational.

Q.E.D.

EXERCISES

1. Prove: $[\![x + n]\!] = [\![x]\!] + n$.
2. Prove: If $x \leq y$ then $[\![x]\!] \leq [\![y]\!]$.
3. Prove: $0 \leq \{x\} \leq \frac{1}{2}$.

4. Prove: $\{x\} = \{y\}$ iff $x + y \in Z$ or $x - y \in Z$.

5. Prove: $(\forall x) \sum_{\alpha=m}^{n} \dfrac{\{4^\alpha x\}}{4^\alpha} < \dfrac{1}{4^m}$.

6. Prove: If $a < b$, then there are infinitely many rational numbers in (a, b).

7. Prove: If $a < b$, then there are infinitely many irrational numbers in (a, b).

8. Prove: If $S \neq \varnothing$ and if S is bounded below, then S has an infimum.

9. Prove: If A is a nonempty subset of B and if sup B exists, then sup A exists and sup $A \leq$ sup B.

10. Prove: If A is a nonempty subset of B and if inf B exists, then inf A exists and inf $A \geq$ inf B.

4.6 Accumulation Points

We have now discussed the real numbers as a complete ordered field and fulfilled our obligation of listing all of the assumptions about the real numbers that the reader is expected to accept. From these assumptions we have deduced many properties of the real numbers, and in the material ahead we will study many more. The remaining part of this chapter we devote to the study of concepts that are basic for the proof of later results. One such concept is that of an *accumulation point*.

Definition 4.60. x is an *accumulation point* of S iff every deleted neighborhood of x contains an element of S, i.e., $(\forall \delta)\, N'(x, \delta) \cap S \neq \varnothing$.

Example.   1 is an accumulation point of $(0, 1)$.

0 is an accumulation point of $\{1/n \mid n \in Z_1\}$.

1 is not an accumulation point of $\{1/n \mid n \in Z_1\}$.

Z has no accumulation point.

From the examples we see that there are sets that have accumulation points, and there are sets that do not, the so-called *discrete sets*. For sets that have a sufficiently simple description it is easy to determine whether or not they have accumulation points. For example, it is easily seen that the interval $(0, 1)$ has accumulation points. Indeed, for each x, if $0 \leq x \leq 1$, then x is an accumulation point of $(0, 1)$. For more general situations, however, we need an existence theorem. As a first step in this direction let us note that if x is an accumulation point of S, then each neighborhood of x not only contains an element of S, it contains infinitely many elements of S.

Theorem 4.61. *x is an accumulation point of S iff $(\forall \delta)\, N(x, \delta) \cap S$ is infinite.*

Proof. If for each δ, $N(x, \delta) \cap S$ is infinite, then clearly $N'(x, \delta) \cap S \neq \varnothing$, and hence x is an accumulation point.

The converse we will prove by contraposition. If for some δ we have that $N(x, \delta) \cap S$ is finite, it then follows that $N'(x, \delta) \cap S$ is also finite. Therefore if δ_1 is the distance from x to the nearest element of S that is in S, i.e.,

$$\delta_1 = \min \{|x - y| \mid y \in N'(x, \delta) \cap S\},$$

then $N'(x, \delta_1) \cap S = \varnothing$, and hence x is not an accumulation point of S. That δ_1 exists is assured by the fact that

$$\{|x - y| \mid y \in N'(x, \delta) \cap S\}$$

is a finite set of positive real numbers. That $N'(x, \delta_1) \cap S = \varnothing$ we leave as an exercise for the reader.

From Theorem 4.61 we see that in order for a set to have an accumulation point, that set must be infinite. Note, however, that Z is an infinite set and has no accumulation points. Some additional condition, besides being infinite, is therefore required to insure that a set has an accumulation point. The needed condition is a very simple one; in addition to being infinite, the set must be bounded.

Theorem 4.62 (Bolzano-Weierstrass). *If S is infinite and bounded, then S has an accumulation point.*

Analysis. Of each real number x we ask the following question. Are there infinitely many elements of S that are smaller than x? The answer, of course, depends upon x. Since S is bounded there exists a number b with the property that if $x \in S$, then $-b < x < b$. Since S is infinite it follows that there are infinitely many elements of S that are smaller than b, but no element of S is smaller than $-b$. Thus if

$$S_x = \{z \in S \mid z \leq x\}$$

then S_b is infinite and S_{-b} is empty. Furthermore if $x < y$ then $S_x \subseteq S_y$. Since subsets of finite sets are finite, since S_{-b} is finite and S_b is infinite, it follows that for some number c which is between $-b$ and b it must be true that if $x < c$ then S_x is finite and if $x > c$ then S_x is infinite. Thus for each δ, $S_{c-\delta}$ is finite and $S_{c+\delta}$ is infinite. Since there are infinitely many elements of S between $c - \delta$ and $c + \delta$, it follows that $N'(c, \delta) \cap S \neq \varnothing$ and c is an accumulation point of S.

The existence of c is established by proving that it is the supremum of

$$\{a \mid S_a \text{ is finite}\}.$$

With this outline we leave the details of the proof to the reader.

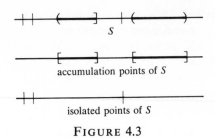

accumulation points of S

isolated points of S

FIGURE 4.3

Clearly each element of a given set either is an accumulation point of the set or is not. Those elements of a set that are not accumulation points are called *isolated* points:

Definition 4.63. x is an *isolated point* of S iff $x \in S$ and $(\exists \delta) \, N'(x, \delta) \cap S = \varnothing$.

Example.   Each element of Z is an isolated point of Z.
Each element of $\{1/n \mid n \in Z_1\}$ is an isolated point of the set.
(0, 1) has no isolated points.

Each element of a set is either an accumulation point of the set or an isolated point. Note, however, that an accumulation point of a set need not be an element of that set. For example, 1 is an accumulation point of (0, 1) but $1 \notin (0, 1)$. Those sets that contain all of their accumulation points are of special interest.

Definition 4.64. S is *closed* iff S contains all of its accumulation points.

Example.   [0, 1] is closed.
Z is closed.
$\varnothing$ is closed.
Q is not closed.
$\{1/n \mid n \in Z_1\}$ is not closed.

Definition 4.65. $\bar{S} = S \cup \{x \mid x$ is an accumulation point of $S\}$.
'$\bar{S}$' is read the *closure of S*.

Example. $\overline{(0, 1)} = \overline{(0, 1]} = \overline{[0, 1)} = [0, 1]$.
$\overline{\varnothing} = \varnothing$

Earlier we pointed out that there are circumstances under which it is important to know that the supremum of a set is in the set. Indeed recall that in the proof of the Archimedean order property we needed to know that every nonempty set of integers that is bounded above has a maximal element. This we proved using the definition of supremum and the fact that there are no integers in $(0, 1)$.

With the notion of an accumulation point we can now prove a more general result concerning maxima and minima.

Theorem 4.66. 1) *If S is nonempty, closed, and bounded above, then* max S *exists.*

2) *If S is nonempty, closed, and bounded below then* min S *exists.*

Proof. 1) If S is nonempty and bounded above then sup S exists. If $b = \sup S$, then we need only prove that $b \in S$. If b is an accumulation point of S, then $b \in S$ because S is closed. If b is not an accumulation point of S, then $(\exists \delta) N'(b, \delta) \cap S = \varnothing$. Since $b = \sup S$ there is an x in S such that $b - \delta < x \le b$. But $N'(b, \delta) \cap S = \varnothing$. Therefore $x = b$ and $b \in S$.

2) The proof is left to the reader.

EXERCISES

1. Prove: Every real number is an accumulation point of rational numbers.

2. Prove: Every real number is an accumulation point of irrational numbers.

3. Prove: If x is an accumulation point of S and $S \subseteq T$, then x is an accumulation point of T.

4. Prove: S has an accumulation point iff S contains a subset that is infinite and bounded.

5. Prove: If for some δ the distance between each pair of elements of S is greater than δ, i.e., $(\exists \delta) \; \forall a \in S, \; \forall b \in S$, if $a \ne b$, then $|a - b| > \delta$, then S has no accumulation points.

6. Prove: If sup S exists and is not an accumulation point of S, then sup $S \in S$.

7. Prove: $[a, b]$, $[a, \infty)$, $(-\infty, a]$, R and $\varnothing$ are closed sets.

8. Prove: If A and B are each closed, then $A \cup B$ and $A \cap B$ are each closed.

9. Prove: The union and the intersection of any finite collection of closed sets are closed.

10. Prove: A is closed iff $A = \overline{A}$.

11. Prove: $\overline{\overline{A}} = \overline{A}$.

12. Prove: If A is closed and $a \in S$, then $\{x \in S \mid x \le a\}$ is closed.

13. Prove: If B is closed and $A \subseteq B$, then $\overline{A} \subseteq B$.

14. What are the accumulation points of $\{m/2^n \mid m \in Z \text{ and } n \in Z\}$?

4.7 Open Sets and the Heine-Borel Theorem

In the last section we found it useful to classify the points in a set as accumulation points or isolated points. We now wish to consider a different classification in which each element of a set is either an *interior point* of the set or a *boundary point*.

If $x \in S$ then one and only one of the following is true.

$$(\exists \delta) \; N(x, \delta) \subseteq S \text{ or } (\forall \delta) \; N(x, \delta) \nsubseteq S.$$

In the event that some neighborhood of x is a subset of S it seems reasonable to describe x as an interior point of S:

Definition 4.70. x is an *interior point* of S iff $(\exists \delta) \; N(x, \delta) \subseteq S$.

Example.   Each element of $(0, 1)$ is an interior point of $(0, 1)$.
$\{1/n \mid n \in Z_1\}$ has no interior points.
Q has no interior points.

We are particularly interested in those sets that consist entirely of interior points.

Definition 4.71. S is *open* iff each element of S is an interior point of S.

Example. $(0, 1)$ is an open set.
R and $\varnothing$ are open sets.
$[0, 1]$ is not an open set.
$\{1/n \mid n \in Z_1\}$ is not an open set.

Theorem 4.72.   *If S and T are open, then $S \cup T$ and $S \cap T$ are open.*

Proof.   If $x \in S \cup T$, then $x \in S$ or $x \in T$. If $x \in S$, then since S is open $(\exists \delta) \; N(x, \delta) \subseteq S$. Since $S \subseteq S \cup T$, it then follows that $N(x, \delta) \subseteq S \cup T$. If $x \in T$ a similar argument brings us to the same conclusion. Therefore $S \cup T$ is open.

If $x \in S \cap T$, then $x \in S$ and $x \in T$. Therefore $(\exists \delta_1)(\exists \delta_2) \; N(x, \delta_1) \subseteq S$ and $N(x, \delta_2) \subseteq T$. Therefore if $\delta = \min \{\delta_1, \delta_2\}$, then $N(x, \delta) \subseteq S \cap T$. Thus $S \cap T$ is open.

Q.E.D.

Corollary 4.73.   *The union and intersection of any infinite collection of open sets is open.*

Corollary 4.74.   *The union of any infinite collection of open sets is open.*

The proofs are left to the reader.

Note that no claim was made concerning the intersection of an infinite collection of open sets. The reason is, of course, that such an intersection need not be an open set. Consider, for example, the collection of open intervals:

$$\{(-x, x) \mid x > 1\}.$$

It is easily proved that the intersection of this set is $[-1, 1]$, which is not open. We leave the details to the reader.

The use of the word 'open' suggests that open sets and closed sets are related in some significant way. This is indeed the case, as we will prove. The relationship is, however, not quite the one that the words 'open' and 'closed' suggest. For example, a set can be neither open nor closed. Consider $(0, 1]$. Since $1 \in (0, 1]$ and 1 is not an interior point of $(0, 1]$, it follows that $(0, 1]$ is not open. On the other hand, 0 is an accumulation point of $(0, 1]$, but $0 \notin (0, 1]$. Thus $(0, 1]$ is not closed.

In contrast to our intuitive feeling about the meaning of the words 'open' and 'closed', a set can be both open and closed. Consider the set of all real numbers. Every accumulation point of R is a real number and hence an element of R. Therefore R is closed. Each real number is an interior point of R, since every neighborhood is a subset of R. Therefore R is open. The empty set is also both open and closed. It is open because the elements of $\varnothing$ have all properties; in particular if $x \in \varnothing$, then x is an interior point of $\varnothing$. It is closed because being a finite set it has no accumulation points; hence every accumulation point of $\varnothing$ is an element of $\varnothing$.

From these examples we see that care must be taken lest we read into the definition for openness and closedness meanings not intended. The basic link between the two concepts we prove as

Theorem 4.75.   *S is open iff R − S is closed.*

Proof.   Since every real number belongs either to S or to $R - S$, it follows that if S contains no accumulation points of $R - S$, then $R - S$ is closed. That S contains no accumulation points of $R - S$ follows easily from the fact that if S is open, then for each x in S there exists a δ for which $N(x, \delta) \subseteq S$. Therefore $N(x, \delta) \cap (R - S) = \varnothing$, and x is not an accumulation point of $R - S$.

Conversely if $R - S$ is closed, then for each x in S, $x \notin R - S$ hence is not an accumulation point of $R - S$. Therefore $(\exists \delta) N(x, \delta) \cap (R - S) = \varnothing$. (Why?) Consequently $N(x, \delta) \subseteq S$, x is an interior point of S and S is open.

Q.E.D.

Theorem 4.76.   1) *If A and B are closed, then $A \cup B$ and $A \cap B$ are closed.*

2) *The union and intersection of any finite collection of closed sets are closed.*

3) *The intersection of any infinite collection of closed sets is closed.*

Proof.   1) From set theory recall that $R - (A \cup B) = (R - A) \cap (R - B)$. Since A and B are closed, it follows from Theorem 4.75 that $R - A$ and $R - B$ are open. Therefore $R - (A \cup B)$ is open, being the intersection of two open sets. From Theorem 4.75 we then conclude that $A \cup B$ is closed. The proof for $A \cap B$ is similar and is left to the reader.

The proofs of 2) and 3) we also leave to the reader with one hint. See Exercise 19, page 46.

Another important result that relates open and closed sets and provides a powerful proof technique is the *Heine-Borel Theorem*. For its statement and proof we need the notion of a *covering*.

Definition 4.77. $\mathscr{C}$ is a *covering* for S iff $\mathscr{C}$ is a set of sets with the property that $S \subseteq \bigcup \mathscr{C}$, that is $\forall x \in S,\ \exists A \in \mathscr{C},\ x \in A$.

$\mathscr{C}$ is an *open* covering for S iff $\mathscr{C}$ is a covering for S and each set in $\mathscr{C}$ is open.

$\mathscr{C}_1$ is a *subcovering* of $\mathscr{C}$ for S iff $\mathscr{C}_1 \subseteq \mathscr{C}$ and $\mathscr{C}_1$ is a covering for S.

$\mathscr{C}$ is a *finite* covering for S iff $\mathscr{C}$ is a finite set and $\mathscr{C}$ is a covering for S.

Example. $\{[0, 1]\}$ is a finite covering for $(0, 1)$.

$\{\{x\} \mid x \in R\}$ is an infinite covering for R.

$\{(1/n, 1) \mid n \in Z_1\}$ is an infinite open covering for $(0, 1)$.

$\{N(1/n, 1) \mid n \in Z_1\}$ is an infinite open covering for $\{1/n \mid n \in Z_1\}$.

$\{N(1/n, 1/(n^2 + n)) \mid n \in Z_1\}$ is an infinite open covering for $\{1/n \mid n \in Z_1\}$.

Theorem 4.78 (Heine-Borel).   *S is closed and bounded iff every open covering for S contains a finite subcovering for S.*

Analysis.   If S is not closed or if S is not bounded, then we can exhibit an open covering for S that contains no finite subcovering. If S is unbounded then

$$\{N(0, n) \mid n \in Z_1\}$$

is a collection of open intervals that covers not only S but all of R. It, however, contains no finite subcovering of S.

If S is not closed then S has an accumulation point a that is not in S. We then consider

$$\left\{ N\left(a, \frac{1}{n}\right) \mid n \in Z_1 \right\}.$$

This is a collection of open intervals. It does not cover S, however, unless $S \subseteq N(a, 1)$. If, however, we consider the closure of each of these intervals

$$\overline{N\left(a, \frac{1}{n}\right)}$$

and then their relative complements with R

$$R - \overline{N\left(a, \frac{1}{n}\right)}$$

it then follows from Theorem 4.75 that $R - \overline{N(a, 1/n)}$ is open. Therefore

$$\left\{ R - \overline{N\left(a, \frac{1}{n}\right)} \mid n \in Z_1 \right\}$$

is a collection of open sets. Furthermore for each x if $x \neq a$, then there exists a positive integer n such that $1/n < |x - a|$. Consequently

$$x \in R - \overline{N\left(a, \frac{1}{n}\right)}.$$

Thus

$$\left\{ R - \overline{N\left(a, \frac{1}{n}\right)} \mid n \in Z_1 \right\}$$

is an open covering for $R - \{a\}$ and hence an open covering for S. However, it contains no finite subcovering of S.

For the proof of the converse we note that since S is bounded, there exists a number b with that property that

$$\forall x \in S, \quad -b < x < b.$$

If $\mathscr{C}$ is an open covering for S, we then ask, for each real number x, if all of the elements in S that are smaller than x can be covered by a finite subset of $\mathscr{C}$; that is, if

$$S_x = \{z \in S \mid z < x\}$$

can S_x be covered by a finite subset of $\mathscr{C}$? Clearly S_{-b} can because $S_{-b} = \varnothing$. If it should be the case that S_b can also, then our proof is complete because $S_b = S$.

Our objective is therefore to prove that for each x, S_x can be covered by a finite subset of $\mathscr{C}$. In other words, if $T = \{x \mid S_x$ can be covered by a finite subset of $\mathscr{C}\}$, then we wish to show that T is the set of all real numbers, i.e., $T = R$. The proof is by contradiction.

We first observe that if $x \in T$ and if $y < x$, then $S_y \subseteq S_x$. Since S_x can be covered by a finite subset of $\mathscr{C}$, it follows that S_y can also be so covered; hence $y \in T$. Thus if $x \in T$ then every number smaller than x is also in T. From this it follows that if $x \notin T$ and if $y > x$, then $y \notin T$; that is, if $x \notin T$ then x is an upper bound for T.

Thus if $T \neq R$ then there exists an x for which $x \notin T$ and x is an upper bound for T. Since $-b \in T$ it then follows that T is a nonempty set that is bounded above. Therefore T has a supremum. If $c = \sup T$, then $c \in S$ or $c \notin S$. Either alternative, however, leads to a contradiction.

If $c \in S$, then since $\mathscr{C}$ is a covering for S, there exists a set A in $\mathscr{C}$ that contains c. Since A is open, there exists a δ such that $N(c, \delta) \subseteq A$. It then follows that $c + \delta \in T$, but $c + \delta$ is greater than c and $c = \sup T$. This is a contradiction.

On the other hand, if $c \notin S$, then since S is closed, c is not an accumulation point of S. Therefore there exists a δ such that $N(c, \delta) \cap S = \varnothing$ and again $c + \delta \in T$.

With this outline we leave the details of the proof to the reader and illustrate the use of the Heine-Borel Theorem by using it to give a second proof of

The Bolzano-Weierstrass Theorem. *If S is infinite and bounded, then S has an accumulation point.*

Proof. It is sufficient to prove that if S has no accumulation points and is bounded, then S is finite. If S has no accumulation points, then S is closed. Therefore if S is also bounded, then by the Heine-Borel Theorem every open covering of S has a finite subcovering. In particular if

$$\mathscr{C} = \{N(a, \delta) \mid \delta > 0, a \in S \text{ and } N'(a, \delta) \cap S = \varnothing\}$$

then since every element of S is not an accumulation point of S, it follows that for each a in S there exists a δ with the property that $N'(a, \delta) \cap S = \varnothing$. Since $a \in N(a, \delta)$ and $N(a, \delta) \in \mathscr{C}$, it follows that $\mathscr{C}$ is an open covering for S. Since S is closed and bounded, $\mathscr{C}$ contains a finite subcovering,

$$\{N(a_1, \delta_1), \ldots, N(a_n, \delta_n)\}.$$

It then follows that $S = \{a_1, \ldots, a_n\}$; that is, S is finite.

Q.E.D.

Each element of a set either is an interior point of that set or is not. Those elements of a set that are not interior points we call *boundary points*. For example, 0 and 1 are boundary points of $[0, 1]$. Indeed, despite the fact that 0 and 1 are not elements of $(0, 1)$, it seems reasonable to call them boundary points also.

Definition 4.79. x is a *boundary point* of S iff every neighborhood of x contains an element of S and an element not in S.

Example. 0 and 1 are boundary points of $(0, 1]$.

Each element of $\{1/n \mid n \in Z_1\}$ is a boundary point.

Each element of $[0, 1]$ is a boundary point of $\{x \in Q \mid 0 \leq x \leq 1\}$

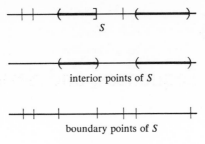

FIGURE 4.4

Note that boundary points are not 'just points on the end'. A finite set, for example, consists entirely of boundary points. Indeed, as we see in the example above, an infinite set can consist entirely of boundary points.

EXERCISES

1. Prove: If $\mathscr{S} = \{[-x, x] \mid 0 < x < 1\}$, then $\bigcup \mathscr{S}$ is not closed.

2. Prove: If $\mathscr{S} = \{(0, x) \mid 1 < x < 2\}$, then $\bigcap \mathscr{S}$ is not open.

3. Prove: If $T \subseteq S$ and $\mathscr{C}$ is a covering for S, then $\mathscr{C}$ is a covering for T.

4. Prove: There exists an open covering of Z that has no finite subcovering.

5. Prove: If $\mathscr{C} = \left\{ \left(\dfrac{1}{2n}, \dfrac{2}{n} \right) \mid n \in Z_1 \right\}$, then $\mathscr{C}$ is an open covering of $\{ 1/n \mid n \in Z_1 \}$, and $\mathscr{C}$ has no finite subcovering.

6. Prove: There exists a covering of $[0, 1]$ that has no finite subcovering.

7. Prove: $(\forall a)(\forall \delta)\, N(a, \delta)$ is open.

CHAPTER 5

Functions, Sequences, and Series

5.0 The Algebra of Functions

In Chapter 3 we discussed functions from a very general point of view. In this chapter, and indeed throughout the remainder of the text, we will confine our discussion almost exclusively to functions whose domain and range are sets of real numbers. Hereafter,

$$f,\ g,\ h,\ \ldots$$

will be understood to be variables on such functions, unless otherwise stated.

Since our functions are defined on sets of real numbers, it is only natural that we look to the real number system as a source of ideas as we begin our search for useful and interesting properties of functions. One such idea, which we define in terms of the order relation on R, is that of a *bounded* function.

Definition 5.00. f is *bounded* iff there exists a number b with the property that

$$\forall x \in \text{Dom } f, \quad |f(x)| \leq b.$$

From the definition, we see that a function is bounded if and only if its range is a bounded set.

The algebraic properties of the real numbers suggest natural definitions for function addition, subtraction, multiplication, and division.

Definition 5.01.
$$f + g = \{(x, f(x) + g(x)) \mid x \in \text{Dom } f \cap \text{Dom } g\}.$$
$$-g = \{(x, -g(x)) \mid x \in \text{Dom } g\}.$$
$$f - g = f + (-g).$$
$$fg = \{(x, f(x)g(x)) \mid x \in \text{Dom } f \cap \text{Dom } g\}.$$
$$\frac{1}{g} = \left\{ \left(x, \frac{1}{g(x)}\right) \mid x \in \text{Dom } g \text{ and } g(x) \neq 0 \right\}.$$
$$\frac{f}{g} = f\frac{1}{g}.$$
$$cf = \{(x, cf(x)) \mid x \in \text{Dom } f\}.$$

124

These operations provide us with useful relationships between functions but also introduce a certain notational awkwardness. For example, we see from the definition that

$$\text{Dom}\,(f + g) = \text{Dom}\,f \cap \text{Dom}\,g$$

and that if $x \in \text{Dom}\,(f + g)$, then $(f + g)(x) = f(x) + g(x)$. Suppose, however, that we are interested in the function

$$\frac{f + g}{f - g}.$$

We then have that

$$\text{Dom}\left(\frac{f + g}{f - g}\right) = \text{Dom}\,f \cap \text{Dom}\,g - \{x \mid f(x) = g(x)\}.$$

Furthermore,

$$\forall\, x \in \text{Dom}\left(\frac{f + g}{f - g}\right),\ \left(\frac{f + g}{f - g}\right)(x) = \frac{f(x) + g(x)}{f(x) - g(x)}.$$

To simplify the notation we will frequently leave much of this information unstated and rely upon the reader to infer it from the context. Thus in an appropriate context we might write

$$\frac{f(x) - f(2)}{x - 2}$$

and expect the reader to understand that we are discussing a function g whose domain is $\text{Dom}\,f - \{2\}$ and if $x \in \text{Dom}\,g$, then

$$g(x) = \frac{f(x) - f(2)}{x - 2}.$$

There are many interesting and useful functions that are of sufficient interest that we choose to name them:

The *identity function*: $f(x) = x$.
The *reciprocal function*: $f(x) = 1/x,\ x \neq 0$.
The *nth root function*: $f(x) = \sqrt[n]{x},\ n \geq 2$ and $x \geq 0$ if n is even.
The *absolute value function*: $f(x) = |x|$.
The *largest integer function*: $f(x) = [\![x]\!]$.
The *distance to integer function*: $f(x) = \{x\}$.
The *rational test function*: $f(x) = 1$ if x is rational, and $f(x) = -1$ if x is irrational.

There are also certain classes of functions that are of special interest. The most elementary of these are the *constant functions*.

Definition 5.02. f is a *constant function* iff there exists a number c with the property that $(\forall x)\, f(x) = c$.

Next after the constant functions, in order of simplicity, are the *polynomial functions*.

Definition 5.03. f is a *polynomial function* iff there exist a nonnegative integer n and real numbers $a_0, a_1, \ldots, a_n$ such that

$$(\forall x)\, f(x) = \sum_{\alpha=0}^{n} a_\alpha x^\alpha.$$

Note that the constant functions are also polynomial functions. The polynomial functions are, in turn, *rational functions*.

Definition 5.04. f is a *rational function* iff there exist polynomial functions g and h such that $\operatorname{Dom} f = R - \{x \mid h(x) = 0\}$ and

$$\forall x \in \operatorname{Dom} f, \quad f(x) = \frac{g(x)}{h(x)}.$$

The representation of polynomial functions as described in Definition 5.03 is, of course, not unique. Indeed, if

$$f(x) = \sum_{\alpha=0}^{n} a_\alpha x^\alpha$$

and if $a_{n+1} = 0$, then

$$f(x) = \sum_{\alpha=0}^{n+1} a_\alpha x^\alpha.$$

Thus, if

$$f(x) = \sum_{\alpha=0}^{n} a_\alpha x^\alpha \text{ and } g(x) = \sum_{\alpha=0}^{m} b_\alpha x^\alpha$$

and if $p = \max\{m, n\}$, then

$$f(x) = \sum_{\alpha=0}^{p} a_\alpha x^\alpha \text{ and } g(x) = \sum_{\alpha=0}^{p} b_\alpha x^\alpha,$$

where $a_{n+1} = 0,\ a_{n+2} = 0, \ldots,\ a_p = 0$ if $n < p$, and $b_{m+1} = 0,\ b_{m+2} = 0, \ldots,$ $b_p = 0$ if $m < p$. We then have that

$$f(x) + g(x) = \sum_{\alpha=0}^{p} a_\alpha x^\alpha + \sum_{\alpha=0}^{p} b_\alpha x^\alpha = \sum_{\alpha=0}^{p} (a_\alpha + b_\alpha) x^\alpha.$$

From this result we see that the sum of two polynomial functions is a polynomial function. That the product of two polynomial functions is also a polynomial function is an immediate consequence of

Lemma 5.05. $\left(\sum_{\alpha=0}^{m} a_\alpha x^\alpha\right)\left(\sum_{\alpha=0}^{n} b_\alpha x^\alpha\right) = \sum_{\alpha=0}^{m+n} \left(\sum_{\beta=\max\{0,\alpha-n\}}^{\min\{\alpha,m\}} a_\beta b_{\alpha-\beta}\right) x^\alpha.$

Before we present the proof, let us observe that in Lemma 5.05 we are claiming that in the product the coefficient of x^α is

$$\sum_{\beta=\max\{0,\alpha-n\}}^{\min\{\alpha,m\}} a_\beta b_{\alpha-\beta}.$$

Note that the peculiar range on β, namely, from $\max\{0, \alpha - n\}$ to $\min\{\alpha, m\}$, is precisely that needed to assure that $0 \le \beta \le m$ and $0 \le \alpha - \beta \le n$. Note also that for each term the sum of the subscripts is α and that every such term is present. This is precisely what we observe when we do the multiplication in special cases, as, for example:

$$(a_0 + a_1 x + a_2 x^2)(b_0 + b_1 x + b_2 x^2)$$
$$= a_0 b_0 + (a_0 b_1 + a_1 b_0)x + (a_0 b_2 + a_1 b_1 + a_2 b_0)x^2$$
$$+ (a_1 b_2 + a_2 b_1)x^3 + a_2 b_2 x^4.$$

Proof. (By induction on n.) If $n = 0$, then we have that for each m

$$\left(\sum_{\alpha=0}^{m} a_\alpha x^\alpha\right)\left(\sum_{\alpha=0}^{n} b_\alpha x^\alpha\right) = \sum_{\alpha=0}^{m} (a_\alpha b_0)x^\alpha = \sum_{\alpha=0}^{m+n} \left(\sum_{\beta=\max\{0,\alpha-n\}}^{\min\{\alpha,m\}} a_\beta b_{\alpha-\beta}\right) x^\alpha.$$

Having established that the result is true for every m, provided $n = 0$, we now assume that it is true for every m and for n, and we consider

$$\left(\sum_{\alpha=0}^{m} a_\alpha x^\alpha\right)\left(\sum_{\alpha=0}^{n+1} b_\alpha x^\alpha\right)$$

$$= \left(\sum_{\alpha=0}^{m} a_\alpha x^\alpha\right)\left(\sum_{\alpha=0}^{n} b_\alpha x^\alpha + b_{n+1} x^{n+1}\right)$$

$$= \left(\sum_{\alpha=0}^{m} a_\alpha x^\alpha\right)\left(\sum_{\alpha=0}^{n} b_\alpha x^\alpha\right) + \sum_{\alpha=0}^{m} a_\alpha b_{n+1} x^{\alpha+n+1}$$

$$= \sum_{\alpha=0}^{m+n} \left(\sum_{\beta=\max\{0,\alpha-n\}}^{\min\{\alpha,m\}} a_\beta b_{\alpha-\beta}\right) x^\alpha + \sum_{\alpha=n+1}^{m+n+1} a_{\alpha-(n+1)} b_{n+1} x^\alpha$$

$$= \sum_{\alpha=0}^{n} \left(\sum_{\beta=\max\{0,\alpha-n\}}^{\min\{\alpha,m\}} a_\beta b_{\alpha-\beta}\right) x^\alpha + \sum_{\alpha=n+1}^{m+n} \left(\sum_{\beta=\max\{0,\alpha-n\}}^{\min\{\alpha,m\}} a_\beta b_{\alpha-\beta}\right) x^\alpha$$

$$+ \sum_{\alpha=n+1}^{m+n+1} a_{\alpha-(n+1)} b_{n+1} x^\alpha.$$

We now observe that if $\alpha \le n$, then $\max\{0, \alpha - n\} = \max\{0, \alpha - (n + 1)\}$, if $n + 1 \le \alpha \le m + n$, then

$$\left(\sum_{\beta=\max\{0,\alpha-n\}}^{\min\{\alpha,m\}} a_\beta b_{\alpha-\beta}\right) + a_{\alpha-(n+1)} b_{n+1} = \sum_{\beta=\max\{0,\alpha-(n+1)\}}^{\min\{\alpha,m\}} a_\beta b_{\alpha-\beta},$$

and if $\alpha = m + n + 1$, then

$$\sum_{\beta = \max\{0, \alpha - (n+1)\}}^{\min\{\alpha, m\}} a_\beta b_{\alpha - \beta} = a_m b_{n+1}.$$

Therefore

$$\left(\sum_{\alpha = 0}^{m} a_\alpha x^\alpha \right) \left(\sum_{\alpha = 0}^{n+1} b_\alpha x^\alpha \right)$$

$$= \sum_{\alpha = 0}^{n} \left(\sum_{\beta = \max\{0, \alpha - (n+1)\}}^{\min\{\alpha, m\}} a_\beta b_{\alpha - \beta} \right) x^\alpha + \sum_{\alpha = n+1}^{m+n+1} \left(\sum_{\beta = \max\{0, \alpha - (n+1)\}}^{\min\{\alpha, m\}} a_\beta b_{\alpha - \beta} \right) x^\alpha$$

$$= \sum_{\alpha = 0}^{m+(n+1)} \left(\sum_{\beta = \max\{0, \alpha - (n+1)\}}^{\min\{\alpha, m\}} a_\beta b_{\alpha - \beta} \right) x^\alpha.$$

Q.E.D.

We now conclude that the set of polynomial functions is closed under function addition and function multiplication. The remaining algebraic properties of the polynomial functions and those of the rational functions we leave as exercises.

In the material ahead we will be studying many particular functions of interest. We urge the reader to draw pictures. A graph of a function can provide a valuable insight into the basic properties of that function. We will make no effort to define the term 'graph'. By not adding this term to our formal language we hope to encourage the reader to draw pictures and use his imagination freely with no compulsion to justify what he has done. Proofs of theorems must, however, stem from basic principles. Pictures may suggest how a proof might go, but will not be an acceptable substitute for a proof.

We will assume that the reader is familiar with the results of analytic geometry and that he can graph functions in rectangular and in polar coordinates. Note that a function is a set of ordered pairs, and as such has different graphs in different coordinate systems. For example, as shown in Figure 5.1, the graph of the identity function in rectangular coordinates is a straight line; in polar coordinates the graph is a spiral.

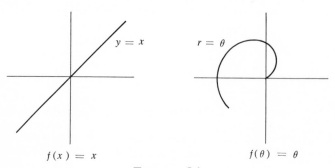

FIGURE 5.1

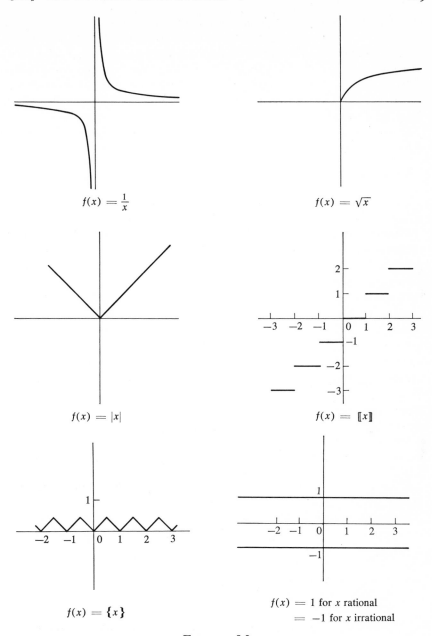

$$f(x) = \frac{1}{x}$$

$$f(x) = \sqrt{x}$$

$$f(x) = |x|$$

$$f(x) = [\![x]\!]$$

$$f(x) = \{x\}$$

$$f(x) = 1 \text{ for } x \text{ rational}$$
$$= -1 \text{ for } x \text{ irrational}$$

FIGURE 5.2

For the purposes we have in mind we have a preference for rectangular coordinates. Therefore, unless otherwise stated, we will speak of *the* graph of a function and we will mean its graph in conventional rectangular coordinates. Thus when we speak of the graphs of the functions previously defined, we will be referring to pictures such as those shown in Figure 5.2.

In graphing the rational test function we have drawn two parallel lines. We understand, of course, that each vertical line can intersect the graph in only one point. Thus the graph consists of those points on the upper line which have rational abscissas and those points on the lower line which have irrational abscissas.

In graphing a function the points of the graph that are on the x-axis are of special interest. These points correspond to the *zeros* of the function.

Definition 5.06. x is a *zero* of f iff $f(x) = 0$.

In addition to function addition and function multiplication we are also interested in function composition. The special properties of composition we leave, however, as exercises. The exercises assume the following definitions.

Definition 5.07. $\displaystyle\sum_{\alpha=1}^{1} f_\alpha = f_1, \ \sum_{\alpha=1}^{n+1} f_\alpha = \left(\sum_{\alpha=1}^{n} f_\alpha\right) + f_{n+1}$ for $n \geq 1$.

$\displaystyle\prod_{\alpha=1}^{1} f_\alpha = f_1, \ \prod_{\alpha=1}^{n+1} f_\alpha = \left(\prod_{\alpha=1}^{n} f_\alpha\right) f_{n+1}$ for $n \geq 1$.

$f^1 = f, \ \ f^{n+1} = f^n f$ for $n \geq 1$.

Definition 5.08. $(\forall c)\ \bar{c}$ is the constant function defined by $\bar{c}(x) = c$.

I is the identity function.

$I^0 = \bar{1}$.

Rat is the rational test function.

EXERCISES

In Exercises 1–6 give a formula for function values and a graph for $f + g$, fg, and $f \circ g$.

    1. $f(x) = x^2 - 1$, $g(x) = x^2 + 1$.

    2. $f(x) = \dfrac{x}{x-1}$, $x \neq 1$, $g(x) = x$.

    3. $f(x) = [\![x]\!]$, $g(x) = 1/(x^2 + 1)$.

    4. $f(x) = \mathrm{Rat}\ x$, $g(x) = x$.

    5. $f(x) = \mathrm{Rat}\ x$, $g(x) = x^2$.

    6. $f(x) = [\![x]\!]$, $g(x) = \{x\}$.

    7. Prove: The rational test function, the distance to integer function, and all constant functions are bounded.

    8. Prove: Function addition is associative and commutative.

    9. Prove: Function multiplication is associative and commutative.

    10. Prove: The set of rational functions is closed under function addition and function multiplication.

11. Prove: The set of polynomial functions is closed under function composition; i.e., if f and g are polynomial functions, then $f \circ g$ is also a polynomial function.

12. Prove: $(\forall a)(\forall b)\, \bar{a} \circ \bar{b} = \bar{a}$.

13. Prove: If $(\forall x) f(x) = \sum_{\alpha=0}^{n} a_\alpha x^\alpha$, then $f = \sum_{\alpha=0}^{n} a_\alpha I^\alpha$.

In Exercises 14–16 give a formula for values of f^{-1}, the inverse of f.

14. $f(x) = x + 1$.   **15.** $f(x) = \sqrt{x} - 2$.

16. $f(x) = (x + 1)/(x - 1)$, $x \neq 1$.

In Exercises 17–22 find all zeros of f.

17. $f(x) = x + 1$.   **18.** $f(x) = \sqrt{x} - 2$.

19. $f(x) = (x + 1)/(x - 1)$, $x \neq 1$.

20. $f(x) = |x|$.   **21.** $f(x) = [\![x]\!]$.

22. $f(x) = \{x\}$.

23. Prove: If f and g each map the set of positive real numbers into itself, then $f + g$, fg, f/g, and $f \circ g$ each map the set of positive real numbers into itself.

24. Prove: If $\forall x \in \text{Dom}\, f$, $f(x) = g(1/x)$, then $f \subseteq g \circ (1/I)$.

5.1 Sequences

In the remainder of this chapter we will study the properties of a very special class of functions called *sequences*. We will be concerned primarily with *infinite* sequences. An infinite sequence is a function whose domain is the set Z_n of all integers that are equal to or greater than some particular integer n. A *finite* sequence is a function whose domain is a finite set of consecutive integers, $\{m, m + 1, m + 2, \ldots, n\}$. Since we will be interested mainly in infinite sequences, we will use the word 'sequence' to mean infinite sequence unless otherwise stated.

It is customary to classify sequences according to the type of elements that constitute their range. A sequence whose range is a set of integers is called a sequence of integers; a sequence whose range is a set of functions is called a sequence of functions. While we are interested in many types of sequences, the first that we will study are sequences of real numbers. As examples we offer

$$1)\ f(n) = \frac{(-1)^n}{n}, \quad n \geq 1.$$

$$2)\ f(n) = (-1)^n, \quad n \geq 0.$$

$$3)\ f(n) = \frac{n + 1}{n}, \quad n \geq 2.$$

$$4)\ f(n) = \frac{(-1)^n n + 1}{n}, \quad n \geq 2.$$

$$5)\ f(n) = 1, \quad n \geq -5.$$

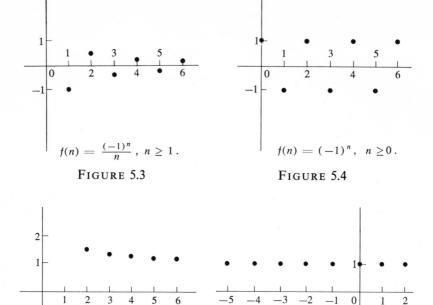

$$f(n) = \frac{(-1)^n}{n}, \quad n \geq 1.$$

FIGURE 5.3

$$f(n) = (-1)^n, \quad n \geq 0.$$

FIGURE 5.4

$$f(n) = \frac{n+1}{n}, \quad n \geq 2.$$

FIGURE 5.5

$$f(n) = 1, \quad n \geq -5.$$

FIGURE 5.6

It is conventional to refer to the values of a sequence as its *terms*, the nth term being the value of the sequence at n. Thus, for example, the first, second, third, fourth, and fifth terms of the sequence 1) above are

$$- 1, \tfrac{1}{2}, - \tfrac{1}{3}, \tfrac{1}{4}, -\tfrac{1}{5},$$

respectively, and the -2nd, -1st, and 0th terms of the sequence 5) are

$$1, 1, 1;$$

indeed for this sequence 1 is the nth term for each n.

A graph can provide a helpful aid in our efforts to understand certain properties of sequences of real numbers. Consider, for example, the graphs in Figures 5.3 to 5.6.

Notice that in Figure 5.3 it appears that for each positive number ϵ, no matter how small, the graph lies almost entirely between the two parallel lines defined by $y = \epsilon$ and $y = -\epsilon$ respectively. That is, these two parallel lines determine a strip of the plane that contains all but a finite number of

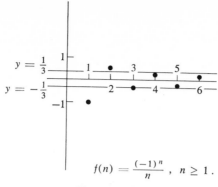

$$f(n) = \frac{(-1)^n}{n}, \quad n \geq 1.$$

FIGURE 5.7

the points of the graph. In Figure 5.7 we have a picture of this strip for $\epsilon = \frac{1}{3}$.

This geometric observation has an obvious interpretation in our theory: If

$$f(n) = \frac{(-1)^n}{n}, \quad n \geq 1,$$

then for each ϵ and for all but a finite number of values of 'n' in $\mathrm{Dom}\, f$ we have that

$$f(n) \in N(0, \epsilon).$$

Indeed when formulated in this way we see a simple proof.

If $n > (1/\epsilon)$, then $(1/n) < \epsilon$ and

$$\left| \frac{(-1)^n}{n} - 0 \right| = \frac{1}{n} < \epsilon;$$

that is, for each n greater than $1/\epsilon$, we have that $f(n) \in N(0, \epsilon)$.

It appears that the function represented in Figure 5.5 has a similar property; that is, its graph lies almost entirely between the parallel lines defined by $y = 1 + \epsilon$ and $y = 1 - \epsilon$ respectively, and this is true for each positive ϵ no matter how small. In nongeometrical terms we claim that for each ϵ and for all but a finite number of values of 'n' in $\mathrm{Dom}\, f$ we have that

$$f(n) \in N(1, \epsilon).$$

This too is easily proved, for if $n \in \mathrm{Dom}\, f$ and if $n > (1/\epsilon)$, then $(1/n) < \epsilon$, and we have that

$$\left| \frac{n+1}{n} - 1 \right| = \frac{1}{n} < \epsilon.$$

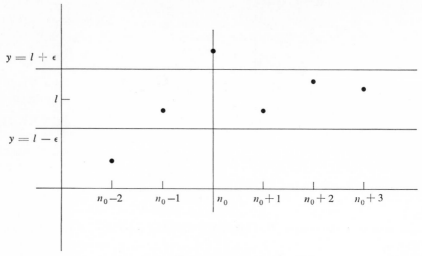

FIGURE 5.8

That is, for each n in Dom f if $n > (1/\epsilon)$, then

$$f(n) \in N(1, \epsilon).$$

Note also in the examples above that 0 and 1 are very special numbers. Zero is special in that it is the only number with the property that for each ϵ

$$\frac{(-1)^n}{n} \in N(0, \epsilon)$$

for all but a finite number of values of 'n' larger than 1. One is special in that it is the only number with the property that for each ϵ

$$\frac{n + 1}{n} \in N(1, \epsilon)$$

for all but a finite number of values of 'n' larger than 1.

Generalizing from these examples we may inquire of each sequence f whether or not there exists a number l with the property that for each ϵ

$$f(n) \in N(l, \epsilon)$$

for all but a finite number of values of 'n' in Dom f. Note that if $f(n) \notin N(l, \epsilon)$ for only a finite number of values of 'n', then there must be a largest integer n_0 such that $f(n_0) \notin N(l, \epsilon)$ and consequently for each n if $n > n_0$, then $f(n) \in N(l, \epsilon)$. Conversely if for a number l and an integer n_0 we have for each n greater than n_0 that $f(n) \in N(l, \epsilon)$, then clearly $f(n) \in N(l, \epsilon)$ for all but a finite number of values of 'n' in Dom f. As illustrated in Figure 5.8 the integer n_0 identifies a point on the x-axis to the right of which the graph of the sequence f lies entirely between the two parallel lines defined by

$y = l + \epsilon$ and $y = l - \epsilon$ respectively. There are two observations that we wish to make. First, it is not necessary that n_0 be an integer. It is sufficient that to the right of some number δ the graph lie entirely between the two parallel lines. Second, we must have such a number δ for each ϵ. But to pair with each positive real number ϵ exactly one positive real number δ is to define a function ϕ that maps the set of positive real numbers into the set of positive real numbers.

From these observations we see that in order to establish that for each ϵ

$$f(n) \in N(l, \epsilon)$$

for all but a finite number of values of 'n' in Dom f, it is sufficient to prove that there exists a function ϕ that maps the set of positive real numbers into the set of positive real numbers and has the property that

$$(\forall\epsilon)(\forall n) \text{ if } n > \phi(\epsilon), \text{ then } f(n) \in N(l, \epsilon).$$

A number l having this property we call a *limit* of the sequence f. It is, of course, important to know that for each sequence f at most one such number l can exist.

Theorem 5.10. *If for a sequence f there exist numbers l_1 and l_2 and there exist functions ϕ_1 and ϕ_2, each of which maps the set of positive real numbers into the set of positive real numbers, with the properties that*

$$(\forall\epsilon)(\forall n) \text{ if } n > \phi_1(\epsilon), \text{ then } f(n) \in N(l_1, \epsilon)$$

and

$$(\forall\epsilon)(\forall n) \text{ if } n > \phi_2(\epsilon), \text{ then } f(n) \in N(l_2, \epsilon),$$

then $l_1 = l_2$.

Proof. From the hypothesis of the theorem we have that if $n > \phi_1(\epsilon/2)$, then $f(n) \in N(l_1, \epsilon/2)$; that is, $|f(n) - l_1| < \epsilon/2$. Similarly, if $n > \phi_2(\epsilon/2)$, then $|f(n) - l_2| < \epsilon/2$. From the Archimedean order property we know that $(\exists n) \, n > \max\{\phi_1(\epsilon/2), \phi_2(\epsilon/2)\}$. Therefore $n > \phi_1(\epsilon/2)$, $n > \phi_2(\epsilon/2)$; and hence

$$|l_1 - l_2| = |l_1 - f(n) + f(n) - l_2| \leq |f(n) - l_1| + |f(n) - l_2|$$

$$< \frac{\epsilon}{2} + \frac{\epsilon}{2} = \epsilon.$$

From this argument we see that for each ϵ we have that $|l_1 - l_2| < \epsilon$. Therefore $l_1 = l_2$.

Q.E.D.

From Theorem 5.10 we see that we may speak of *the* limit of a sequence. If l is the limit of the sequence f, then we say that f *converges* to l. The test of whether or not a given sequence f converges to a given number l is, of course, whether or not there exists a function ϕ with the prescribed properties. For this reason we choose to call functions that map the set of positive real numbers into the set of positive real numbers *convergence tests*. We will use the symbols

$$\phi, \psi, \eta$$

as variables on convergence tests. From Exercise 23, page 131, it is clear that the sum, product, quotient, and composite of two convergence tests are convergence tests.

Definition 5.11.   The number l is the *limit* of the sequence f iff there exists a convergence test ϕ with the property that for each ϵ and for each n

if $n > \phi(\epsilon)$, then $f(n) \in N(l, \epsilon)$.

The sequence f *converges* iff its limit exists and *diverges* iff its limit does not exist.

In order to apply Definition 5.11 we must have both a sequence and a number that is a candidate for the limit. We are then required to produce a convergence test. Let us illustrate by proving that if

$$f(n) = \frac{1}{n}, \quad n \geq 1,$$

then f converges to 0.

Analysis.   We wish to exhibit a convergence test ϕ with the property that for each n larger than $\phi(\epsilon)$ we will have that $f(n) \in N(0, \epsilon)$; that is,

$$|f(n) - 0| < \epsilon.$$

Since

$$f(n) = \frac{1}{n} \text{ and } \left| \frac{1}{n} - 0 \right| = \frac{1}{n}$$

it follows that if $n > 1/\epsilon$, then

$$|f(n) - 0| < \epsilon.$$

This suggests that we define ϕ by

$$\phi(\epsilon) = \frac{1}{\epsilon}.$$

Proof.   If ϕ is defined by $\phi(\epsilon) = 1/\epsilon$ and if $n > \phi(\epsilon)$, then

$$|f(n) - 0| = \frac{1}{n} < \frac{1}{\phi(\epsilon)} = \epsilon.$$

Q.E.D.

A point worthy of note in the foregoing argument is that if the domain of f had been Z_m rather than Z_1 with $m > 1$, then by only a slight modification of the argument, namely, that the convergence test be defined by

$$\phi(\epsilon) = m + \frac{1}{\epsilon},$$

we would again have that for each n

$$\text{if } n > \phi(\epsilon), \text{ then } f(n) \in N(0, \epsilon).$$

Thus f would still converge to 0. We then see that there are infinitely many sequences, each of which converges to 0 because its values are defined by the form '$1/n$'.

To indicate this dependence of the limit of a sequence on its defining form we introduce the notation

$$\operatorname*{Lim}_{n \to \infty} F_n,$$

where 'F_n' is a variable that may be replaced by any singular form in the variable 'n'. The information deduced above we then summarize as

Theorem 5.12. $\operatorname*{Lim}_{n \to \infty} \dfrac{1}{n} = 0.$

Definition 5.13.   For each sequence f,

$$\operatorname*{Lim}_{n \to \infty} f(n) = l$$

iff l is the limit of f.

'$\operatorname*{Lim}_{n \to \infty} f(n)$' is read the *limit of $f(n)$ as n tends to ∞*.

The collection of all sequences of real numbers is, however, so vast that there are sequences whose values are not given by any existing form. In spite of this the same general observations made above hold; that is, if f and g are sequences with the property that for some integer m and for every n greater than m we have that $f(n) = g(n)$, then f and g either both have the same limit or both have no limit. Indeed it is not vital that the equality be between nth term and nth term.

Theorem 5.14.   *If f and g are sequences and if there exist integers m and p such that*

$$\forall n \in Z_m, \qquad f(n) = g(n + p),$$

then

$$\operatorname*{Lim}_{n \to \infty} f(n) = l \text{ iff } \operatorname*{Lim}_{n \to \infty} g(n) = l.$$

Proof. If f converges to l, then there exists a convergence test ϕ such that for each n greater than $\phi(\epsilon)$

$$|f(n) - l| < \epsilon.$$

Therefore if $\psi(\epsilon) = |m| + |p| + \phi(\epsilon)$ and if $n > \psi(\epsilon)$, then $n - p \in Z_m$ and $n - p > \phi(\epsilon)$. It then follows that $f(n - p) = g(n)$ and

$$|g(n) - l| = |f(n - p) - l| < \epsilon;$$

that is,

$$\operatorname*{Lim}_{n \to \infty} g(n) = l.$$

The proof of the converse we leave to the reader.

As one would expect, the order properties of the real numbers provide much useful information for the study of sequences of real numbers. As an elementary example recall that if $0 < x < 1$, then positive powers of x are smaller than x. Indeed if $n > m$, then $x^n < x^m$. This suggests that

$$\operatorname*{Lim}_{n \to \infty} x^n = 0.$$

For the proof of this and other such assertions, success rests heavily upon the ability of the solver to recall facts that can be related to the problem at hand. By way of illustration we present an interesting use of Bernoulli's inequality to prove

Theorem 5.15. *If $|x| < 1$, then $\operatorname*{Lim}_{n \to \infty} x^n = 0$.*

Analysis. We wish to exhibit a convergence test ϕ with the property that

$$\forall n > \phi(\epsilon), \qquad |x^n - 0| < \epsilon.$$

Since $|x^n - 0| = |x|^n$ it is sufficient to show that $|x|^n < \epsilon$. From Bernoulli's inequality we have that

$$(1 + h)^n > hn$$

provided that $h > 0$ and $n \geq 1$. Therefore if

$$h = \frac{1 - |x|}{|x|},$$

it then follows that $h > 0$ and

$$|x|^n = \frac{1}{(1 + h)^n} < \frac{1}{hn}.$$

From this inequality we see that if $n > 1/h\epsilon$ then $|x|^n < \epsilon$. This suggests that we define our convergence test ϕ by

$$\phi(\epsilon) = \frac{1}{h\epsilon}.$$

We leave the details of the proof to the reader.

In proving that the limit of a sequence f is l, we are required by Definition 5.11 to prove the existence of a convergence test ϕ with the property that

$$\forall n > \phi(\epsilon), \qquad |f(n) - l| < \epsilon.$$

As the preceding examples illustrate, we frequently arrive at a satisfactory definition for ϕ by establishing a chain of inequalities beginning with $|f(n) - l|$ and building up to ϵ. For example, in Theorem 5.15 the chain of inequalities is

$$|x^n - 0| < \frac{1}{hn} < \epsilon.$$

Suppose that in analyzing a given problem we discover a chain of inequalities building up from $|f(n) - l|$, not to ϵ, but to 2ϵ or $\epsilon/3$. In such an event it is always possible to alter the computations so that the end result is exactly ϵ. To do so in every limit problem is, however, a nuisance involving very dull and uninteresting computations. We, therefore, dispose of the need for such alterations by proving

Theorem 5.16.   *If f is a sequence of real numbers and if for some number c and some convergence test ϕ we have that $\forall n > \phi(\epsilon)$, $|f(n) - l| < c\epsilon$, then*

$$\operatorname*{Lim}_{n \to \infty} f(n) = l.$$

Proof.   Since, under the given conditions, we have that $c > 0$, it follows that $\epsilon/c > 0$ for each ϵ. Consequently if we define ψ by $\psi(\epsilon) = \phi(\epsilon/c)$, then ψ is a convergence test. Furthermore if $n > \psi(\epsilon)$, then $n > \phi(\epsilon/c)$ and hence

$$|f(n) - l| = c \cdot \frac{\epsilon}{c} = \epsilon.$$

Therefore f converges to l.

Q.E.D.

In our search for interesting limit properties of sequences we will find that the bounded sequences play a special role. Recall from our earlier definition that a sequence of real numbers f is bounded if and only if there exists a number b with the property that

$$\forall n \in \operatorname{Dom} f, \qquad |f(n)| \leq b.$$

Example.   If $f(n) = (-1)^n$, $n \geq 1$, then f is bounded, because if $n \in Z_1$, then $|(-1)^n| \leq 1$.

If $f(n) = 1/n$, $n \geq 1$, then f is bounded, because if $n \in Z_1$, then $|1/n| < 2$.

If $f(n) = n$, $n \geq 1$, then f is unbounded.

One reason for our interest in bounded sequences is that the collection of bounded sequences contains all of the convergent sequences.

Theorem 5.17.   *Every convergent sequence is bounded.*

Proof.   If f is convergent, then there exists a number l and a convergence test ϕ such that

$$\text{if } n > \phi(\epsilon), \text{ then } |f(n) - l| < \epsilon.$$

In particular, if $n > \phi(1)$, then $|f(n) - l| < 1$. Since $|f(n)| - |l| \le |f(n) - l|$, we have that if $n > \phi(1)$, then $|f(n)| < 1 + |l|$. Therefore if $\operatorname{Dom} f = Z_m$, then $\operatorname{Ran} f = \{f(n) \mid m \le n \le \phi(1)\} \cup \{f(n) \mid n > \phi(1)\}$. Since $\operatorname{Ran} f$ is the union of two bounded sets, it is bounded, and hence f is a bounded sequence.

Q.E.D.

Since most of the elementary properties of limits are easily proved, we leave them as exercises with one final theorem to serve as an additional guide for their proof.

Theorem 5.18.   *If f is a sequence that converges to l_1, if g is a sequence that converges to l_2, and if c is a real number, then cf, $f + g$, and fg each converge and*

1) $\displaystyle \operatorname*{Lim}_{n \to \infty} cf(n) = cl_1$.

2) $\displaystyle \operatorname*{Lim}_{n \to \infty} (f(n) + g(n)) = l_1 + l_2$.

3) $\displaystyle \operatorname*{Lim}_{n \to \infty} f(n)g(n) = l_1 l_2$.

Proof.   1) Since

$$\operatorname*{Lim}_{n \to \infty} f(n) = l_1$$

there exists a convergence test ϕ_1 with the property that for each ϵ and for each n greater than $\phi_1(\epsilon)$

$$|f(n) - l_1| < \epsilon.$$

It then follows that if $c \ne 0$,

$$|cf(n) - cl_1| = |c|\,|f(n) - l_1| < |c|\epsilon.$$

From Theorem 5.16 we then conclude that

$$\operatorname*{Lim}_{n \to \infty} cf(n) = cl_1.$$

If $c = 0$ the proof is obvious.

2) If ϕ_1 and ϕ_2 are convergence tests for f and g respectively, and if we define ϕ by $\phi(\epsilon) = \phi_1(\epsilon) + \phi_2(\epsilon)$, it follows that if $n > \phi(\epsilon)$, then $n > \phi_1(\epsilon)$ and $n > \phi_2(\epsilon)$. Therefore

$$|(f(n) + g(n)) - (l_1 + l_2)| = |f(n) - l_1 + g(n) - l_2|$$
$$\leq |f(n) - l_1| + |g(n) - l_2| < \epsilon + \epsilon = 2\epsilon.$$

We conclude that

$$\operatorname*{Lim}_{n \to \infty} (f(n) + g(n)) = l_1 + l_2.$$

3) If ϕ is defined as in 2), and if b is a bound for g, then for each n greater than $\phi(\epsilon)$ we have that

$$|f(n)g(n) - l_1 l_2| = |f(n)g(n) - l_1 g(n) + l_1 g(n) - l_1 l_2|$$
$$\leq |f(n) - l| \, |g(n)| + |l_1| \, |g(n) - l_2|$$
$$< \epsilon b + |l_1|\epsilon = (b + |l_1|)\epsilon.$$

Q.E.D.

E X E R C I S E S

In Exercises 1–4 find the limit and provide a convergence test.

1. $\operatorname*{Lim}_{n \to \infty} 1^n$ **2.** $\operatorname*{Lim}_{n \to \infty} \dfrac{n-1}{n}$ **3.** $\operatorname*{Lim}_{n \to \infty} \dfrac{1}{n!}$ **4.** $\operatorname*{Lim}_{n \to \infty} \dfrac{2n^2 + 3n}{3^n + 2}$

In the following exercises 'f', 'g', and 'h' are variables on sequences of real numbers.

5. Prove: If $f(n) = l$, $n \geq m$, then f converges to l.

6. Prove: If $f(n) \in N\left(l, \dfrac{1}{n}\right)$, $n \geq m$, then $\operatorname*{Lim}_{n \to \infty} f(n) = l$.

7. Prove: $\operatorname*{Lim}_{n \to \infty} f(n) = 0$ iff $\operatorname*{Lim}_{n \to \infty} |f(n)| = 0$.

8. Prove: If $\operatorname*{Lim}_{n \to \infty} f(n) = l_1$ and $\operatorname*{Lim}_{n \to \infty} g(n) = l_2$, then $\operatorname*{Lim}_{n \to \infty} (f(n) - g(n)) = l_1 - l_2$.

9. Prove: If $|x| > 1$ and if $f(n) = x^n$, $n \geq m$, then f is unbounded and hence diverges.

10. Give an example of a bounded sequence that is divergent.

11. Prove: If f is a sequence of nonzero numbers, if $\operatorname*{Lim}_{n \to \infty} f(n) = l$, and if $l \neq 0$, then $\operatorname*{Lim}_{n \to \infty} \dfrac{1}{f(n)} = \dfrac{1}{l}$.

12. Prove: If g is a sequence of nonzero numbers, if $\operatorname*{Lim}_{n \to \infty} f(n) = l_1$, $\operatorname*{Lim}_{n \to \infty} g(n) = l_2$, and if $l_2 \neq 0$, then $\operatorname*{Lim}_{n \to \infty} \dfrac{f(n)}{g(n)} = \dfrac{l_1}{l_2}$.

13. Prove: If f and g each converge and for some integer m we have that $f(n) \leq g(n)$, $n \geq m$, then $\underset{n \to \infty}{\text{Lim}} f(n) \leq \underset{n \to \infty}{\text{Lim}} g(n)$.

14. Prove: If $\underset{n \to \infty}{\text{Lim}} f(n) = \underset{n \to \infty}{\text{Lim}} h(n) = l$ and if for some integer m we have that $f(n) \leq g(n) \leq h(n)$, $n \geq m$, then $\underset{n \to \infty}{\text{Lim}} g(n) = l$.

15. To what values do the following sequences converge?

a) $f(n) = \dfrac{n^2}{n^3 + 1}$,

b) $f(n) = \dfrac{(-1)^n}{n}$,

c) $f(n) = \dfrac{n^2 + 1}{n^2 - 1}$,

d) $f(n) = \dfrac{n}{(n + 1)2^n}$.

16. Prove: If f is bounded and $\text{Lim}_{n \to \infty} g(n) = 0$, then $\text{Lim}_{n \to \infty} f(n)g(n) = 0$.

17. Prove: If for some ϵ we have $|f(m) - f(n)| < \epsilon$ for all m and n that are greater than p, then f is bounded.

18. Prove: If $\text{Ran} f$ is finite, then $(\exists l)\{n \in \text{Dom} f \,|\, f(n) = l\}$ is infinite.

19. Prove: If $\text{Ran} f$ is finite and $\text{Lim}_{n \to \infty} f(n) = l$, then there exists an integer m such that $f(n) = l$ if $n > m$.

20. Prove: If $\text{Ran} f$ is infinite and $\text{Lim}_{n \to \infty} f(n) = l$, then l is an accumulation point of $\text{Ran} f$.

21. Prove: If f converges, then $\text{Ran} f$ has at most one accumulation point.

22. Prove: If there exists an integer m such that $f(n) \in S$ for $n > m$ and if $\text{Lim}_{n \to \infty} f(n) = l$, then $l \in S$ or l is an accumulation point of S. In particular if S is closed, then $l \in S$.

23. Prove: If $f(n) = \sum_{\alpha=1}^{n} 1/\alpha$, $n \geq 0$, then f is unbounded and hence divergent. (Hint: Exercise 23, page 106.)

24. Prove: If $f(n) = \sum_{\alpha=1}^{n} 1/\alpha^2$, $n \geq 0$, then f is bounded. (Hint: Exercise 23, page 106.)

5.2 Convergence

As we observed earlier we need both a sequence and a number in order to apply the definition of limit. In a particular problem, however, we may be given only a sequence and be left to our own ingenuity to make a reasonable choice of a number to test for the honor of being the limit. In making this choice we may, and indeed should, draw upon all sources of useful information available to us. However, from experience in other contexts we know that before we spend much time searching for the limit of a given sequence we should ask if the thing we are searching for exists. In this section we will establish certain conditions for the existence of limits, including one very important one known as the *Cauchy convergence criterion*. For our first result, however, we need

Definition 5.20. If f is a sequence of real numbers and 'm' and 'n' are variables on its domain, then

1) f is *monotone increasing* iff $m < n$ implies $f(m) \leq f(n)$.
2) f is *monotone strictly increasing* iff $m < n$ implies $f(m) < f(n)$.
3) f is *monotone decreasing* iff $m < n$ implies $f(m) \geq f(n)$.
4) f is *monotone strictly decreasing* iff $m < n$ implies $f(m) > f(n)$.
5) f is *monotone* iff f is monotone increasing or f is monotone decreasing.

Thus, for example, if $f(n) = 1$, $n \geq 1$, then f is both monotone increasing and monotone decreasing; if $f(n) = n$, $n \geq 1$, then f is monotone strictly increasing; if $f(n) = 1/n$, $n \geq 1$, then f is monotone strictly decreasing; and if $f(n) = (-1)^n$, $n \geq 1$, then f is not monotone.

It follows easily from Definition 5.20 that every bounded monotone sequence is convergent.

Theorem 5.21. 1) *If f is a monotone increasing sequence that is bounded above, then f converges.*

2) *If f is a monotone decreasing sequence that is bounded below, then f converges.*

Analysis. 1) If f is monotone increasing and bounded above, then Ran f is nonempty, bounded above, and hence has a supremum. If $l = \sup \text{Ran} f$, then each neighborhood of l must contain a term of f. (Why?) Therefore for each ϵ there exists an integer m such that

$$f(m) \in N(l, \epsilon).$$

But since f is monotone increasing we have for each n greater than m that

$$f(n) \geq f(m).$$

Therefore

$$f(m) \leq f(n) \leq l;$$

that is, $f(n) \in N(l, \epsilon)$. With this outline we leave the details of the proof to the reader.

Example. Consider a sequence f defined inductively by $f(1) = 1$ and

$$f(n + 1) = \frac{f(n)[3a + (f(n))^2]}{3(f(n))^2 + a}, \quad a > 0.$$

Does this sequence converge and, if so, to what value? We will show that it does converge by proving that it is monotone and bounded. For notational convenience we will write 'x_n' for '$f(n)$'. The defining property for f then becomes

$$x_{n+1} = \frac{x_n(3a + x_n^2)}{3x_n^2 + a}, \quad a > 0.$$

We first note that for each n we have, $x_n > 0$. This is proved by induction, the details of which we leave to the reader. We note further that

$$a - x_{n+1}^2 = a - \frac{x_n^2(3a - x_n^2)^2}{(3x_n^2 + a)^2} = \frac{a(3x_n^2 + a)^2 - x_n^2(3a + x_n^2)^2}{(3x_n^2 + a)^2} = \frac{(a - x_n^2)^3}{(3x_n^2 + a)^2}.$$

From this it follows that if $a > 1$, then since $x_1 = 1$ we have that $x_1^2 < a$, and hence by induction $x_n^2 < a$ for each $n \geq 1$. Therefore $x_n < \sqrt{a}$; that is, the sequence is bounded above. Furthermore we have

$$2x_n^2 < 2a,$$
$$3x_n^2 + a < 3a + x_n^2,$$
$$1 < \frac{3a + x_n^2}{3x_n^2 + a},$$
$$x_n < \frac{x_n(3a + x_n^2)}{3x_n^2 + a} = x_{n+1}.$$

Thus if $a > 1$, then the sequence is monotone increasing and bounded above. If $a < 1$, then a similar argument establishes that the sequence is monotone decreasing and bounded below. In either case it follows that the sequence converges. But to what value does it converge? This is a little like asking who is buried in Grant's Tomb. Having established that the given sequence converges, we know that

$$\lim_{n \to \infty} x_n$$

is a name with denotation; hence the value to which the sequence converges is

$$\lim_{n \to \infty} x_n.$$

This trivial response we would not accept as a satisfactory answer to our question. Our question is intended to convey the following. We know that the sequence converges, and this information gives us one conception of the number in question. If this is all we know about this number, then we know very little. We are therefore asking for additional information.

Since for some number l,

$$\lim_{n \to \infty} x_n = l,$$

it follows that

$$\lim_{n \to \infty} x_{n+1} = l.$$

Therefore since

$$x_{n+1} = \frac{x_n(3a + x_n^2)}{3x_n^2 + a},$$

it follows that

$$\operatorname*{Lim}_{n\to\infty} x_{n+1} = \operatorname*{Lim}_{n\to\infty} \frac{x_n(3a + x_n^2)}{3x_n^2 + a},$$

$$l = \frac{l(3a + l^2)}{3l^2 + a},$$

$$l(3l^2 + a) = l(3a + l^2),$$

$$l(2l^2 - 2a) = 0,$$

$$l = 0 \text{ or } l = -\sqrt{a} \text{ or } l = \sqrt{a}.$$

From the monotonicity properties of the sequence it is clear that $l \neq 0$ and $l \neq -\sqrt{a}$. We conclude that for each a greater than zero the sequence converges to $\sqrt{a}$.

The notation introduced in the previous example is very useful for discussing properties of sequences. We therefore introduce it formally for general use.

Definition 5.22.

$f = \{x_n\}_k$ iff $\operatorname{Dom} f = Z_k$ and $\forall n \in \operatorname{Dom} f, \ f(n) = x_n$.

$f = \{x_n\}_k^p$ iff $\operatorname{Dom} f = \{k, k + 1, \ldots, p\}$ and $\forall n \in \operatorname{Dom} f, \ f(n) = x_n$.

With this notation the five sequences defined on page 131 would be denoted by

$$\left\{\frac{(-1)^n}{n}\right\}_1, \quad \{(-1)^n\}_0, \quad \left\{\frac{n+1}{n}\right\}_2, \quad \left\{\frac{(-1)^n n + 1}{n}\right\}_2, \quad \{1^n\}_{-5},$$

respectively.

Since every convergent sequence is bounded, it follows that every unbounded sequence is divergent. Thus a monotone sequence is convergent if and only if it is bounded. We know, of course, that there exist bounded sequences that are divergent. Thus, except for monotone sequences, some additional condition besides boundedness is required to insure convergence. Some insight into the problem can be obtained by considering the range of the sequence in question. If the range is a finite set, then from Exercise 19, page 142, we see that the sequence will converge if and only if all of the terms beyond a certain point are equal—that is, if and only if for some integer p we have $f(n) = f(m)$ for $m > p$ and $n > p$. If the range of a bounded sequence is an infinite set, then it must contain an accumulation point. From Exercises 20–21, page 142, we see that if such a sequence has a limit, then its range has exactly one accumulation point. If the range of a sequence has two or more accumulation points, then clearly all of its terms cannot cluster around a single point. On the other hand, there is a subset of terms that do cluster around a single point. This observation prompts us to introduce the notion of a *subsequence*.

If f is a monotone strictly increasing sequence of integers that maps Z_p into Z_k and if from $\{x_n\}_k$ we define $\{y_n\}_p$ by

$$y_n = x_{f(n)}, \quad n \geq p,$$

then $\{y_n\}_p$ is related to $\{x_n\}_k$ in an interesting and useful way. Intuitively we may think of $\{y_n\}_p$ as having been defined by deleting certain terms of $\{x_n\}_k$ and then "renumbering in order" as illustrated in the following diagram:

$$x_k, \ x_{k+1}, \ x_{k+2}, \ x_{k+3}, \ x_{k+4}, \ \ldots.$$

$$\begin{array}{cc} \uparrow & \uparrow \\ f(p) & f(p+1) \\ | & | \\ y_p & y_{p+1} \end{array}$$

Definition 5.23. $\{y_n\}_p$ is a subsequence of $\{x_n\}_k$ iff there exists a monotone strictly increasing sequence of integers f that maps Z_p into Z_k and

$$\forall n \in Z_p, \quad y_n = x_{f(n)}.$$

Example. $\{2n\}_1$ is a subsequence of $\{n\}_1$. $f(n) = 2n$.

$\left\{\dfrac{1}{n^2}\right\}_1$ is a subsequence of $\left\{\dfrac{1}{n}\right\}_1$. $f(n) = n^2$.

$\{1^n\}_1$ is a subsequence of $\{(-1)^n\}_1$. $f(n) = 2n$.

From the definition of subsequence it is easy to prove

Theorem 5.24. *If $\{a_n\}_k$ converges to l, then every infinite subsequence of $\{a_n\}_k$ converges to l.*

Proof. If $\{a_n\}_k$ converges to l, then there exists a convergence test ϕ with the property that if $n > \phi(\epsilon)$ then $|a_n - l| < \epsilon$. If $\{b_n\}_p$ is a subsequence of $\{a_n\}_k$, then there exists a monotone strictly increasing sequence of integers f that maps Z_p into Z_k such that for each n in Z_p we have that $b_n = a_{f(n)}$. Since f is a monotone strictly increasing sequence of integers, it is unbounded above. Therefore for each ϵ the range of f contains integers that are larger than $\phi(\epsilon)$. By the well-ordering principle Ran f must contain a smallest integer that is larger than $\phi(\epsilon)$. If

$$\psi(\epsilon) = \min \{n \in Z_p \mid f(n) > \phi(\epsilon)\}$$

then ψ is a convergence test. If $n > \psi(\epsilon)$, then $f(n) > \phi(\epsilon)$ and hence

$$|b_n - l| = |a_{f(n)} - l| < \epsilon.$$

$$\text{Q.E.D.}$$

Every sequence has infinitely many subsequences. By defining the monotone strictly increasing sequence of integers f in special ways we are able to select from $\{c_n\}_k$ subsequences of special interest. One such special subsequence which we will call the *subsequence of positive terms* is obtained by defining f in the following way.

$$f(k) = \min \{m \in Z_k \mid c_m > 0\},$$
$$f(n + 1) = \min \{m \in Z_k \mid c_m > 0 \text{ and } m > f(n)\}, \quad n \geq k.$$

If there are infinitely many values of 'm' for which $c_m > 0$, then f is a monotone strictly increasing sequence of integers that maps Z_k into Z_k. Therefore if

$$a_n = c_{f(n)}, \quad n \geq k,$$

then $\{a_n\}_k$ is a subsequence of $\{c_n\}_k$. This subsequence we will call the subsequence of positive terms of $\{c_n\}_k$.

If there are only a finite number of values of 'm' for which $c_m > 0$, then f will be a finite sequence. If Ran $f = \{k, k + 1, \ldots, p\}$, and if

$$a_n = c_{f(n)} \text{ for } k \leq n \leq p,$$

then $\{a_n\}_k^p$ we will also call the *subsequence of positive terms* of $\{c_n\}_k$.

In a similar way we can define the *subsequence of negative terms* of $\{c_n\}_k$. We leave the details as an exercise for the reader. From the definition of subsequence it is easy to prove the following.

Corollary 5.25. *If every subsequence of $\{a_n\}_k$ converges, then they all converge to the same value.*

Proof. If every subsequence of $\{a_n\}_k$ converges, then in particular $\{a_n\}_k$ converges. Therefore every subsequence converges to the same value by Theorem 5.24.

$$\text{Q.E.D.}$$

We have now established that a sequence converges if and only if every subsequence converges. It then follows that every divergent sequence must contain divergent subsequences. Can a divergent sequence contain a convergent subsequence? For bounded sequences the answer is that it not only can, it must.

Theorem 5.26. *Every bounded sequence has a convergent subsequence.*

Analysis. If $\{a_n\}_k$ is a bounded sequence with a finite range, then from Exercise 18, page 142, it follows that for some number l

$$\{n \in Z_k \mid a_n = l\}$$

is infinite. Therefore if we define $\{b_n\}_1$ by $b_n = l$, then clearly $\{b_n\}_1$ converges to l. It is intuitively apparent that $\{b_n\}_1$ is a subsequence of $\{a_n\}_k$. A proof, however, requires that we produce a monotone strictly increasing sequence of integers f that maps Z_1 into Z_k such that $b_n = a_{f(n)}$. This we do inductively in the following way. If

$$f(1) = \min \{n \in Z_k \mid a_n = l\}.$$

then $b_1 = a_{f(1)}$. Suppose that we have succeeded in defining $f(1), f(2), \ldots,$ $f(m)$ in such a way that $f(1) < f(2) < \cdots < f(m)$ and $b_1 = a_{f(1)}$, $b_2 = a_{f(2)}$, $\ldots, b_m = a_{f(m)}$. If

$$f(m + 1) = \min \{n \in Z_k \mid a_n = l \text{ and } n > f(m)\},$$

then $f(m + 1) > f(m)$ and $b_{m+1} = a_{f(m+1)}$.

If $\{a_n\}_k$ is bounded and has an infinite range, then the range must contain an accumulation point l. It then follows that every neighborhood of l contains infinitely many terms of $\{a_n\}_k$. In particular, for each positive integer p, there are infinitely many terms of $\{a_n\}_k$ in $N(l, 1/p)$. We wish to define $\{b_n\}_1$ as a subsequence of $\{a_n\}_k$ with the property that $b_n \in N(l, 1/n)$. From Exercise 6, page 141, it will then follow that $\{b_n\}_1$ converges to l. To accomplish this we define f inductively in a manner similar to that above.

$$f(1) = \min \{n \in Z_k \mid a_n \in N(l, 1)\}$$

$$f(m + 1) = \min \left\{n \in Z_k \mid a_n \in N\left(l, \frac{1}{m + 1}\right) \text{ and } n > f(m)\right\}$$

It then follows that f is monotone strictly increasing and if $b_n = a_{f(n)}$, then $b_n \in N(l, 1/n)$. The details of the proof we leave to the reader.

We are now prepared to prove a very basic convergence criterion which is due to Cauchy. It is suggested by the following observation. If $\{x_n\}_k$ converges, then there exists a number l to which it converges and there exists a convergence test ϕ such that

$$\text{if } n > \phi(\epsilon), \text{ then } |x_n - l| < \epsilon.$$

In particular, if $n > \phi(\epsilon/2)$ and $m > \phi(\epsilon/2)$, then

$$|x_m - x_n| = |x_m - l + l - x_n| \le |x_m - l| + |l - x_n| < \frac{\epsilon}{2} + \frac{\epsilon}{2} = \epsilon.$$

We not only have that x_n is near l for large n, but for large m and n we have that x_m and x_n are near each other. The Cauchy test for convergence asserts that this condition is both necessary and sufficient for convergence. That is, if for large m and n we have that x_m and x_n are near each other, then $\{x_n\}_k$ converges.

Theorem 5.27 (Cauchy's Convergence Criterion for Sequences). $\{x_n\}_k$ *converges iff there exists a convergence test ϕ with the property that for each ϵ and for each m and n greater than $\phi(\epsilon)$*

$$|x_m - x_n| < \epsilon.$$

Analysis. If for $m > \phi(\epsilon)$ and $n > \phi(\epsilon)$ we have that $|x_m - x_n| < \epsilon$, then it can be proved that $\{x_n\}_k$ is bounded. The sequence must therefore have a convergent subsequence, $\{x_{f(n)}\}_p$. If $\{x_{f(n)}\}_p$ converges to l and has ϕ_1 as a convergence test, it follows that

$$\text{if } n > \phi_1(\epsilon), \text{ then } |x_{f(n)} - l| < \epsilon.$$

From the Archimedean order property it follows that there exists an integer m such that $m > \phi_1(\epsilon)$ and $f(m) > \phi(\epsilon)$. Since $m > \phi_1(\epsilon)$ we have that

$$|x_{f(m)} - l| < \epsilon.$$

Furthermore, if $n > \phi(\epsilon)$, then since $f(m) > \phi(\epsilon)$

$$|x_n - l| = |x_n - x_{f(m)} - x_{f(m)} - l| \leq |x_n - x_{f(m)}| + |x_{f(m)} - l|$$
$$< \epsilon + \epsilon = 2\epsilon.$$

Consequently

$$\operatorname*{Lim}_{n \to \infty} x_n = l.$$

The details of the proof we leave to the reader.

We have now presented some very useful tests for the convergence of sequences. One reason for our interest in convergent sequences is, of course, the fact that a convergent sequence uniquely determines the number to which it converges. There are also useful ways of pairing numbers with divergent sequences. One such method is suggested by the fact that every bounded sequence has a convergent subsequence.

If $\{a_n\}_k$ is bounded and if A is the set of all numbers that are limits of subsequences of $\{a_n\}_k$, then A is nonempty and bounded. Consequently A has both a supremum and an infimum. The supremum of A we call the *limit superior* of $\{a_n\}_k$ and the infimum of A we call the *limit inferior* of $\{a_n\}_k$. The limit superior and the limit inferior of $\{a_n\}_k$ we denote respectively by

$$\overline{\operatorname*{Lim}_{n \to \infty}} a_n \quad \text{and} \quad \underline{\operatorname*{Lim}_{n \to \infty}} a_n.$$

Definition 5.28. $\overline{\operatorname*{Lim}_{n \to \infty}} a_n = l$ iff $\{a_n\}_k$ is bounded above and $l = \sup \{x \mid x \text{ is the limit of some subsequence of } \{a_n\}_k\}$.

$\underline{\operatorname*{Lim}_{n \to \infty}} a_n = l$ iff $\{a_n\}_k$ is bounded below and $l = \inf \{x \mid x \text{ is the limit of some subsequence of } \{a_n\}_k\}$.

Example. $\overline{\text{Lim}}_{n\to\infty} (-1)^n = 1, \quad \underline{\text{Lim}}_{n\to\infty} (-1)^n = -1.$

$$\overline{\text{Lim}}_{n\to\infty} \frac{1}{n} = 0, \quad \underline{\text{Lim}}_{n\to\infty} \frac{1}{n} = 0.$$

The elementary properties of limits superior and limits inferior we leave as exercises and conclude this section with a final observation about divergent sequences. Certain sequences—as, for example, the unbounded monotone sequences—diverge but do so in a rather "orderly manner." We find it convenient to identify this type of divergence.

Definition 5.29. $\{a_n\}_k$ *diverges to infinity* iff for each positive real number ϵ there exists a number δ with the property that if $n > \delta$, then $a_n > \epsilon$.

$\{a_n\}_k$ *diverges to minus infinity* iff for each positive real number ϵ there exists a number δ with the property that if $n > \delta$, then $a_n < -\epsilon$.

Example. $\{n\}_1$ and $\{n!\}_1$ each diverge to infinity.

EXERCISES

1. Prove: $\{x_n\}_k$ is monotone increasing iff $x_n \le x_{n+1}, n \ge k$.

2. Prove: 1) A monotone increasing sequence is bounded iff it is bounded above. 2) A monotone decreasing sequence is bounded iff it is bounded below.

3. Prove: If $\{m_n\}_k$ is a monotone strictly increasing sequence of integers with $m_k \ge p$ then $\{x_{m_n}\}_k = \{x_n\}_p \circ \{m_n\}_k$.

4. Prove: If $\{m_n\}_k$ is a monotone strictly increasing sequence of integers, then $\forall n \in Z_k, m_n \ge m_k + n - k$.

5. Prove: Every monotone strictly increasing sequence of integers diverges to infinity.

6. Prove: Every monotone increasing sequence of real numbers that is not bounded diverges to infinity.

7. Prove: Every monotone decreasing sequence of real numbers that is not bounded diverges to minus infinity.

8. Prove: If the subsequence of positive terms of $\{x_n\}_1$ is infinite and if we define f on Z_1 by

$$f(1) = 1 \text{ if } x_1 > 0, \quad f(n+1) = f(n) + 1 \text{ if } x_{n+1} > 0,$$
$$= 0 \text{ if } x_1 \le 0, \quad\quad\quad = f(n) \quad\quad \text{ if } x_{n+1} \le 0,$$

then f diverges to infinity.

9. Define f so that $\{x_{f(n)}\}_k$ is the subsequence of $\{x_n\}_k$ of rational terms.

10. Prove: If $a > 0$ then $\{\sqrt[n]{a}\}_1$ is monotone and converges to 1.

11. If $\{x_n\}_k$ is a bounded sequence of positive real numbers must $\{x_{n+1}/x_n\}_k$ also be bounded?

12. Prove: A monotone sequence is bounded iff it has a bounded subsequence.

13. Does every sequence that is bounded above have a limit superior? Does every sequence that is bounded below have a limit inferior?

14. Prove: If $\{x_n\}_k$ is bounded, then $\overline{\operatorname{Lim}}_{n\to\infty} x_n$ and $\underline{\operatorname{Lim}}_{n\to\infty} x_n$ each exist and $\underline{\operatorname{Lim}}_{n\to\infty} x_n \leq \overline{\operatorname{Lim}}_{n\to\infty} x_n$.

15. Prove: If $\{x_n\}_k$ is bounded above and if $\overline{\operatorname{Lim}}_{n\to\infty} x_n = l$, then for each ϵ, $\{n \in Z_k \mid x_n > l - \epsilon\}$ is infinite and $\{n \in Z_k \mid x_n > l + \epsilon\}$ is finite.

16. Prove: If $\{x_n\}_k$ is bounded below and if $\underline{\operatorname{Lim}}_{n\to\infty} x_n = l$ then for each ϵ, $\{n \in Z_k \mid x_n < l + \epsilon\}$ is infinite and $\{n \in Z_k \mid x_n < l - \epsilon\}$ is finite.

17. Prove: $\operatorname{Lim}_{n\to\infty} x_n$ exists iff $\underline{\operatorname{Lim}}_{n\to\infty} x_n$ and $\overline{\operatorname{Lim}}_{n\to\infty} x_n$ each exist and are equal.

18. Prove: Limits superior are *limits maximum*; that is, if $\overline{\operatorname{Lim}}_{n\to\infty} x_n = l$ then there is a subsequence of $\{x_n\}_k$ that converges to l.

19. Prove: Limits inferior are *limits minimum*.

20. Does $\overline{\operatorname{Lim}}_{n\to\infty} \dfrac{x_{n+1}}{x_n}$ exist for every sequence of positive reals $\{x_n\}_k$?

Does $\underline{\operatorname{Lim}}_{n\to\infty} \dfrac{x_{n+1}}{x_n}$ exist for every sequence of positive reals $\{x_n\}_k$?

21. If $\{x_n\}_k$ is a sequence of positive reals and if $\overline{\operatorname{Lim}}_{n\to\infty} \dfrac{x_{n+1}}{x_n}$ exists, must $\underline{\operatorname{Lim}}_{n\to\infty} \dfrac{x_{n+1}}{x_n}$ exist?

22. Prove: There exists a sequence $\{x_n\}_1$ having the property that for each real number l some subsequence of $\{x_n\}_1$ converges to l.

5.3 Series

Much valuable information concerning sequences has arisen from the search for ways of obtaining new sequences from old. One method which has proved to be quite useful consists of defining the terms of the new sequence as sums of terms of the old. Thus from $\{a_n\}_k$ we obtain

$$\left\{ \sum_{\alpha=k}^{n} a_\alpha \right\}_k .$$

Such sequences are the subject matter of the theory of *infinite series*.

Definition 5.30. An *infinite series* is an ordered pair of sequences,

$$\left(\{a_n\}_k, \left\{ \sum_{\alpha=k}^{n} a_\alpha \right\}_k \right).$$

The first entry is the *sequence of terms* of the series, and the second entry is the *sequence of partial sums* of the series. A series is said to *converge* if its sequence of partial sums converges and is said to *diverge* if its sequence of partial sums diverges. A series *converges to l* iff its sequence of partial sums converges to *l*.

For the discussion of the properties of series we require an additional special symbol

Definition 5.31. $\displaystyle \sum_{\alpha=k}^{\infty} a_\alpha = \operatorname*{Lim}_{n \to \infty} \sum_{\alpha=k}^{n} a_\alpha.$

The symbol '$\sum_{k}^{\infty} a_\alpha$' will be used as an abbreviation for

$$\sum_{\alpha=k}^{\infty} a_\alpha.$$

Both symbols are read the *sum from α equal k to infinity of a_α*. We will use the symbol 's_n' as a variable on partial sums, that is, if $\{a_n\}_k$ is the sequence of terms of a series, then $\{s_n\}_k$ will be understood to be its sequence of partial sums; i.e.,

$$s_n = \sum_{\alpha=k}^{n} a_\alpha, \quad n \geq k.$$

Before taking up the study of series we point out that the symbol '$\sum_{k}^{\infty} a_\alpha$' has traditionally been used ambiguously. It is sometimes used to refer to a series and sometimes used to refer to the value to which a series converges. For example, if we assert that '$\sum_{k}^{\infty} a_\alpha$ converges', it is clear that the symbol '$\sum_{k}^{\infty} a_\alpha$' refers to that series whose sequence of terms is $\{a_n\}_k$ and whose sequence of partial sums is $\{\sum_{k}^{n} a_\alpha\}_k$. If, however, we assert that $\sum_{k}^{\infty} a_\alpha = 2$, it is clear that '$\sum_{k}^{\infty} a_\alpha$' is being used to denote the value to which the series converges. We will continue to use this symbol in both ways and rely upon the context to make the meaning clear.

From the foregoing definitions we see that when we assert that a certain series converges we are simply claiming that a certain sequence has a limit. It is, therefore, not surprising that we can infer elementary properties of series from the elementary properties of sequences. For example, from the convergence properties of $\{x^n\}_0$ we can infer the following result concerning the so-called *geometric series*

$$\sum_{\alpha=0}^{\infty} x^\alpha.$$

Theorem 5.32.   1) *If $|x| < 1$, then $\displaystyle\sum_{\alpha=0}^{\infty} x^\alpha$ converges to $1/(1-x)$.*

2) *If $|x| \geq 1$, then $\displaystyle\sum_{\alpha=0}^{\infty} x^\alpha$ diverges.*

Proof. If $x \neq 1$, then

$$\sum_{\alpha=0}^{n} x^\alpha = \frac{1 - x^{n+1}}{1 - x}.$$

It then follows that if $|x| < 1$, then

$$\lim_{n \to \infty} \sum_{\alpha=0}^{n} x^\alpha = \frac{1}{1 - x};$$

that is, $\sum_0^\infty x^\alpha$ converges to $1/(1 - x)$. If $|x| > 1$, then $\sum_0^\infty x^\alpha$ diverges. If $|x| = 1$, then $x = 1$ or $x = -1$. If $x = -1$, then $\sum_0^\infty x^\alpha$ diverges because $\{(-1)^n\}_0$ is divergent and

$$\sum_{\alpha=0}^{n} x^\alpha = \frac{1 - (-1)^{n+1}}{2}.$$

If $x = 1$, then $\sum_0^\infty x^\alpha$ diverges because $\{n + 1\}_0$ is divergent and

$$\sum_{\alpha=0}^{n} x^\alpha = n + 1.$$

Q.E.D.

From Theorem 5.18 it is easy to prove

Theorem 5.33. *If $\sum_k^\infty a_\alpha$ and $\sum_k^\infty b_\alpha$ each converge, then $(\forall c)$ $\sum_k^\infty (ca_\alpha)$ converges, $\sum_k^\infty (a_\alpha + b_\alpha)$ converges, and*

$$1)\ \sum_{\alpha=k}^{\infty} (ca_\alpha) = c \sum_{\alpha=k}^{\infty} a_\alpha,$$

$$2)\ \sum_{\alpha=k}^{\infty} (a_\alpha + b_\alpha) = \sum_{\alpha=k}^{\infty} a_\alpha + \sum_{\alpha=k}^{\infty} b_\alpha.$$

Corollary 5.34. *If $|x| < 1$, then $\sum_{\alpha=0}^{\infty} cx^\alpha = c/(1 - x)$.*

The proofs are left to the reader.

Because the question of the convergence of series is the question of the convergence of a particular type of sequence—namely, a sequence of partial sums—there are special tests for the convergence of series. We turn now to a study of these special convergence tests. Our first result is a rather simple observation which we present as

Theorem 5.35 (The nth Term Test). *If a series converges then its sequence of terms converges to 0.*

First Proof. If $\{a_n\}_k$ and $\{s_n\}_k$ are respectively the sequence of terms and sequence of partial sums of a convergent series, then for some number l.

$$\lim_{n \to \infty} s_n = l.$$

We then also have that

$$\text{Lim}_{n \to \infty} s_{n-1} = l.$$

Therefore since $a_n = s_n - s_{n-1}$ (why?), it follows that

$$\text{Lim}_{n \to \infty} a_n = \text{Lim}_{n \to \infty} s_n - \text{Lim}_{n \to \infty} s_{n-1} = 0.$$

Q.E.D.

Second Proof.   From the Cauchy criterion it follows that there exists a convergence test ϕ such that for each ϵ and each m and n greater than $\phi(\epsilon)$

$$|s_m - s_n| < \epsilon.$$

In particular, if $n > \phi(\epsilon) + 1$, then $n > \phi(\epsilon)$, $n - 1 > \phi(\epsilon)$, and

$$|a_n| = |s_n - s_{n-1}| < \epsilon.$$

Therefore

$$\text{Lim}_{n \to \infty} a_n = 0.$$

Q.E.D.

Note that for the purpose of investigating the convergence of series the nth term test is a negative test; that is, if the sequence of terms of a given series does not converge to 0 then the series diverges.

Example.   The series

$$\sum_{\alpha=1}^{\infty} \alpha, \quad \sum_{\alpha=1}^{\infty} 2^\alpha, \quad \sum_{\alpha=1}^{\infty} (-1)^\alpha, \quad \sum_{\alpha=1}^{\infty} \alpha!, \quad \text{and} \quad \sum_{\alpha=1}^{\infty} \frac{\alpha+1}{\alpha}$$

are each divergent, since in each case the sequence of terms does not converge to 0.

It should be noted that the nth term test is not an if and only if condition. There do exist divergent series whose sequence of terms converge to 0. For the proof of this claim we appeal to the following results.

Theorem 5.36.   *If $\{x_n\}_k$ is a sequence of nonnegative real numbers, then $\sum_k^\infty x_\alpha$ converges iff its sequence of partial sums is bounded.*

Proof.   If $\{x_n\}_k$ is a sequence of nonnegative real numbers and if

$$s_n = \sum_{\alpha=k}^{n} a_\alpha, \quad n \geq k,$$

then

$$s_n \leq s_{n+1}, \quad n \geq k.$$

Therefore the sequence of partial sums $\{s_n\}_k$ is monotone increasing and hence converges if and only if it is bounded above. But it is bounded above if and only if it is bounded.

Q.E.D.

Corollary 5.37.   1) $\sum\limits_{\alpha=1}^{\infty} 1/\alpha$ *diverges.*

   2) $\sum\limits_{\alpha=1}^{\infty} 1/\alpha^2$ *converges.*

Analysis.   1) If $s_n = \sum_1^n 1/\alpha$ then it is sufficient to prove that $\{s_n\}_1$ is unbounded. For this purpose note that $s_1 = 1$, $s_2 = s_1 + \frac{1}{2}$, $s_4 = s_2 + \frac{1}{3} + \frac{1}{4}$, and in general

$$s_{2^{n+1}} = s_{2^n} + \frac{1}{2^n + 1} + \frac{1}{2^n + 2} + \cdots + \frac{1}{2^{n+1}}.$$

Thus $s_{2^{n+1}}$ is obtained by adding to s_{2^n} a sum of 2^n terms each of which is larger than or equal to $1/2^{n+1}$. Since $2^n/2^{n+1} = \frac{1}{2}$, it follows that

$$s_{2^{n+1}} \geq s_{2^n} + \frac{1}{2}$$

Since $s_{2^0} = 1$, it is easily proved by induction that

$$s_{2^n} \geq 1 + \frac{n}{2}.$$

It then follows that $\{s_{2^n}\}_1$ is unbounded, and hence $\{s_n\}_1$ is unbounded.

   2) If $s_n = \sum_1^n 1/\alpha^2$, then we wish to prove that $\{s_n\}_1$ is bounded. We note that

$$s_1 = 1, \qquad s_3 = s_1 + \frac{1}{2^2} + \frac{1}{3^2}, \qquad s_7 = s_3 + \frac{1}{4^2} + \frac{1}{5^2} + \frac{1}{6^2} + \frac{1}{7^2},$$

and in general

$$s_{2^{n+1}-1} = s_{2^n-1} + \frac{1}{(2^n)^2} + \frac{1}{(2^n+1)^2} + \cdots + \frac{1}{(2^{n+1}-1)^2}, \quad n \geq 1.$$

Thus $s_{2^{n+1}-1}$ is obtained by adding to s_{2^n-1} a sum of 2^n terms each of which is equal to or smaller than $1/(2^n)^2$. Since $2^n/(2^n)^2 = 1/2^n$, it follows that

$$s_{2^{n+1}-1} \leq s_{2^n-1} + \frac{1}{2^n}.$$

Since $s_{2^1-1} = 1$, it is easily proved by induction that

$$s_{2^{n+1}-1} \leq \sum_{\alpha=0}^{n} \frac{1}{2^\alpha}.$$

But

$$(\forall n) \sum_{\alpha=0}^{n} \frac{1}{2^\alpha} < 2;$$

therefore $\{s_{2^n-1}\}_1$ is bounded, and since $\{s_n\}_1$ is monotone, it must also be bounded. The details of the proof we leave to the reader.

Corollary 5.37 provides an example of a divergent series whose sequence of terms converges to 0.

From Theorem 5.36 we easily deduce

Theorem 5.38 (The Comparison Test). *If $\sum_k^\infty x_\alpha$ and $\sum_k^\infty y_\alpha$ are series of nonnegative terms such that for each $n \geq k$*

$$x_n \leq y_n,$$

then $\sum_k^\infty x_\alpha$ converges if $\sum_k^\infty y_\alpha$ converges and $\sum_k^\infty y_\alpha$ diverges if $\sum_k^\infty x_\alpha$ diverges.

Proof. Since for each $n \geq k$ we have $x_n \leq y_n$, it follows that for each $n \geq k$ we also have that

$$\sum_{\alpha=k}^n x_\alpha \leq \sum_{\alpha=k}^n y_\alpha.$$

From this we see that if the partial sums of $\sum_k^\infty y_\alpha$ are bounded, then the partial sums of $\sum_k^\infty x_\alpha$ are bounded. It then follows that if $\sum_k^\infty y_\alpha$ converges, then $\sum_k^\infty x_\alpha$ converges. Similarly if $\sum_k^\infty x_\alpha$ diverges, then its sequence of partial sums is unbounded. The sequence of partial sums of $\sum_k^\infty y_\alpha$ is therefore unbounded; consequently $\sum_k^\infty y_\alpha$ diverges.

Q.E.D.

Example. If $p > 2$, then $1/n^p < 1/n^2$. Since $\sum_1^\infty 1/\alpha^2$ converges, it follows that $\sum_1^\infty 1/\alpha^p$ converges.

Example. If $n > 1$, then $\sqrt{n} < n$ and hence $(1/\sqrt{n}) > (1/n)$. Since $\sum_1^\infty 1/\alpha$ diverges, it follows that $\sum_1^\infty 1/\sqrt{\alpha}$ diverges.

As an interesting application of the results of this section we will prove that every real number has a decimal representation. Since every positive real number x is the sum of an integer, $[\![x]\!]$, and a positive real number that is less than 1, $x - [\![x]\!]$, it is sufficient to prove that positive real numbers that are less than 1 have a decimal representation. We must, of course, agree on what is meant by a decimal representation.

We would surely agree that by the repeating decimal

$$.333\cdots$$

we mean

$$\frac{3}{10} + \frac{3}{10^2} + \frac{3}{10^3} + \cdots;$$

that is, when we assert that $.333\cdots$ is $\frac{1}{3}$, we are claiming that the series

$$\sum_{\alpha=1}^\infty \frac{3}{10^\alpha}$$

converges to $\frac{1}{3}$. From the properties of geometric series we see that this is true. Indeed if $\{a_n\}_1$ is a sequence whose terms are nonnegative integers that are less than 10, then since

$$\frac{a_n}{10^n} \le \frac{9}{10^n}, \quad n \ge 1,$$

and since

$$\sum_{\alpha=1}^{\infty} \frac{9}{10^\alpha}$$

converges, it follows, from the comparison test, that

$$\sum_{\alpha=1}^{\infty} \frac{a_\alpha}{10^\alpha}$$

converges to a nonnegative number that is less than or equal to 1.

Theorem 5.39. *If $0 < x < 1$ then there exists a sequence of integers $\{a_n\}_1$ with $0 \le a_n \le 9$, $n \ge 1$, for which*

$$\sum_{\alpha=1}^{\infty} \frac{a_\alpha}{10^\alpha} = x.$$

Proof. The sequence of integers $\{a_n\}_1$ we will define inductively in the following way. If

$$a_1 = [\![10x]\!],$$

then since $0 < x < 1$, it follows that $0 < 10x < 10$. Therefore, $0 \le a_1 \le 9$. We then have that $0 < 10x - a_1 < 1$. If

$$a_2 = \left[\!\left[10^2\left(x - \frac{a_1}{10}\right) \right]\!\right],$$

then since $0 < 10^2[x - (a_1/10)] < 10$, it follows that $0 \le a_2 \le 9$.

Assume that we have succeeded in defining $a_1, a_2, \ldots, a_n$ in such a way that for $0 \le m \le n$ we have that $0 \le a_m \le 9$ and

$$a_m = \left[\!\left[10^m\left(x - \sum_{\alpha=1}^{m-1} \frac{a_\alpha}{10^\alpha}\right) \right]\!\right],$$

then in particular we would have that

$$a_n = \left[\!\left[10^n\left(x - \sum_{\alpha=1}^{n-1} \frac{a_\alpha}{10^\alpha}\right) \right]\!\right]$$

and $0 \le a_n \le 9$. Consequently

$$0 \le 10^n\left(x - \sum_{\alpha=1}^{n-1} \frac{a_\alpha}{10^\alpha}\right) - a_n < 1,$$

$$0 \le 10^{n+1}\left(x - \sum_{\alpha=1}^{n} \frac{a_\alpha}{10^\alpha}\right) < 10.$$

Therefore if

$$a_{n+1} = \left[\!\left[10^{n+1}\!\left(x - \sum_{\alpha=1}^{n} \frac{a_\alpha}{10^\alpha} \right) \right]\!\right],$$

then $0 \le a_{n+1} \le 9$.

With $\{a_n\}_1$ as defined, we have for each positive n that

$$0 \le 10^{n+1}\!\left(x - \sum_{\alpha=1}^{n} \frac{a_\alpha}{10^\alpha} \right) < 10,$$

$$0 \le x - \sum_{\alpha=1}^{n} \frac{a_\alpha}{10^\alpha} < \frac{1}{10^n}.$$

Since

$$\operatorname*{Lim}_{n \to \infty} \frac{1}{10^n} = 0,$$

we conclude that

$$\sum_{\alpha=1}^{\infty} \frac{a_\alpha}{10^\alpha} = x.$$

Q.E.D.

Combining Theorem 5.39 with the earlier result, that every positive integer has a decimal representation, it follows that for each positive real number x there exists a nonnegative integer n and a sequence $\{a_m\}_{-n}$ with $0 \le a_m \le 9$ for $m \ge -n$, such that

$$x = \sum_{\alpha=-n}^{\infty} \frac{a_\alpha}{10^\alpha}.$$

We have now established that every real number has a decimal representation. It is natural to ask if each number has only one such representation. The answer is no, as we see from the fact that

$$1 = .999\cdots.$$

It is interesting that this example is characteristic of all numbers that do not have a unique decimal representation. That is, every number that has more than one decimal representation can be proved to have exactly two, one involving an infinite sequence of zeros and the other an infinite sequence of nines. For the proof of this fact we need the following.

Lemma.   *If $\{a_n\}_1$ is a sequence of integers with $|a_n| \le 9$, $n \ge 1$, and if*

$$\sum_{\alpha=1}^{\infty} \frac{a_\alpha}{10^\alpha} = 1,$$

then $a_n = 9$, $n \ge 1$.

Proof. (By contradiction.) If for some positive integer m we have that $a_m \neq 9$, then $a_m < 9$. If $n > m$, then

$$\sum_{\alpha=1}^{n} \frac{a_\alpha}{10^\alpha} \leq \sum_{\alpha=1}^{n} \frac{9}{10^\alpha} - \frac{1}{10^m}.$$

Therefore

$$\lim_{n \to \infty} \sum_{\alpha=1}^{n} \frac{a_\alpha}{10^\alpha} \leq 1 - \frac{1}{10^m} < 1.$$

This is a contradiction that forces us to conclude that $a_n = 9$ for all positive n.

Q.E.D.

From this lemma it then follows that each number has at most two decimal representations, for suppose that

$$\sum_{\alpha=1}^{\infty} \frac{a_\alpha}{10^\alpha} = \sum_{\alpha=1}^{\infty} \frac{b_\alpha}{10^\alpha}$$

and that for some positive integer m we have that $a_m \neq b_m$. It then follows that there is a smallest positive integer k such that $a_k \neq b_k$. Without loss of generality we may assume that $a_k > b_k$.

We then have that $a_1 = b_1, a_2 = b_2, \ldots, a_{k-1} = b_{k-1}$, and

$$\sum_{\alpha=1}^{\infty} \frac{a_\alpha - b_\alpha}{10^\alpha} = 0.$$

Therefore

$$\frac{a_k - b_k}{10^k} = \sum_{\alpha=k+1}^{\infty} \frac{b_\alpha - a_\alpha}{10^\alpha};$$

hence

$$0 < a_k - b_k = 10^k \sum_{\alpha=k+1}^{\infty} \frac{b_\alpha - a_\alpha}{10^\alpha} \leq 1.$$

Since $a_k - b_k$ is a positive integer, we conclude that

$$10^k \sum_{\alpha=k+1}^{\infty} \frac{b_\alpha - a_\alpha}{10^\alpha} = 1.$$

From the lemma above it then follows that

$$b_n - a_n = 9, \quad n \geq k + 1.$$

Since b_n and a_n are nonnegative integers that are smaller than 10, it follows that

$$b_n = 9, \quad n \geq k + 1, \quad \text{and} \quad a_n = 0, \quad n \geq k + 1.$$

From this result we see that a one-to-one correspondence can be established between real numbers and decimal representations by prescribing for those real numbers that have two representatives which one of the two we shall use, the one having an infinite sequence of zeros or the one having an infinite sequence of nines.

EXERCISES

In Exercises 1–4 decide whether or not the series converge. For those that do, find the values to which they converge.

1. $\sum_{\alpha=2}^{\infty} \frac{1}{2^{\alpha}}$.

2. $\sum_{\alpha=1}^{\infty} \frac{1}{\alpha(\alpha+1)}$.

3. $\sum_{\alpha=1}^{\infty} \frac{\alpha-1}{\alpha}$.

4. $\sum_{\alpha=2}^{\infty} \frac{1}{(2\alpha-1)(2\alpha+1)}$.

5. Prove: $\sum_{\alpha=0}^{\infty} \frac{\{4^{\alpha}x\}}{4^{\alpha}}$ converges for all x.

6. For what values of 'x' does $\sum_{0}^{\infty} (x + |x|)^{\alpha}$ converge?

7. Prove (Cauchy condensation test): If $\{x_n\}_0$ is a monotone decreasing sequence that converges to 0, then $\sum_{0}^{\infty} x_{\alpha}$ converges iff $\sum_{0}^{\infty} 2^{\alpha}x_{2\alpha}$ converges. (Hint: Exercises 23 and 24, page 142.)

8. Prove: x is rational iff x has a repeating decimal representation.

9. Prove: If for $\{a_n\}_k$ and $\{b_n\}_l$ there exists an integer m such that $m \geq k$, $m \geq l$ and

$$0 \leq a_n \leq b_n \text{ for } n \geq m,$$

then $\sum_{k}^{\infty} a_{\alpha}$ converges if $\sum_{l}^{\infty} b_{\alpha}$ converges and $\sum_{l}^{\infty} b_{\alpha}$ diverges if $\sum_{k}^{\infty} a_{\alpha}$ diverges.

10. Prove: The two series $\sum_{k}^{\infty} a_{\alpha}$ and $\sum_{k}^{\infty} b_{\alpha}$ both converge or both diverge if for some integer m greater than or equal to k, we have that

$$a_n = b_n, \quad n \geq m.$$

11. If, in Exercise 10, $\sum_{k}^{\infty} a_{\alpha}$ converges to l, to what value does $\sum_{k}^{\infty} b_{\alpha}$ converge?

12. Prove: If the sequence of terms of $\sum_{k}^{\infty} a_{\alpha}$ contains only a finite subsequence of positive terms or only a finite subsequence of negative terms, then $\sum_{k}^{\infty} a_{\alpha}$ converges iff $\sum_{k}^{\infty} |a_{\alpha}|$ converges.

13. Prove (Cauchy convergence criterion for series): $\sum_{k}^{\infty} a_{\alpha}$ converges iff $(\exists\phi)(\forall\epsilon)$ if $\phi(\epsilon) < m \leq n$, then $|\sum_{m}^{n} a_{\alpha}| < \epsilon$.

14. Prove: If $\{m_n\}_1$ is a sequence of positive integers that diverges to infinity and if $\sum_{1}^{\infty} a_{\alpha}$ converges, then $\text{Lim}_{n\to\infty} \sum_{1}^{m_n} a_{\alpha} = \sum_{1}^{\infty} a_{\alpha}$.

15. Prove: If $\{a_n\}_0$ is a bounded sequence of nonnegative real numbers and if $0 \leq x < 1$, then $\sum_{0}^{\infty} a_{\alpha}x^{\alpha}$ converges.

16. Prove: If $\{a_n\}_0$ is a sequence of nonnegative real numbers, and if $0 \leq x \leq y$, then

1) $\sum_{0}^{\infty} a_{\alpha}x^{\alpha}$ converges if $\sum_{0}^{\infty} a_{\alpha}y^{\alpha}$ converges,

2) $\sum_{0}^{\infty} a_{\alpha}y^{\alpha}$ diverges if $\sum_{0}^{\infty} a_{\alpha}x^{\alpha}$ diverges.

17. Prove: If $\sum_k^\infty a_\alpha$ is a series of positive terms and if $\{a_{n+1}/a_n\}_k$ is unbounded, must the series diverge?

18. Prove: If $\sum_0^\infty a_\alpha$ and $\sum_0^\infty b_\alpha$ are convergent series with non-negative terms, then $\sum_0^\infty a_\alpha b_\alpha$ converges.

19. Prove: Every positive real number has a ternary representation; that is, if $x > 0$, then there exists a positive integer n and a sequence $\{a_m\}_{-n}$ with $0 \le a_m \le 2$ such that

$$x = \sum_{\alpha=-n}^\infty \frac{a_\alpha}{3^\alpha}.$$

5.4 More on Convergence

In the last section we presented a few of the elementary properties of series including one basic test for the convergence of series, the comparison test. In this section we will present several other tests for convergence. It is instructive to note the role of the comparison test in each proof.

Theorem 5.40. *If $\sum_k^\infty a_\alpha$ and $\sum_k^\infty b_\alpha$ are series of positive terms and if*

$$\lim_{n \to \infty} \frac{a_n}{b_n} = c, \quad c \ne 0,$$

then the two series either both converge or both diverge.

Proof. Since $\{a_n/b_n\}_k$ converges to c, there exists a convergence test ϕ with the property that for each ϵ

$$\text{if } n > \phi(\epsilon), \text{ then } \left| \frac{a_n}{b_n} - c \right| < \epsilon.$$

In particular, since $c > 0$, it follows that if $n > \phi(c/2)$, then

$$\left| \frac{a_n}{b_n} - c \right| < \frac{c}{2}.$$

Consequently

$$-\frac{c}{2} < \frac{a_n}{b_n} - c < \frac{c}{2},$$

$$\frac{c}{2} < \frac{a_n}{b_n} < \frac{3c}{2},$$

$$\frac{c}{2} b_n < a_n < \frac{3c}{2} b_n.$$

It then follows that if $\sum_k^\infty b_\alpha$ converges, then $\sum_k^\infty (3c/2)b_\alpha$ converges and hence $\sum_k^\infty a_\alpha$ converges. Furthermore if $\sum_k^\infty a_\alpha$ converges, then $\sum_k^\infty (c/2)b_\alpha$ converges and hence $\sum_k^\infty b_\alpha$ converges. Thus $\sum_k^\infty a_\alpha$ converges iff $\sum_k^\infty b_\alpha$ converges.

$$\text{Q.E.D.}$$

Example. $\sum\limits_{\alpha=2}^{\infty} \alpha/(\alpha^2 - 2)$ diverges because $\sum\limits_{\alpha=2}^{\infty} 1/\alpha$ diverges and

$$\lim_{n \to \infty} \frac{n}{n^2 - 2}\frac{n}{1} = 1.$$

$\sum\limits_{\alpha=1}^{\infty} (\alpha + 1)/(2\alpha^3 + 2\alpha - 1)$ converges because $\sum\limits_{\alpha=1}^{\infty} 1/\alpha^2$ converges and

$$\lim_{n \to \infty} \frac{n + 1}{2n^3 + 2n - 1} \cdot \frac{n^2}{1} = \frac{1}{2}.$$

From these examples we see that Theorem 5.40 is particularly useful in testing series whose terms are rational in n. We see in fact that such a series converges iff the denominator polynomial is of degree at least two larger than that of the numerator.

Another interesting consequence of the comparison test we present as

Theorem 5.41 (Ratio Test). *If* $\sum\limits_{\alpha=k}^{\infty} a_\alpha$ *is a series of positive terms and if*

$$\lim_{n \to \infty} \frac{a_{n+1}}{a_n} = r$$

then $\sum\limits_{\alpha=k}^{\infty} a_\alpha$ *converges if* $r < 1$ *and diverges if* $r > 1$.

Proof. Since $\{a_{n+1}/a_n\}_k$ converges to r, there exists a convergence test ϕ such that for each ϵ

$$\text{if } n > \phi(\epsilon), \text{ then } \left| \frac{a_{n+1}}{a_n} - r \right| < \epsilon.$$

In particular,

$$\text{if } r < 1, \text{ then } \frac{1 - r}{2} > 0$$

and hence

$$\text{if } n > \phi\left(\frac{1-r}{2}\right), \text{ then } \left| \frac{a_{n+1}}{a_n} - r \right| < \frac{1-r}{2}.$$

Consequently

$$\frac{a_{n+1}}{a_n} - r < \frac{1-r}{2},$$

$$\frac{a_{n+1}}{a_n} < \frac{1+r}{2},$$

$$a_{n+1} < \frac{1+r}{2} a_n.$$

Finally if

$$m > \phi\left(\frac{1-r}{2}\right),$$

then by induction, the details of which we leave to the reader, we can prove that

$$a_n \le \left(\frac{1+r}{2}\right)^{n-m} a_m, \quad n \ge m.$$

Since $(1 + r)/2 < 1$ it follows that

$$\sum_{\alpha=m}^{\infty} \left(\frac{1+r}{2}\right)^{\alpha} a_m$$

converges and hence by the comparison test $\sum_k^{\infty} a_\alpha$ converges.

However, if $r > 1$, then $r - 1 > 0$ and

$$\text{if } n > \phi(r - 1), \text{ then } \left|\frac{a_{n+1}}{a_n} - r\right| < r - 1.$$

Consequently

$$1 - r < \frac{a_{n+1}}{a_n} - r,$$

$$1 < \frac{a_{n+1}}{a_n},$$

$$a_n < a_{n+1}.$$

Thus if $m > \phi(r - 1)$, then again by induction we can prove that

$$a_m < a_n, \text{ for } n \ge m.$$

But $0 < a_m$; therefore $\{a_n\}_k$ does not converge to zero and hence the series diverges by the nth term test.

Q.E.D.

Example. $\sum_{\alpha=1}^{\infty} 1/\alpha!$ converges because

$$\lim_{n\to\infty} \frac{1}{(n+1)!} \cdot \frac{n!}{1} = \lim_{n\to\infty} \frac{1}{n+1} = 0.$$

Example. If $r \ge 0$, then $\sum_{\alpha=0}^{\infty} r^\alpha$ converges for $r < 1$ and diverges for $r > 1$ because

$$\lim_{n\to\infty} \frac{r^{n+1}}{r^n} = r.$$

It should be observed that the ratio test assumes the existence of

$$\lim_{n\to\infty} \frac{a_{n+1}}{a_n}.$$

There exist convergent series for which this limit does not exist, as for example

$$1 + \frac{1}{2^2} + \frac{1}{2^3} + \frac{1}{3^2} + \frac{1}{2^4} + \frac{1}{5^2} + \frac{1}{2^6} + \cdots$$

and there exist divergent series for which the limit does not exist, as for example

$$1 + \tfrac{1}{2} + 1 + \tfrac{1}{4} + 1 + \tfrac{1}{6} + \cdots.$$

It should also be noted that even if the limit exists, the ratio test gives no information if the limit is 1. That this is not just a shortcoming of the method of proof is established by the fact that $\sum_1^\infty 1/\alpha$ is divergent, $\sum_1^\infty 1/\alpha^2$ is convergent, and for each series the limit of the ratio of the $(n + 1)$th term to the nth term is 1.

We conclude our discussion of series of nonnegative terms with one final result. This is the so-called Cauchy root test. Note that the tests above all require the existence of a certain limit. If that limit fails to exist, the test is simply not applicable. We know that every convergent sequence is bounded, but not all bounded sequences converge. While bounded sequences exist that do not have a limit, every bounded sequence has a limit superior.

Theorem 5.42. *If $\sum\limits_{\alpha=k}^{\infty} a_\alpha$ is a series of positive terms and if*

$$\overline{\mathrm{Lim}}_{n \to \infty} \sqrt[n]{a_n} = r,$$

then $\sum\limits_{\alpha=k}^{\infty} a_\alpha$ converges if $r < 1$ and diverges if $r > 1$.

Proof. If

$$\overline{\mathrm{Lim}}_{n \to \infty} \sqrt[n]{a_n} = r,$$

then from Exercise 15, page 151, it follows that for each ϵ there exists an integer m such that

$$\sqrt[n]{a_n} < r + \epsilon, \quad n \geq m.$$

In particular, if $r < 1$, then $(1 - r)/2 > 0$ and hence there exists an integer m such that

$$\sqrt[n]{a_n} < r + \frac{1 - r}{2} = \frac{1 + r}{2}, \quad n \geq m.$$

From this we have that

$$a_n < \left(\frac{1 + r}{2} \right)^n, \quad n \geq m.$$

Since $(1 + r)/2 < 1$, it follows that

$$\sum_{\alpha = k}^{\infty} \left(\frac{1 + r}{2} \right)^{\alpha}$$

converges. Hence by the comparison test

$$\sum_{\alpha = k}^{\infty} a_{\alpha}$$

converges.

On the other hand, we also have that for each ϵ there are infinitely many values of 'n' for which

$$\sqrt[n]{a_n} > r - \epsilon.$$

Therefore if $r > 1$, then $r - 1 > 0$ and hence if $\epsilon = r - 1$, it follows that there are infinitely many values of 'n' for which

$$\sqrt[n]{a_n} > 1$$

and hence

$$a_n > 1.$$

Thus $\{a_n\}_k$ contains a subsequence that does not converge to 0; therefore $\{a_n\}_k$ does not converge to 0; hence the series diverges by the nth term test.

Q.E.D.

It should be noted that Theorem 5.42 provides no convergence information if $r = 1$.

EXERCISES

In Exercises 1–6 determine whether or not the given series are convergent.

1. $\displaystyle\sum_{\alpha = 1}^{\infty} \frac{\alpha - 1}{\alpha + 1}.$ 2. $\displaystyle\sum_{\alpha = 1}^{\infty} \frac{\alpha - 1}{(\alpha + 1)^2}.$ 3. $\displaystyle\sum_{\alpha = 1}^{\infty} \frac{\alpha - 1}{(\alpha + 1)^3}.$

4. $\displaystyle\sum_{\alpha = 1}^{\infty} \frac{\alpha!}{(\alpha + 1)!}.$ 5. $\displaystyle\sum_{\alpha = 1}^{\infty} \frac{1}{\sqrt{\alpha^3 + 1}}.$ 6. $\displaystyle\sum_{\alpha = 1}^{\infty} \frac{a^{\alpha}}{\alpha!}, \ a \geq 0.$

5.5 Absolute Convergence

The tests for convergence that we have developed thus far are all tests for series with nonnegative terms. In this section we will consider a more general class of series. The main result that we will prove is that

$$\sum_{\alpha = k}^{\infty} a_{\alpha}$$

converges provided

$$\sum_{\alpha=k}^{\infty} |a_\alpha|$$

converges.

Definition 5.50. $\sum_{\alpha=k}^{\infty}$ converges *absolutely* iff $\sum_{\alpha=k}^{\infty} |a_\alpha|$ converges.

The reader is cautioned to read into Definition 5.50 no more than is there. By this definition the phrase '$\sum_k^\infty a_\alpha$ converges absolutely' is only a curious, though traditional, way to say that $\sum_k^\infty |a_\alpha|$ converges.

Theorem 5.51. *If* $\sum_{\alpha=k}^{\infty} a_\alpha$ *converges absolutely, then it converges.*

Proof. From the Cauchy criterion for series the convergence of $\sum_k^\infty |a_\alpha|$ implies the existence of a convergence test ϕ such that

$$\text{if } \phi(\epsilon) < m \le n, \text{ then } \left| \sum_{\alpha=m}^{n} |a_\alpha| \right| < \epsilon.$$

But since

$$\left| \sum_{\alpha=m}^{n} a_\alpha \right| \le \sum_{\alpha=m}^{n} |a_\alpha|,$$

it follows that

$$\text{if } \phi(\epsilon) < m \le n, \text{ then } \left| \sum_{\alpha=m}^{n} a_\alpha \right| \le \sum_{\alpha=m}^{n} |a_\alpha| < \epsilon;$$

hence by the Cauchy criterion $\sum_k^\infty a_\alpha$ also converges.

Q.E.D.

That the converse of Theorem 5.51 is false is established by the following.

Example. The series

$$\sum_{\alpha=1}^{\infty} \frac{(-1)^{\alpha+1}}{\alpha}$$

is not absolutely convergent since

$$\left| \frac{(-1)^{\alpha+1}}{\alpha} \right| = \frac{1}{\alpha}$$

and $\sum_1^\infty 1/\alpha$ diverges. On the other hand,

$$\sum_{\alpha=1}^{\infty} \frac{(-1)^{\alpha+1}}{\alpha}$$

is a convergent series as we see by the following argument, in which we examine two subsequences of the sequence of partial sums $\{s_n\}_1$ individually. First we observe that

$$s_{2m} = (1 - \tfrac{1}{2}) + (\tfrac{1}{3} - \tfrac{1}{4}) + \cdots + \left(\frac{1}{2m - 1} - \frac{1}{2m}\right)$$

Associated this way, we see that s_{2m} is a sum of positive numbers and $\{s_{2m}\}_1$ is a monotone increasing sequence. On the other hand,

$$s_{2m} = 1 - (\tfrac{1}{2} - \tfrac{1}{3}) - (\tfrac{1}{4} - \tfrac{1}{5}) - \cdots - \left(\frac{1}{2m - 2} - \frac{1}{2m - 1}\right) - \frac{1}{2m}.$$

From this we see that

$$s_{2m} < 1 \text{ for } m \geq 1.$$

Thus $\{s_{2m}\}_1$ is a bounded monotone increasing sequence and hence converges, say, to l.

Next we have that

$$s_{2m-1} = 1 - (\tfrac{1}{2} - \tfrac{1}{3}) - (\tfrac{1}{4} - \tfrac{1}{5}) - \cdots - \left(\frac{1}{2m - 2} - \frac{1}{2m - 1}\right).$$

Thus $\{s_{2m-1}\}_1$ is a decreasing sequence. But

$$s_{2m-1} = (1 - \tfrac{1}{2}) + (\tfrac{1}{3} - \tfrac{1}{4}) + \cdots + \left(\frac{1}{2m - 3} - \frac{1}{2m - 2}\right) + \frac{1}{2m - 1};$$

that is,

$$s_{2m-1} > 0 \text{ for } m \geq 1.$$

We then have that $\{s_{2m-1}\}_1$ is a bounded monotone sequence and hence converges, say, to l'. But

$$s_{2m} - s_{2m-1} = \frac{1}{2m}.$$

Therefore since $\{s_{2m}\}_1$ converges to l, since $\{s_{2m-1}\}_1$ converges to l', and since $\{1/2m\}_1$ converges to 0,

$$l - l' = 0.$$

With the knowledge that $l = l'$, it is then a simple matter to prove that $\{s_n\}_1$ converges to l. Indeed from the convergence properties of $\{s_{2m}\}_1$ and $\{s_{2m-1}\}_1$ we know that there exist convergence tests ϕ_1 and ϕ_2 such that

$$|s_{2m} - l| < \epsilon \text{ if } m > \phi_1(\epsilon),$$
$$|s_{2m-1} - l| < \epsilon \text{ if } m > \phi_2(\epsilon).$$

Consequently if ϕ is defined by

$$\phi(\epsilon) = 2\phi_1(\epsilon) + 2\phi_2(\epsilon)$$

and if $n > \phi(\epsilon)$, then there exists an integer m such that $n = 2m$ or $n = 2m - 1$. In either case we have that $m > \phi_1(\epsilon)$ and $m > \phi_2(\epsilon)$; consequently

$$|s_n - l| < \epsilon.$$

Thus $\{s_n\}_1$ converges to l, that is,

$$\sum_{\alpha=1}^{\infty} \frac{(-1)^{\alpha+1}}{\alpha} = l.$$

This example has an immediate generalization whose proof so closely parallels the argument above that we leave it as an exercise for the reader.

Theorem 5.52 (Leibniz: Alternating Series Test). *If $\{a_n\}_k$ is a monotone decreasing sequence of positive terms that converges to 0, then $\sum_k^{\infty} (-1)^{\alpha} a_{\alpha}$ converges.*

The knowledge that there are series that converge but do not converge absolutely prompts

Definition 5.53. $\sum_k^{\infty} a_{\alpha}$ converges *conditionally* iff $\sum_k^{\infty} a_{\alpha}$ converges but $\sum_k^{\infty} |a_{\alpha}|$ diverges.

EXERCISES

Test the following series for convergence and absolute convergence.

1. $\sum_{\alpha=1}^{\infty} (-1)^{\alpha} \dfrac{\alpha - 1}{\alpha + 1}$ 2. $\sum_{\alpha=1}^{\infty} \dfrac{(-1)^{\alpha}(\alpha - 1)}{(\alpha + 1)^2}$ 3. $\sum_{\alpha=1}^{\infty} \dfrac{(-1)^{\alpha}(\alpha - 1)}{(\alpha + 1)^3}$

4. Prove: If $\sum_k^{\infty} a_{\alpha}$ converges and $\sum_k^{\infty} b_{\alpha}$ converges absolutely, then $\sum_k^{\infty} a_{\alpha} b_{\alpha}$ converges absolutely.

5. Prove: If $\sum_0^{\infty} a_{\alpha}$ converges and if $|x| < 1$, then $\sum_0^{\infty} a_{\alpha} x^{\alpha}$ converges.

6. Prove: For each nonintegral real number x,

$$\frac{1}{1 + x} + \frac{1}{1 - x} + \frac{1}{2 + x} + \frac{1}{2 - x} + \cdots \text{ diverges and}$$

$$\frac{1}{x + 1} + \frac{1}{x - 1} + \frac{1}{x + 2} + \frac{1}{x - 2} + \cdots \text{ converges.}$$

5.6 The Arithmetic of Series

The concept of an infinite series is in some sense a generalization of the ordinary notion of addition. It then seems natural to ask if the elementary arithmetic properties of addition hold for series. For example, ordinary addition is both associative and commutative; indeed we have a generalized associative law which asserts that the results of adding any finite collection of numbers is independent of the method of associating terms. Is this also true when "adding" an infinite sequence of numbers?

To formulate the problem more precisely, note that if we think of the $\sum_1^\infty a_\alpha$ as an infinite sum

$$a_1 + a_2 + a_3 + \cdots,$$

then the definition of the partial sums requires that the terms be associated from the left, that is,

$$((a_1 + a_2) + a_3) + \cdots.$$

Let us agree that by an association of the terms we mean that the terms are first grouped in blocks, and the sum of blocks are then added by associating from the left, for example,

$$(a_1 + a_2) + (a_3 + a_4 + a_5) + \cdots.$$

More formally, if $\{m_n\}_1$ is a monotone strictly increasing sequence of positive integers, then $\{m_n\}_1$ can be used to block off terms of $\{a_n\}_1$ thus

$$b_1 = a_1 + a_2 + \cdots + a_{m_1},$$
$$b_2 = a_{m_1+1} + a_{m_1+2} + \cdots + a_{m_2},$$
$$\vdots$$
$$b_n = a_{m_{n-1}+1} + a_{m_{n-1}+2} + \cdots + a_{m_n}.$$

We then have an infinite collection of series $\sum_1^\infty b_\alpha$, one for each $\{m_n\}_1$. It also seems reasonable to consider these series as different associations of the same basic series, namely $\sum_1^\infty a_\alpha$. But the question remains, do they all converge and, if so, do they all converge to the same value? This question has a simple and interesting answer. If $\{t_n\}_1$ and $\{s_n\}_1$ are the sequences of partial sums of $\sum_1^\infty b_\alpha$ and $\sum_1^\infty a_\alpha$ respectively, then

$$t_n = \sum_{\alpha=1}^n b_\alpha = \sum_{\alpha=1}^{m_n} a_\alpha = s_{m_n}.$$

Therefore $\{t_n\}_1$ is a subsequence of $\{s_n\}_1$. Thus, an association of terms as defined above amounts to the selection of a subsequence of the sequence of partial sums. Conversely, the selection of a subsequence of the sequence of partial sums determines a particular association of terms. Since subsequences of convergent sequences do converge and in fact, to the same value, it follows that if $\sum_1^\infty a_\alpha$ converges, then each of the reassociated series $\sum_1^\infty b_\alpha$ also converges and converges to the same value.

On the other hand, a divergent sequence can have convergent subsequences. It follows that if $\sum_1^\infty a_\alpha$ diverges, then the reassociated series need not behave alike—some may diverge, some may converge, and they may converge to different values. For example, if $a_n = (-1)^n$ then $\sum_1^\infty a_\alpha$ is divergent. But $\{s_{2n}\}_1$ converges to 0, that is,

$$(-1 + 1) + (-1 + 1) + (-1 + 1) + \cdots = 0$$

and $\{s_{2n-1}\}_1$ converges to -1.

The question of the commutative property has an even more interesting answer. The basic question that we pose is this. If

$$b_1, b_2, \ldots$$

is a rearrangement of

$$a_1, a_2, \ldots$$

and if $\sum_1^\infty a_\alpha$ converges, does $\sum_1^\infty b_\alpha$ converge to the same value? The answer is "Not necessarily!"

Let us begin by defining "rearrangement."

Definition 5.60. $\{b_n\}_k$ is a *rearrangement* of $\{a_n\}_k$ iff $(\exists h)\, h\colon Z_k \xrightarrow[\text{onto}]{1\text{-}1} Z_k$ and

$$b_n = a_{h(n)} \text{ for } n \geq k.$$

Our first result is a condition under which the rearranged series does converge to the same value.

Theorem 5.61.   *If $\{a_n\}_k$ is a sequence of nonnegative terms and if $\{b_n\}_k$ is a rearrangement of $\{a_n\}_k$, then $\sum_k^\infty a_\alpha$ converges iff $\sum_k^\infty b_\alpha$ converges. Furthermore, if the series converge they converge to the same value.*

Proof.   Since $\{b_n\}_k$ is a rearrangement of $\{a_n\}_k$ there exists a sequence h which maps Z_k one-to-one onto Z_k and for which

$$b_n = a_{h(n)} \text{ for } n \geq k.$$

If $\{s_n\}_k$ and $\{t_n\}_k$ are the sequence of partial sums for $\{a_n\}_k$ and $\{b_n\}_k$ respectively, and if

$$f(n) = \max \{h(\alpha) \mid k \leq \alpha \leq n\} \text{ for } n \geq k,$$

then

$$t_n = \sum_{\alpha=k}^{n} b_\alpha \leq \sum_{\alpha=k}^{f(n)} a_\alpha = s_{f(n)}.$$

From this inequality we see that any upper bound for $\{s_n\}_k$ is an upper bound for $\{t_n\}_k$. Consequently, $\sum_k^\infty b_\alpha$ converges if $\sum_k^\infty a_\alpha$ converges. In fact from the same inequality we have that if they converge, then

$$\sum_{\alpha=k}^{\infty} b_\alpha \leq \sum_{\alpha=k}^{\infty} a_\alpha.$$

Similarly if

$$g(n) = \max \{h^{-1}(\alpha) \mid k \leq \alpha \leq n\} \text{ for } n \geq k$$

then

$$s_n = \sum_{\alpha=k}^{n} a_\alpha \leq \sum_{\alpha=k}^{g(n)} b_\alpha = t_{g(n)}$$

from which we conclude that $\sum_{k}^{\infty} a_\alpha$ converges if $\sum_{k}^{\infty} b_\alpha$ converges, and if they converge,

$$\sum_{\alpha=k}^{\infty} a_\alpha \leq \sum_{\alpha=k}^{\infty} b_\alpha.$$

Therefore if one series converges so does the other and

$$\sum_{\alpha=k}^{\infty} a_\alpha = \sum_{\alpha=k}^{\infty} b_\alpha.$$

Q.E.D.

Theorem 5.62. *If $\{c_n\}_k$ is a sequence whose subsequence of positive terms is $\{a_n\}_k$ and whose subsequence of negative terms is $\{-b_n\}_k$, then $\sum_{k}^{\infty} c_\alpha$ converges absolutely iff $\sum_{k}^{\infty} a_\alpha$ and $\sum_{k}^{\infty} b_\alpha$ converge. Furthermore, if $\sum_{k}^{\infty} a_\alpha$ and $\sum_{k}^{\infty} b_\alpha$ do converge, then*

$$\sum_{\alpha=k}^{\infty} c_\alpha = \sum_{\alpha=k}^{\infty} a_\alpha - \sum_{\alpha=k}^{\infty} b_\alpha.$$

Proof. If $\sum_{k}^{\infty} c_\alpha$ converges absolutely, then since $\{a_n\}_k$ and $\{-b_n\}_k$ are subsequences of $\{c_n\}_k$ there exist sequences f and g such that

$$a_n = c_{f(n)} \quad b_n = -c_{g(n)} \text{ for } n \geq k.$$

Consequently

$$\sum_{\alpha=k}^{n} a_\alpha \leq \sum_{\alpha=k}^{f(n)} |c_\alpha| \text{ and } \sum_{\alpha=k}^{n} b_\alpha \leq \sum_{\alpha=k}^{g(n)} |c_\alpha|.$$

Since $\sum_{k}^{\infty} c_\alpha$ converges absolutely, it follows that $\sum_{k}^{\infty} a_\alpha$ and $\sum_{k}^{\infty} b_\alpha$ each converge. (Why?)

Conversely, if $\sum_{k}^{\infty} a_\alpha$ and $\sum_{k}^{\infty} b_\alpha$ converge and if f and g are so defined that $f(n)$ and $g(n)$ are the number of positive terms and the number of negative terms respectively of $\{c_m\}_k^n$ (see Exercise 8, page 150), then

$$\underset{n \to \infty}{\text{Lim}} \sum_{\alpha=k}^{f(n)} a_\alpha = \sum_{\alpha=k}^{\infty} a_\alpha \text{ and } \underset{n \to \infty}{\text{Lim}} \sum_{\alpha=k}^{g(n)} b_\alpha = \sum_{\alpha=k}^{\infty} b_\alpha.$$

Therefore since

$$\sum_{\alpha=k}^{n} |c_\alpha| = \sum_{\alpha=k}^{f(n)} a_\alpha + \sum_{\alpha=k}^{g(n)} b_\alpha,$$

it follows that $\sum_{k}^{\infty} |c_{\alpha}|$ not only converges but

$$\sum_{\alpha=k}^{\infty} |c_{\alpha}| = \sum_{\alpha=k}^{\infty} a_{\alpha} + \sum_{\alpha=k}^{\infty} b_{\alpha}.$$

Moreover, since

$$\sum_{\alpha=k}^{n} c_{\alpha} = \sum_{\alpha=k}^{f(n)} a_{\alpha} - \sum_{\alpha=k}^{g(n)} b_{\alpha},$$

we have that

$$\sum_{\alpha=k}^{\infty} c_{\alpha} = \sum_{\alpha=k}^{\infty} a_{\alpha} - \sum_{\alpha=k}^{\infty} b_{\alpha}.$$

Q.E.D.

Theorem 5.63. *If $\sum_{k}^{\infty} c_{\alpha}$ converges absolutely and if $\{c'_n\}_k$ is a rearrangement of $\{c_n\}_k$, then $\sum_{k}^{\infty} c'_n$ converges absolutely, hence converges and*

$$\sum_{\alpha=k}^{\infty} c'_{\alpha} = \sum_{\alpha=k}^{\infty} c_{\alpha}.$$

Proof. If $\{c_n\}_k$ contains an infinite subsequence of positive terms, $\{a_n\}_k$, and an infinite subsequence of negative terms, $\{-b_n\}_k$, and if $\{a'_n\}_k$ and $\{-b'_n\}_k$ are respectively the subsequence of positive terms and the subsequence of negative terms of $\{c'_n\}_k$, then $\{a'_n\}_k$ is a rearrangement of $\{a_n\}_k$ and $\{-b'_n\}_k$ is a rearrangement of $\{b_n\}_k$. (Why?) Therefore, since $\sum_{k}^{\infty} c_{\alpha}$ converges absolutely, we have from Theorem 5.62 that $\sum_{k}^{\infty} a_{\alpha}$ and $\sum_{k}^{\infty} b_{\alpha}$ converge, and

$$\sum_{\alpha=k}^{\infty} c_{\alpha} = \sum_{\alpha=k}^{\infty} a_{\alpha} - \sum_{\alpha=k}^{\infty} b_{\alpha}.$$

From Theorem 5.61 we have that $\sum_{k}^{\infty} a'_{\alpha}$ and $\sum_{k}^{\infty} b'_{\alpha}$ also converge;

$$\sum_{\alpha=k}^{\infty} a_{\alpha} = \sum_{\alpha=k}^{\infty} a'_{\alpha} \text{ and } \sum_{\alpha=k}^{\infty} b_{\alpha} = \sum_{\alpha=k}^{\infty} b'_{\alpha}.$$

Thus $\sum_{k}^{\infty} c'_{\alpha}$ converges and

$$\sum_{\alpha=k}^{\infty} c'_{\alpha} = \sum_{\alpha=k}^{\infty} a'_{\alpha} - \sum_{\alpha=k}^{\infty} b'_{\alpha} = \sum_{\alpha=k}^{\infty} a_{\alpha} - \sum_{\alpha=k}^{\infty} b_{\alpha} = \sum_{\alpha=k}^{\infty} c_{\alpha}.$$

The proof for the case in which $\{c_n\}_k$ contains only a finite subsequence of positive terms or only a finite subsequence of negative terms we leave as an exercise for the reader.

With the aid of Theorem 5.63 we can now prove the following interesting result concerning conditionally convergent series.

Theorem 5.64. *If $\sum_k^\infty c_\alpha$ is conditionally convergent, then its subsequence of positive terms, $\{a_n\}_k$, is infinite, its subsequence of negative terms, $\{-b_n\}_k$ is infinite, and both $\sum_k^\infty a_\alpha$ and $\sum_k^\infty b_\alpha$ diverge.*

Proof. If either the subsequence of positive terms or the subsequence of negative terms of $\{c_n\}_k$ is finite, then $\sum_k^\infty c_\alpha$ converges if and only if $\sum_k^\infty |c_\alpha|$ converges. Therefore if $\sum_k^\infty c_\alpha$ converges conditionally, then the subsequence of positive terms and the subsequence of negative terms of $\{c_n\}_k$ are each infinite. If f and g are sequences defined on Z_k in such a way that $f(n)$ is "the number of positive terms" of $\{c_m\}_k^n$ and $g(n)$ is "the number of negative terms" of $\{c_m\}_k^n$ (see Exercise 8, page 150) then both f and g diverge to infinity and

$$\sum_{\alpha=k}^{n} c_\alpha = \sum_{\alpha=k}^{f(n)} a_\alpha - \sum_{\alpha=k}^{g(n)} b_\alpha.$$

If $\sum_k^\infty a_\alpha$ converges, then since

$$\operatorname*{Lim}_{n\to\infty} \sum_{\alpha=k}^{f(n)} a_\alpha = \sum_{\alpha=k}^{\infty} a_\alpha$$

and since

$$\sum_{\alpha=k}^{g(n)} b_\alpha = \sum_{\alpha=k}^{f(n)} a_\alpha - \sum_{\alpha=k}^{n} c_\alpha,$$

it follows that

$$\operatorname*{Lim}_{n\to\infty} \sum_{\alpha=k}^{g(n)} b_\alpha = \sum_{\alpha=k}^{\infty} a_\alpha - \sum_{\alpha=k}^{\infty} c_\alpha.$$

Thus $\sum_k^\infty b_\alpha$ converges. But from Theorem 5.63 the convergence of $\sum_k^\infty a_\alpha$ and $\sum_k^\infty b_\alpha$ implies the absolute convergence of $\sum_k^\infty c_\alpha$. It then follows that $\sum_k^\infty a_\alpha$ diverges. In a similar manner we can prove that $\sum_k^\infty b_\alpha$ diverges.

Q.E.D.

EXERCISES

1. Test for convergence: $\sum_1^\infty (-1)^\alpha a_\alpha$ where $a_{2n} = 1/n^2$ and $a_{2n-1} = 1/n$.

2. Test for convergence: $\sum_1^\infty (-1)^\alpha a_\alpha$ where $a_{2n} = 1/n^2$ and $a_{2n-1} = 1/n^3$.

3. Prove: Given any number l there is a rearrangement, $\{a_n\}_1$, of $\{(-1)^n/n\}_1$ such that

$$\sum_{\alpha=1}^{\infty} a_\alpha = l.$$

(Hint: Define $a_1 = -1$, $a_{n+1} = \max\{\{1/2\alpha|\ \alpha \in Z_1\} - \{a_1 \cdots a_n\}\}$ if $\sum_1^n a_\alpha \le l$. $a_{n+1} = \min\{\{-1/(2\alpha - 1)|\ \alpha \in Z_1\} - \{a_1 \cdots a_n\}\}$ if $l < \sum_1^n a_\alpha$.)

4. Prove: For each conditionally convergent sequence $\{a_n\}_k$ and for each number l there exists a rearrangement of $\{a_n\}_k$ which converges to l.

5.7 Countability

Sequences provide an interesting and useful means of extending the notion of counting. To count a given collection of objects we point to each object in turn and name a positive integer starting with one and proceeding in the usual way. Such a pairing of integers and objects defines a function that is one-to-one and onto. For the purpose of determining the number of apples in a basket, such "counting functions" are of little interest; but for the purpose of studying counting itself, they are quite useful. Indeed the one-to-one functions provide a method for comparing infinite sets and extending the notion of number to enable us to speak of the "number of elements" in an infinite set. For the purpose of this section we will be content to deal with those infinite sets which are *denumerable* in the sense of

Definition 5.70. *A is denumerable iff* $(\exists f)f:Z_1 \xrightarrow[\text{onto}]{1-1} A$. *A is countable iff A is finite or denumerable.*

One interesting fact about infinite sets is that an infinite set can be mapped one-to-one onto a proper subset of itself. For example, the set of positive even integers is a proper subset of the set of positive integer Z_1. If

$$f(n) = 2n, \quad n \geq 1,$$

then f maps Z_1 one-to-one onto the set of positive even integers. From Definition 5.70 it follows that the set of positive even integers is denumerable.

It is easily proved that the set of all integers is denumerable. Indeed if f is defined by

$$f(0) = 1, \quad f(n) = 2n, \quad n > 0, \quad \text{and} \quad f(n) = 1 - 2n, \quad n < 0,$$

then f maps Z one-to-one onto Z_1. (Why?) Since f is one-to-one it has an inverse, and f^{-1} maps Z_1 one-to-one onto Z.

Note that the mapping f counts the integers in the order in which they are represented graphically on the spiral shown in Figure 5.9. By a similar argument it is easy to prove that any set of real numbers is countable if its subset of positive numbers is countable and there exists a one-to-one correspondence between its subset of positive numbers and its subset of negative numbers. We leave the proof as an exercise for the reader.

That the integers are denumerable is not particularly surprising. A result of greater interest is that the rational numbers are also denumerable. It is sufficient to prove that the positive rationals are denumerable. This we

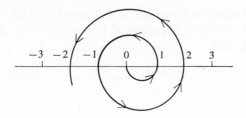

FIGURE 5.9

prove in two stages. We first prove that $Z_1 \times Z_1$ is denumerable. We propose to count the ordered pairs of positive integers beginning with $(1, 1)$ and counting in the order indicated by the arrows in the following diagram:

$$(1, 1), (2, 1), (3, 1), (4, 1), \ldots$$
$$(1, 2), (2, 2), (3, 2), (4, 2), \ldots$$
$$(1, 3), (2, 3), (3, 3), (4, 3), \ldots$$

How should we define our counting function f in order to accomplish this? Clearly we wish to have $f(1, 1) = 1$. Indeed for the pairs $(m, 1)$ that are represented at the "end" of each diagonal we see that we wish

$$f(m, 1) = 1 + 2 + 3 + \cdots + m = \frac{m(m + 1)}{2}.$$

Since each pair (m, n) is represented as the mth element on the diagonal that contains it, it follows that if (m, n) is represented on the rth diagonal, then we wish to have

$$f(m, n) = \frac{(r - 1)r}{2} + m.$$

Note also that for each ordered pair represented on a particular diagonal the sums of the first and second entries are the same. Thus (m, n) is represented on the first diagonal if and only if $m + n = 2$, the second diagonal if and only $m + n = 3$, etc. Since (m, n) is the nth ordered pair represented on the $m + n - 1$ diagonal we chose to define f by

$$f(m, n) = \frac{(m + n - 2)(m + n - 1)}{2} + m.$$

Since $(m + n - 2)(m + n - 1)$ is even it follows that f maps $Z_1 \times Z_1$ into Z_1. That the mapping is onto follows from the fact that if $s \in Z_1$ then $s = 1$ or $s > 1$. If $s = 1$ then $f(1, 1) = s$. If $s > 1$, then there exists a largest positive integer r such that

$$\frac{(r - 1)r}{2} < s.$$

Since r is the largest such integer, it follows that if $m = s - (r - 1)r/2$ then $0 < m \le r$. (Why?) Therefore if $n = r + 1 - m$, then $n > 0$ and $(m, n) \in Z_1 \times Z_1$. But

$$f(m, n) = \frac{(m + n - 2)(m + n - 1)}{2} + m = \frac{(r - 1)r}{2} + m = s.$$

Thus f is onto.

To prove that f is one-to-one we note that since $n \ge 1$,

$$m + n - 1 \ge m,$$

$$\frac{(m + n - 1)(m + n - m - n + 2)}{2} \ge m,$$

$$\frac{(m + n - 1)(m + n)}{2} - \frac{(m + n - 2)(m + n - 1)}{2} \ge m,$$

$$\frac{(m + n - 1)(m + n)}{2} \ge \frac{(m + n - 2)(m + n - 1)}{2} + m.$$

But

$$\frac{(m + n - 2)(m + n - 1)}{2} + m > \frac{(m + n - 2)(m + n - 1)}{2}.$$

Therefore if r is the largest positive integer such that

$$\frac{(r - 2)(r - 1)}{2} < f(m, n),$$

then $r = m + n$. From this we see if $f(m, n) = f(m_1, n_1)$, then r is also the largest positive integer such that

$$\frac{(r - 2)(r - 1)}{2} < f(m_1, n_1)$$

and hence $r = m_1 + n_1$. It then follows that $m + n = m_1 + n_1$. Therefore

$$\frac{(m + n - 2)(m + n - 1)}{2} = \frac{(m_1 + n_1 - 2)(m_1 + n_1 - 1)}{2}.$$

But, since $f(m, n) = f(m_1, n_1)$, we have that

$$\frac{(m + n - 2)(m + n - 1)}{2} + m = \frac{(m_1 + n_1 - 2)(m_1 + n_1 - 1)}{2} + m_1.$$

From this it follows that $m = m_1$, $n = n_1$, and hence f is one-to-one. Since $f : Z_1 \times Z_1 \xrightarrow[\text{onto}]{1-1} Z_1$, it follows that $f^{-1} : Z_1 \xrightarrow[\text{onto}]{1-1} Z_1 \times Z_1$.

We next define a mapping g by $g(m, n) = m/n$. It then follows that $g : Z_1 \times Z_1 \xrightarrow[\text{onto}]{} \{x \in Q \mid x > 0\}$ (why?) and consequently $g \circ f^{-1} : Z_1 \xrightarrow[\text{onto}]{} \{x \in Q \mid x > 0\}$. However this mapping is not one-to-one. (Why?) We wish to prove that a one-to-one mapping can be defined. Such a mapping h we define in the following way:

$$h(1) = g \circ f^{-1}(1).$$

$h(k + 1) = g \circ f^{-1}(n)$ where n is the smallest positive integer such that $g \circ f^{-1}(n) \notin \{h(1), h(2), \ldots, h(k)\}$. Since the set of rational numbers is infinite, it follows that Dom $h = Z_1$. Furthermore for each positive rational number x there exists a smallest positive integer n such that $g \circ f^{-1}(n) = x$, and hence for some positive integer k that is less than or equal to n we have that $h(k) = x$. (Why?) Thus h is onto.

To prove that h is one-to-one we note that if k and l are in Z_1 with $k < l$, then $h(k) \in \{h(1), h(2), \ldots, h(l-1)\}$. But $h(l) \notin \{h(1), h(2), \ldots, h(l-1)\}$, hence $h(k) \neq h(l)$. Thus $h(k) = h(l)$ implies $k = l$. Consequently

$$h : Z_1 \xrightarrow[\text{onto}]{1-1} \{x \in Q \mid x > 0\}$$

and we have proved

Theorem 5.71.   *The set of rational numbers is denumerable.*

If we think about the rational numbers graphically, recalling the fact that they are dense in the reals, then their denumerability may seem surprising. Indeed we might wonder whether or not all sets are countable.

That all sets are not countable we will prove by showing that in particular $(0, 1)$ is not countable. We first observe that $(0, 1)$ is not finite because it contains an infinite subset $\{1/n \mid n \in Z_1\}$. That $(0, 1)$ is not denumerable we will prove by a very clever argument due to Cantor. The proof is by contradiction.

If there exists a function f such that

$$f : Z_1 \xrightarrow[\text{onto}]{1-1} (0, 1),$$

then $f(n)$ has a unique decimal representation, for each positive integer n, if we reject infinite sequences of 9's. (See Theorem 5.39 and the discussion that follows.) If

$$f(n) = .a_{n1}a_{n2}\cdots,$$

where $0 \leq a_{nm} \leq 9$, we then have a decimal representation for each real number in $(0, 1)$.

$$f(1) = .a_{11}a_{12}a_{13}\cdots$$
$$f(2) = .a_{21}a_{22}a_{23}\cdots$$
$$f(3) = .a_{31}a_{32}a_{33}\cdots$$
$$\cdots$$

We now consider the real number, b, whose decimal representation is

$$.c_1c_2c_3\cdots$$

where $c_n = 5$ if $a_{nn} \neq 5$ and $c_n = 6$ if $a_{nn} = 5$. Clearly this is the decimal representation of a number in $(0, 1)$. But this number is not $f(1)$ because $c_1 \neq a_{11}$. It is not $f(2)$ because $c_2 \neq a_{22}$. Indeed for each positive integer n we have that $f(n) \neq .c_1 c_2 \cdots$ because $c_n \neq a_{nn}$. We have found a number in $(0, 1)$ which is not the image of any element of Z_1 under the mapping f. This is a contradiction.

We have proved

Theorem 5.72. $(0, 1)$ *is not countable.*

Note that in the preceding argument it is only a matter of convenience that dictates that $c_n = 5$ or $c_n = 6$. There is nothing special about 5's and 6's. The basic property that we wish is that $c_n \neq a_{nn}$ and $c_n \neq 9$ for all sufficiently large n. This can be done with only a ternary notation. Note that if

$$A = \{x \in [0, 1] \mid x \text{ has a ternary representation involving no 1's}\},$$

then each element in A has one and only one ternary representation involving no 1's (see Exercise 19, page 161). We are then prepared to prove that A is not countable. A is clearly not finite. (Why?) That A is not denumerable we prove by contradiction, again using Cantor's method.

If

$$f : Z_1 \xrightarrow[\text{onto}]{1-1} A,$$

then for each positive integer n, $f(n)$ has a unique ternary representation which involves no 1's

$$.a_{n1} a_{n2} \cdots$$

where $a_{nm} = 0$ or $a_{nm} = 2$. Then

$$.c_1 c_2 \cdots$$

where $c_n = 0$ if $a_{nn} = 2$ and $c_n = 2$ if $a_{nn} = 0$, is the ternary representation of a number in A that is not $f(n)$ for any n. Thus A is nondenumerable.

The set A is commonly referred to as the Cantor set. We have, therefore, proved

Theorem 5.73. *The Cantor set is not countable.*

Because of our method of introducing the Cantor set it is not surprising that it is not countable. Note, however, the following curious property. Each x in A has a ternary representation

$$.c_1 c_2 \cdots$$

where $c_n = 0$ or $c_n = 2$. In particular, $c_1 \neq 1$; therefore no elements of A lie in $(\frac{1}{3}, \frac{2}{3})$; that is,

$$A \subseteq [0, \tfrac{1}{3}] \cup [\tfrac{2}{3}, 1].$$

Thus A is a subset of the union of two intervals whose total length is $\frac{2}{3}$. If $c_1 = 0$, then $x \in [0, \frac{1}{3}]$ and if $c_1 = 2$, then $x \in [\frac{2}{3}, 1]$. But in either case, since $c_2 \neq 1$, x cannot lie in the middle third of either interval. Therefore

$$A \subseteq [0, \tfrac{1}{9}] \cup [\tfrac{2}{9}, \tfrac{1}{3}] \cup [\tfrac{2}{3}, \tfrac{7}{9}] \cup [\tfrac{8}{9}, 1];$$

that is, A is a subset of the union of four intervals whose total length is $\frac{4}{9}$. Again, since $c_3 \neq 1$, x cannot lie in the middle third of each of these four intervals. Inductively we see that since $c_\alpha \neq 1$, $\alpha = 1, \ldots, n$, the set A is a subset of the union of 2^n intervals whose total length is $(\frac{2}{3})^n$. Since for each ϵ there exists an integer n for which $(\frac{2}{3})^n < \epsilon$, we have the following interesting result. The set A is not denumerable, yet for each ϵ there exists a finite collection of closed intervals whose total length is less than ϵ and whose union contains A as a subset. If we were to attempt to extend the notion of length to sets other than intervals, it would therefore seem reasonable to assign to the Cantor set the length 0. We would then have an example of a set that is nondenumerable and of length 0. On the other hand, consider the set B of rational numbers that lie in $(0, 1)$. This set is denumerable and it is easily proved that the total length of any finite collection of intervals whose union contains B must be at least 1.

The Cantor 'diagonal' argument used to prove the last two theorems is of sufficient interest that we offer one more result using it.

Theorem 5.74. *The set A, of all sequences that map Z_1 into $\{0, 1\}$ is not countable.*

Proof. Clearly A is not finite. (Why?) If $h : Z_1 \xrightarrow[\text{onto}]{1-1} A$, then we define a sequence g in the following way: If $h(n) = f_n$, then

$$g(n) = 0 \text{ if } f_n(n) = 1 \text{ and } g(n) = 1 \text{ if } f_n(n) = 0.$$

Then $g \in A$, but for each n in Z_1, $h(n) \neq g$ because $f_n(n) \neq g(n)$. Thus A is not countable.

                                                                    Q.E.D.

The set of all sequences that map Z_1 into $\{0, 1\}$ is a subset of the set of all functions that map real numbers into real numbers. That the set of all functions from real numbers to real numbers is nondenumerable then follows from Theorem 5.74 and

Theorem 5.75. *Every subset of a countable set is countable.*

Proof. Since subsets of finite sets are finite, it is sufficient to prove that if A is denumerable and B is an infinite subset of A, then B is denumerable. Indeed if A is denumerable, then there exists a function f such that

$$f : Z_1 \xrightarrow[\text{onto}]{1-1} A.$$

We then define g by

$g(1) = f(n)$ where n is the smallest integer such that $f(n) \in B$.

$g(k + 1) = f(n)$ where n is the smallest integer such that

$$f(n) \in B - \{g(1) \cdots g(k)\}.$$

The verification that

$$g : Z_1 \xrightarrow[\text{onto}]{1-1} B$$

we leave as an exercise for the reader.

Q.E.D.

That the set of all real numbers is not countable follows from Theorem 5.75 and the fact that $(0, 1)$ is not countable.

⋆5.8 The Axiom of Choice

In the foregoing material we have frequently been confronted with the problem of proving that there exists a function that has some specified property. One approach, which we have used repeatedly, is to define (i.e., name) a specific function and then prove that the function defined has the given property. For example, to prove that

$$\lim_{n \to \infty} \frac{1}{n} = 0,$$

it is necessary to prove that there exists a convergence test ϕ with the property that

$$\text{if } n > \phi(\epsilon) \text{ then } \left| \frac{1}{n} \right| < \epsilon.$$

Our method of proof was to define a convergence test ϕ by

$$\phi(\epsilon) = \frac{1}{\epsilon}$$

and then prove that this convergence test had the desired property. That is, we proved the existence of a function having a prescribed property by exhibiting a function that has the property.

There are, however, other contexts in which we infer the existence of a function without exhibiting one. For example, if we are given two convergent sequences it is not necessary to exhibit a convergence test for their sum in order to know that such a convergence test exists; its existence is assured by Theorem 5.18.

Consider now the following situation (Figure 5.10). Given any set A and given, for each element x in A, one and only one nonempty set S_x does there exist a function f with domain A with the property that

$$\forall x \in A, \qquad f(x) \in S_x?$$

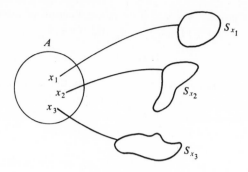

FIGURE 5.10

Intuitively we are quite confident that such a function does exist. This seems to be inherent in what we mean by a nonempty set. Since for each x in A we have that S_x is nonempty, there exists an element y in S_x. If we pair x and y taking care not to pair more than one element with each x in A, then is not this collection of all ordered pairs a function with the prescribed property? Clearly we have not exhibited a function, for unless each S_x contains exactly one element, there is more than one choice of a y in S_x that can be paired with x, and we have not specified which one to use. To define a function we must give a procedure that determines exactly one y in S_x for each x in A. For example, if each S_x is a closed and bounded set of real numbers, we might specify that y is to be the maximum of S_x; if each S_x is a finite interval, we might specify that y is to be the midpoint of S_x. But every procedure for determining y that we can think of requires some property for S_x that is not common to all sets.

The fact that we cannot give a procedure which would enable us to exhibit a function does not mean that such a function does not exist. Surely the existence of such a function can be inferred from the axioms of set theory. Since the nineteenth century many able mathematicians have labored unsuccessfully to do this. The fact that they failed to find an existence proof does not in itself mean that no proof exists. However, in 1963 Professor Paul Cohen of Stanford University proved that indeed the existence of such a function cannot be deduced.

We have, therefore, reached an interesting and indeed exciting juncture when intuition and logic seem not to agree. If we wish our intuitive belief to be reinforced by logic, we must postulate the existence of a function with the properties previously described. Since this function is to have a value in S_x for each x in A, it enables us to choose an element from each of the sets in the collection

$$\{S_x \mid x \in A\}.$$

It is customary to refer to such a function as a choice function and to the axiom that affirms its existence as

The Axiom of Choice. $\forall A \ \forall \mathcal{S}$ if $\mathcal{S}$ is a collection of nonempty sets and if $(\exists h) \ h: A \to \mathcal{S}$, then $(\exists f)$ Dom $f = A$, and $\forall x \in A$

$$f(x) \in h(x).$$

For the interested reader we point out that there are many equivalent formulations of the axiom of choice. The formulation we have chosen is, in fact, not the most convenient one for most mathematical purposes. It is, however, intuitive and adequate for the proof of

Theorem 5.80. *If a is an element of S or an accumulation point of S, then there exists a sequence of elements of S that converges to a.*

Proof. If $a \in S$ and $f(n) = a$, $n \geq 1$, then f is a sequence of elements of S that converges to a.

If a is an accumulation point of S, then for each positive n

$$N\left(a, \frac{1}{n}\right) \cap S \neq \varnothing.$$

Therefore if $S_n = N(a, 1/n) \cap S$, then $\{S_n \mid n \in Z_1\}$ is a collection of nonempty sets, and by the axiom of choice there exists a function f whose domain is Z_1 which has the property that

$$f(n) \in S_n \text{ for } n \geq 1;$$

hence

$$f(n) \in S \text{ and } f(n) \in N\left(a, \frac{1}{n}\right).$$

Therefore f is a sequence of elements of S that converges to a. (Why?)

$$\text{Q.E.D.}$$

Theorem 5.81. *If a is an accumulation point of S, then there exists a sequence of elements of S that converges to a which has the property that $\forall n \in$ Dom f, $f(n) \neq a$.*

The proof is left to the reader. As another application of the axiom of choice we prove

Theorem 5.82. *If S is closed and bounded and if $\mathcal{C}$ is an open covering of S, then there exists a number δ with the property that $\forall x \in S$, $\exists A \in \mathcal{C}$, $N(x, \delta) \subseteq A$.*

Proof. (By contradiction.) If the conclusion were false, then for each δ there would exist an x in S with the property that

$$\forall A \in \mathcal{C}, \qquad N(x, \delta) \nsubseteq A.$$

In particular, for each positive n, with $\delta = 1/n$, there would exist an x in S with the property that

$$\forall A \in \mathscr{C}, \qquad N\left(x, \frac{1}{n}\right) \nsubseteq A.$$

Therefore if

$$S_n = \left\{x \in S \mid \forall A \in \mathscr{C}, N\left(x, \frac{1}{n}\right) \nsubseteq A\right\},$$

then S_n is not empty. By the axiom of choice there exists a sequence $\{x_n\}_1$ such that

$$x_n \in S_n \text{ for } n \geq 1.$$

Since for each positive n we have that $S_n \subseteq S$, and since S is bounded, it follows that $\{x_n\}_1$ is a bounded sequence, and hence it contains a convergent subsequence $\{x_{m_n}\}_1$. If

$$\operatorname*{Lim}_{n \to \infty} x_{m_n} = a,$$

then since S is closed it follows that $a \in S$. Therefore there exists an element A in $\mathscr{C}$ such that $a \in A$. Since A is open, there is a number ϵ such that

$$N(a, \epsilon) \subseteq A.$$

Furthermore, since $\{x_{m_n}\}_1$ converges to a, there exists an integer n for which

$$x_{m_n} \in N\left(a, \frac{\epsilon}{2}\right) \text{ and } \frac{1}{m_n} < \frac{\epsilon}{2}.$$

It is then easily proved that

$$N\left(x_{m_n}, \frac{1}{m_n}\right) \subseteq N(a, \epsilon) \subseteq A.$$

But this contradicts the definition of S_{m_n}.

Q.E.D.

*5.9 Recursive Definitions

In the past material we have made frequent use of so-called *inductive* or *recursive* definitions—as, for example, the definition of powers of real numbers:

$$x^0 = 1,$$
$$x^{n+1} = x^n \cdot x, \quad n \geq 0.$$

This type of definition is quite different from others that we have used. For example, a definition that appeared early in Chapter 4 is the following:

$$\frac{x}{y} = x \cdot y^{-1}.$$

As a particular instance of this definition we have that

$$\tfrac{2}{3} = 2 \cdot 3^{-1}.$$

We interpret this equation as defining '$\tfrac{2}{3}$' in terms of the primitive symbols and previously defined symbols that occur on the right side of the equality. If, however, we wish to know the meaning of say '2^{100}' we have from the definition of powers that

$$2^{100} = 2^{99} \cdot 2.$$

However, '2^{99}' does not derive its meaning from any previously given definition but rather from the same formula that defines 2^{100}.

This apparent circularity prompts us to pause and ask what our definition of powers defines and how it defines. It is, of course, our intention that the definition give meaning to 'x^n' for every x and every nonnegative n. Thus for each x the definition should, in fact, define an infinite sequence $\{x^n\}_0$ with the property that its 0th term is 1 and its $(n + 1)$th term is obtained by multiplying its nth term by x. But are these conditions sufficient to define a sequence? Does there really exist a sequence f with the property that

$$f(0) = 1,$$

$$f(n + 1) = f(n) \cdot x \text{ for } n \geq 0,$$

and if so, why cannot two different sequences exist having this property?

That at most one such sequence can exist is easily proved by induction, for if f and g are sequences each having domain Z_0 and if $f(0) = 1$, $g(0) = 1$, $f(n + 1) = f(n) \cdot x$ for $n \geq 1$, and $g(n + 1) = g(n) \cdot x$ for $n \geq 1$, then

$$f(0) = g(0).$$

If as induction hypothesis we have that $f(n) = g(n)$, then

$$f(n + 1) = f(n) \cdot x = g(n) \cdot x = g(n + 1).$$

Since for each n in Z_0 we have $f(n) = g(n)$, we conclude that $f = g$.

To establish the existence of at least one sequence with the properties specified above let us return to our earlier example of 2^{100} for another observation. We have pointed out that the equation

$$2^{100} = 2^{99} \cdot 2$$

defines '2^{100}' only after '2^{99}' has been defined. But

$$2^{99} = 2^{98} \cdot 2$$

and hence '2^{99}' is defined if '2^{98}' is defined. Repeating this process we see that after a finite number of steps we will arrive at

$$2^1 = 2^0 \cdot 2$$

and 2^0 has been defined. Thus in order to define the 100th power of 2 it is necessary to define all smaller powers of 2.

In general to define 'x^n' we must, in fact, define a finite sequence $\{x^m\}_0^n$ whose 0th term is 1 and whose $m + 1$th term is obtained by multiplying the mth term by x. The nth term of this sequence is then x^n. While in practice we know that we cannot carry out the steps necessary to define $\{x^m\}_0^n$ for large values of 'n', nevertheless our intuition tells us that at least in theory it can be done. We then ask if there are logical grounds for believing what our intuition so strongly insists. It is sufficient to prove that for each non-negative n there exists one and only one finite sequence f_n with domain $\{0, 1, \ldots, n\}$ having the properties that

$$f_n(0) = 1,$$
$$f_n(m + 1) = f_n(m) \cdot x \text{ for } 0 \le m < n.$$

That at most one such sequence exists we leave as an exercise for the reader. That at least one such sequence exists we prove by induction.

If $f_0 = \{(0, 1)\}$, then Dom $f_0 = \{0\}$ and $f_0(0) = 1$. Therefore the base of the induction is established. If as our induction hypothesis we assume the existence of a finite sequence f_n with domain $\{0, 1, \ldots, n\}$ having the properties that

$$f_n(0) = 1,$$
$$f_n(m + 1) = f_n(m) \cdot x \text{ for } 0 \le m < n,$$

and we define f_{n+1} by

$$f_{n+1}(m) = f_n(m) \text{ for } 0 \le m < n,$$
$$f_{n+1}(n + 1) = f_n(n) \cdot x,$$

then Dom $f_{n+1} = \{0, 1, \ldots, n + 1\}$ and $f_{n+1}(0) = f_n(0) = 1$. Furthermore if $0 \le m < n$, then

$$f_{n+1}(m + 1) = f_n(m + 1) = f_n(m) \cdot x = f_{n+1}(m) \cdot x,$$
$$f_{n+1}(n + 1) = f_n(n) \cdot x = f_{n+1}(n) \cdot x.$$

Thus

$$f_{n+1}(m + 1) = f_{n+1}(m) \cdot x \text{ for } 0 \le m < n + 1;$$

therefore f_{n+1} has the desired properties and the induction is complete.

Having established for each nonnegative n the existence of one and only one finite sequence f_n with domain $\{0, 1, \ldots, n\}$ for which

$$f_n(0) = 1,$$
$$f_n(m + 1) = f_n(m) \cdot x \text{ for } 0 \le m < n,$$

we can now define an infinite sequence f with domain Z_0 by requiring that

$$f(n) = f_n(n), \quad n \ge 0.$$

It then follows that $f(0) = f_0(0) = 1$. Furthermore, if $n \ge 0$, then

$$f(n + 1) = f_{n+1}(n + 1) = f_{n+1}(n) \cdot x = f_n(n) \cdot x = f(n) \cdot x.$$

Thus there exists one and only one sequence f with domain Z_0 for which

$$f(0) = 1,$$
$$f(n + 1) = f(n) \cdot x.$$

For the enthusiastic reader who may feel that he has been "taken in" by the inductive definition of 'x^n' and that the "proper" definition is

$$x^n = f(n),$$

we point out that no one was "taken in" by the inductive definition, for we have just proved that it is logically sound.

Another inductive definition of special interest is that of the $\sum$ notation, which is defined thus:

$$\sum_{\alpha = k}^{n} a_\alpha = 0 \text{ if } n < k,$$

$$\sum_{\alpha = k}^{n+1} a_\alpha = \sum_{\alpha = k}^{n} a_\alpha + a_{n+1} \text{ if } n \geq k - 1.$$

As in the case of the definition of powers the first part of this definition poses no problem. The second part, however, implies the existence of a sequence, $\{\sum_{k}^{n} a_\alpha\}_k$, whose kth term is a_k and whose nth term is obtained by adding a_n to its $(n - 1)$th term. Does such a sequence exist? Does there exist a sequence f with domain Z_k having the property that

$$f(k) = a_k,$$
$$f(n + 1) = f(n) + a_{n+1} \text{ for } n \geq k,$$

and if so does only one such sequence exist?

That at most one such sequence can exist is easily proved by induction, for if $f(k) = a_k$ and $g(k) = a_k$, then $f(k) = g(k)$, and if $f(n) = g(n)$, then

$$f(n + 1) = f(n) + a_{n+1} = g(n) + a_{n+1} = g(n + 1).$$

That there is at least one such sequence we prove as before by first showing that for each n in Z_k there is one and only one finite sequence f_n with domain $\{k, k + 1, \ldots, n\}$ having the property that

$$f_n(k) = a_k,$$
$$f_n(m + 1) = f_n(m) + a_{n+1}, \quad k \leq m < n.$$

That at most one such finite sequence can exist we leave as an exercise for the reader. That at least one such sequence must exist we prove by induction.

If f_k is defined by $f_k(k) = a_k$, then Dom $f_k = \{k\}$ and the base of the induction is established. If as our induction hypothesis we assume the existence of a sequence f_n with domain $\{k, \ldots, n\}$ having the properties

$$f_n(k) = a_k,$$
$$f_n(m + 1) = f_n(m) + a_{m+1}, \quad k \leq m < n,$$

and if we define f_{n+1} by

$$f_{n+1}(m) = f_n(m), \quad k \le m \le n,$$
$$f_{n+1}(n + 1) = f_n(n) + a_{n+1},$$

then $\text{Dom } f_{n+1} = \{k, \ldots, n + 1\}$ and $f_{n+1}(k) = f_n(k) = a_k$. Furthermore, if $k < m \le n$, then

$$f_{n+1}(m) = f_n(m) = f_n(m - 1) + a_m = f_{n+1}(m - 1) + a_m.$$

Thus

$$f_{n+1}(m + 1) = f_{n+1}(m) + a_{m+1}, \; k \le m < n + 1.$$

This completes the induction.

We then define a sequence f with domain Z_k by

$$f(n) = f_n(n), \quad n \ge k.$$

It then follows that

$$f(k) = f_k(k) = a_k,$$
$$f(n + 1) = f_{n+1}(n + 1) = f_{n+1}(n) + a_{n+1}$$
$$= f_n(n) + a_{n+1} = f(n) + a_{n+1}.$$

Thus there is one and only one sequence whose kth term is a_k and whose nth term is obtained by adding a_n to its $(n - 1)$th term.

At this point we invite the reader to provide a justification for the $\prod$ notation:

$$\prod_{\alpha=k}^{n} a_\alpha = 1, \quad n < k,$$

$$\prod_{\alpha=k}^{n+1} a_\alpha = \left(\prod_{\alpha=k}^{n} a_\alpha\right) a_{n+1}, \quad n \ge k - 1.$$

Assuming that the reader patterned his argument after the two preceding examples, we now point out some rather striking similarities in the three arguments. In each case we use the same method of proof to establish the existence of one and only one sequence having certain properties. In each of the three cases the properties required of this sequence are very similar.

x^n	$\displaystyle\sum_{\alpha=k}^{n} a_\alpha$	$\displaystyle\prod_{\alpha=k}^{n} a_\alpha$
$f(0) = 1$	$f(k) = a_k$	$f(k) = a_k$
$f(n + 1) = f(n) \cdot x$	$f(n + 1) = f(n) + a_{n+1}$	$f(n + 1) = f(n) \cdot a_{n+1}$

It surely must be the case that all three are particular instances of a more general result. Note that in each problem f is required to have a specified value at a specified point and its value at $n + 1$ is defined in terms of its value at n by means of a multiplication or an addition. But multiplication and addition are particular binary functions. If we use functional notation, M for multiplication, A for addition, our three cases become

$$f(0) = 1 \qquad\qquad f(k) = a_k \qquad\qquad f(k) = a_k$$

$$f(n + 1) = M(f(n), x) \quad f(n + 1) = A(f(n), a_{n+1}) \quad f(n + 1) = M(f(n), a_{n+1})$$

Each of these is then a special case of

$$f(k) = a_k$$
$$f(n + 1) = F(f(n), a_{n+1})$$

This suggests the following.

Theorem 5.90. *If* $F : A \times B \to A$ *if* $\{a_n\}_k$ *is a sequence of elements of* B *with* $a_k \in A$ *then there exists one and only one sequence* f *with domain* Z_k *having the property that*

$$f(k) = a_k,$$
$$f(n + 1) = F(f(n), a_{n+1}).$$

The proof is a repetition of the previous argument, and we leave it as an exercise for the reader.

CHAPTER 6

Limits and Continuity

6.0 Introduction

In this chapter we will define two important concepts: the concept of *limit* and the concept of *continuity*. The idea of continuity is suggested by numerous instances in the physical world of relationships in which small changes produce small effects. For example, the weight of an object is known to depend upon the distance of the object from the center of the earth. This dependency is, however, such that the weight of the object does not change much if its distance from the center of the earth is changed only a small amount.

Suppose that for an object we have a function f with the property that for each a in Dom f the object weighs $f(a)$ pounds if its distance from the center of the earth is a miles. It then seems reasonable that the function f should also have the property that for each x in Dom f, if x is a number near a, then $f(x)$ is a number near $f(a)$. Indeed we should be able to compel $f(x)$ to be as close to $f(a)$ as we please by restricting x to a sufficiently small neighborhood of a. This is our intuitive idea of continuity that we will make more precise in a later section.

The limit concept that we will define is quite similar to that of continuity except that it is somewhat more general. We are interested in functions f having the property at a given point a that for every x in Dom f if x is near a then $f(x)$ is near some number l. Furthermore we can compel $f(x)$ to be as close to l as we please by restricting x to a sufficiently small neighborhood of a. We will not insist that l be $f(a)$ or even that $f(a)$ exist. Indeed we find it convenient to ignore completely the question of the existence of $f(a)$ and interpret our requirement that x be near a to mean that x is in some deleted neighborhood of a.

The statement that $f(x)$ can be compelled to be as near l as we please by restricting x to a sufficiently small deleted neighborhood of a we will interpret to mean that

$$(\forall \epsilon)(\exists \delta) \, \forall x \in N'(a, \delta) \cap \text{Dom} f, \quad f(x) \in N(l, \epsilon),$$

or in other words if $x \in \text{Dom} f$ and $0 < |x - a| < \delta$, then $|f(x) - l| < \epsilon$.

We would be assured of the existence of a δ for each ϵ if there exists a convergence test ϕ with the property

$$(\forall \epsilon) \; \forall x \in N'(a, \phi(\epsilon)) \cap \mathrm{Dom} f, \quad f(x) \in N(l, \epsilon).$$

We must, of course, have some assurance that there is at most one number l with this property. Suppose, however, that there exists a δ for which

$$N'(a, \delta) \cap \mathrm{Dom} f = \varnothing.$$

It would then follow that for each x in $N'(a, \delta) \cap \mathrm{Dom} f$

$$f(x) \in N(l, \epsilon)$$

for every ϵ and for every l. To assure uniqueness it is then necessary that

$$(\forall \delta) N'(a, \delta) \cap \mathrm{Dom} f \neq \varnothing,$$

that is, a must be an accumulation point of $\mathrm{Dom} f$. With this condition uniqueness is easily proved.

Theorem 6.00. *If a is an accumulation point of* $\mathrm{Dom} f$, *then there is at most one number l with the property that there exists a convergence test ϕ and*

$$(\forall \epsilon) \; \forall x \in N'(a, \phi(\epsilon)) \cap \mathrm{Dom} f, \quad f(x) \in N(l, \epsilon).$$

Proof. If l_1 and l_2 each have the property, then there exist convergence tests ϕ_1 and ϕ_2 such that

$$(\forall \epsilon) \; \forall x \in N'(a, \phi_1(\epsilon)) \cap \mathrm{Dom} f, \quad f(x) \in N(l_1, \epsilon),$$
$$(\forall \epsilon) \; \forall x \in N'(a, \phi_2(\epsilon)) \cap \mathrm{Dom} f, \quad f(x) \in N(l_2, \epsilon).$$

If $l_1 \neq l_2$, and if

$$\epsilon_1 = \frac{|l_1 - l_2|}{2},$$

then, since a is an accumulation point of $\mathrm{Dom} f$, there exists an element x_1 in $N(a, \phi_1(\epsilon_1)) \cap N(a, \phi_2(\epsilon_1)) \cap \mathrm{Dom} f$. Furthermore

$$f(x_1) \in N(l_1, \epsilon_1) \text{ and } f(x_1) \in N(l_2, \epsilon_1).$$

But since

$$\epsilon_1 = \frac{|l_1 - l_2|}{2}$$

it follows that

$$N(l_1, \epsilon_1) \cap N(l_2, \epsilon_1) = \varnothing.$$

This is a contradiction that forces us to conclude that $l_1 = l_2$.

Q.E.D.

A number l having the property specified in Theorem 6.00 we will denote by the symbol '$L(f, a)$', which is read the *limit of f at a*. Since many of the functions that interest us are defined by forms, it is convenient to have a limit notation that is applicable to forms and can be used in a computational context. In such a context we will use the notation

$$\operatorname*{Lim}_{x \to a} f(x)$$

which is read the *limit of f(x) as x tends to a*. If, for example, f were defined by the form '$1/x$' we would write

$$\operatorname*{Lim}_{x \to a} \frac{1}{x}.$$

Since no function symbol appears here it is understood that the function under discussion is the one that is defined by the form and whose domain is the set of all real numbers for which the form has a value.

Definition 6.01. $L(f, a) = l$ iff a is an accumulation point of $\operatorname{Dom} f$ and there exists a convergence test ϕ with the property that for each ϵ and for each x in $N'(a, \phi(\epsilon)) \cap \operatorname{Dom} f$

$$f(x) \in N(l, \epsilon).$$

Let us illustrate the definition by proving for the function f defined on the set of rational numbers Q by $f(x) = x^2$ that

$$L(f, \sqrt{2}) = 2.$$

Since every real number is an accumulation point of rational numbers, it follows that $\sqrt{2}$ is an accumulation point of Q. We now wish to define a convergence test ϕ in such a way that for each rational number x in $N'(\sqrt{2}, \phi(\epsilon))$ we will have that $|f(x) - 2| < \epsilon$. Let us begin with the observation that

$$|f(x) - 2| = |x^2 - 2| = |x + \sqrt{2}|\,|x - \sqrt{2}|.$$

Note in particular that if $x \in N(\sqrt{2}, 1)$ then

$$|x| - \sqrt{2} \le |x - \sqrt{2}| < 1,$$
$$|x| < 1 + \sqrt{2},$$
$$|x + \sqrt{2}| \le |x| + \sqrt{2} < 1 + 2\sqrt{2}.$$

Furthermore, if

$$\epsilon_1 = \frac{\epsilon}{1 + 2\sqrt{2}}$$

and if $x \in N(\sqrt{2}, \epsilon_1)$, then

$$|x - \sqrt{2}| < \frac{\epsilon}{1 + 2\sqrt{2}}.$$

Thus if $\phi(\epsilon) = \min\{1, \epsilon_1\}$, then for each rational number x in $N'(\sqrt{2}, \phi(\epsilon))$

$$x \in N(\sqrt{2}, 1), \quad \text{hence } |x + \sqrt{2}| < 1 + 2\sqrt{2},$$

$$x \in N(\sqrt{2}, \epsilon_1), \quad \text{hence } |x - \sqrt{2}| < \frac{\epsilon}{1 + 2\sqrt{2}},$$

and consequently

$$|f(x) - 2| = |x^2 - 2|$$
$$= |x + \sqrt{2}|\,|x - \sqrt{2}| < (1 + 2\sqrt{2})\frac{\epsilon}{1 + 2\sqrt{2}} = \epsilon.$$

Therefore

$$L(f, \sqrt{2}) = 2.$$

This example illustrates a proof technique that is applicable to many limit problems. In general, to prove that

$$L(f, a) = l$$

we are required to establish the existence of a convergence test ϕ with the property that

$$(\forall \epsilon)\ \forall x \in N'(a, \phi(\epsilon)) \cap \operatorname{Dom} f, \quad f(x) \in N(l, \epsilon).$$

But $f(x) \in N(l, \epsilon)$ if and only if $|f(x) - l| < \epsilon$. Since for each x in $N'(a, \phi(\epsilon)) \cap \operatorname{Dom} f$ we have that $x \neq a$, it follows that

$$f(x) - l = (x - a)\frac{f(x) - l}{x - a}.$$

Consider the function g defined by

$$g(x) = \frac{f(x) - l}{x - a}, \quad x \in \operatorname{Dom} f - \{a\}.$$

Suppose that there exists a neighborhood of a in which g is bounded, that is, suppose that there exists a δ_1 and a positive number b such that

$$\forall x \in N(a, \delta_1) \cap \operatorname{Dom} g, \quad |g(x)| < b.$$

It would then follow that

$$\forall x \in N'(a, \delta_1) \cap \operatorname{Dom} f, \quad |f(x) - l| < |x - a|b.$$

Therefore, if $\phi(\epsilon) = \min\{\delta_1, \epsilon/b\}$, then for each x in $N'(a, \phi(\epsilon)) \cap \operatorname{Dom} f$

$$|f(x) - l| = |x - a|\left|\frac{f(x) - l}{x - a}\right| < |x - a|b < \frac{\epsilon}{b} \cdot b = \epsilon.$$

Let us illustrate with another example. If $f(x) = 1/x$, $x \neq 0$, then since $f(\frac{1}{2}) = 2$ and since reciprocals of numbers near $\frac{1}{2}$ ought to be near 2, we conjecture that

$$\operatorname*{Lim}_{x \to 1/2} \frac{1}{x} = 2.$$

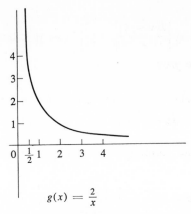

$$g(x) = \frac{2}{x}$$

FIGURE 6.1

Since

$$f(x) - 2 = \frac{1}{x} - 2 = -\frac{2(x - \frac{1}{2})}{x}$$

we define g by

$$g(x) = \frac{2}{x}, \quad x \neq 0.$$

The graph of g is a hyperbola (see Figure 6.1). It is apparent from the graph and from the definition of g that g is not bounded in those neighborhoods of $\frac{1}{2}$ that have 0 as an interior point or as a boundary point. If, however, δ_1 is smaller than $\frac{1}{2}$, for example, if $\delta_1 = \frac{1}{4}$, then for each x in $N(\frac{1}{2}, \frac{1}{4})$

$$|x - \tfrac{1}{2}| < \tfrac{1}{4}.$$

Therefore, since

$$\tfrac{1}{2} - |x| \leq |x - \tfrac{1}{2}| < \tfrac{1}{4}$$

we have that

$$\tfrac{1}{4} < |x|,$$

$$\frac{1}{|x|} < 4,$$

$$\left|\frac{2}{x}\right| < 8.$$

Thus if $\phi(\epsilon) = \min\{\frac{1}{4}, \epsilon/8\}$ and if $x \in N'(\frac{1}{2}, \phi(\epsilon)) \cap \operatorname{Dom} f$, then $x \in N(\frac{1}{2}, \frac{1}{4})$ and $x \in N(\frac{1}{2}, \epsilon/8)$. Consequently

$$\left|\frac{2}{x}\right| < 8, \quad |x - \tfrac{1}{2}| < \frac{\epsilon}{8},$$

and

$$\left|\frac{1}{x} - 2\right| = \left|\frac{2(x - \frac{1}{2})}{x}\right| = \left|\frac{2}{x}\right| |x - \tfrac{1}{2}| < 8 \cdot \frac{\epsilon}{8} = \epsilon.$$

As a final example we prove

Theorem 6.02. *If* $f(x) = \sqrt[n]{x}$, $n \geq 2$ *and if* $x \geq 0$ *when* n *is even, then*
$$\forall a \in \operatorname{Dom} f, \quad L(f, a) = f(a).$$

Analysis. From the formula for factoring the difference of two nth powers we have that

$$x - a = (\sqrt[n]{x} - \sqrt[n]{a}) \sum_{\alpha = 0}^{n-1} (\sqrt[n]{x})^{\alpha}(\sqrt[n]{a})^{n-1-\alpha}.$$

Thus if $a \neq 0$ and $x \neq 0$, then

$$f(x) - f(a) = \sqrt[n]{x} - \sqrt[n]{a} = \frac{x - a}{\displaystyle\sum_{\alpha = 0}^{n-1} (\sqrt[n]{x})^{\alpha}(\sqrt[n]{a})^{n-1-\alpha}}.$$

Therefore if

$$g(x) = \frac{1}{\displaystyle\sum_{\alpha = 0}^{n-1} (\sqrt[n]{x})^{\alpha}(\sqrt[n]{a})^{n-1-\alpha}}$$

and if $x \in N(a, |a|/2)$ it follows that each term of

$$\sum_{\alpha = 0}^{n-1} (\sqrt[n]{x})^{\alpha}(\sqrt[n]{a})^{n-1-\alpha}$$

has the same sign. (Why?) In view of this fact

$$\left|\sum_{\alpha = 0}^{n-1} (\sqrt[n]{x})^{\alpha}(\sqrt[n]{a})^{n-1-\alpha}\right| = \sum_{\alpha = 0}^{n-1} (\sqrt[n]{|x|})^{\alpha}(\sqrt[n]{|a|})^{n-1-\alpha}.$$

Since a sum of positive numbers must be greater than any particular term of the sum, it follows that

$$\sum_{\alpha = 0}^{n-1} (\sqrt[n]{|x|})^{\alpha}(\sqrt[n]{|a|})^{n-1-\alpha} > |a|^{(n-1)/n}$$

and hence

$$|g(x)| < |a|^{(1-n)/n}.$$

We leave the remaining details of the proof to the reader.

EXERCISES

1. How close to 1 must x be in order for

    a) $|x^2 - 1| < \dfrac{1}{2}$,   b) $|x^2 - 1| < \dfrac{1}{100}$,   c) $|x^2 - 1| < \dfrac{1}{2n}$?

In Exercises 2–10 prove or disprove the given assertion.

2. $\underset{x \to 2}{\text{Lim}}\, x = 2.$

3. $\underset{x \to 0}{\text{Lim}}\, x^2 = 0.$

4. $\underset{x \to 2}{\text{Lim}}\, \dfrac{1}{1 - x} = -1.$

5. $\underset{x \to 0}{\text{Lim}}\, \dfrac{x^2}{|x|} = 0.$

6. $\underset{x \to 1}{\text{Lim}}\, \dfrac{x}{1 + x} = \dfrac{1}{2}.$

7. $\underset{x \to 2}{\text{Lim}}\, (x^3 - 3x) = 2.$

8. $\underset{x \to 1}{\text{Lim}}\, (x - 1)^3 = 0.$

9. $\underset{x \to 0}{\text{Lim}}\, x^2 \text{ Rat } x = 0.$

10. $\underset{x \to 1}{\text{Lim}}\, \{x\} = 1.$

In Exercises 11–19 prove or disprove the assertion for every a.

11. $\underset{x \to a}{\text{Lim}}\, x = a.$

12. $\underset{x \to a}{\text{Lim}}\, x^2 = a^2.$

13. $\underset{x \to a}{\text{Lim}}\, \dfrac{1}{1 - x} = \dfrac{1}{1 - a}.$

14. $\underset{x \to a}{\text{Lim}}\, |x| = |a|.$

15. $\underset{x \to a}{\text{Lim}}\, \dfrac{x}{1 + x} = \dfrac{a}{1 + a}.$

16. $\underset{x \to a}{\text{Lim}}\, (x^3 - 3x) = a^3 - 3a.$

17. $\underset{x \to a}{\text{Lim}}\, (x - 1)^3 = (a - 1)^3.$

18. $\underset{x \to a}{\text{Lim}}\, [\![x]\!] = [\![a]\!].$

19. $\underset{x \to a}{\text{Lim}}\, \left(x + \left[\!\!\left[\dfrac{1}{1 + x^2} \right]\!\!\right] \right) = a.$

20. Prove: If $(\forall x)\, f(x) = c$, then $(\forall a)\, L(f, a) = c$.

21. Prove: If $g \subseteq f$, if $L(f, a) = l$ and if a is an accumulation point of Dom g, then $L(g, a) = l$.

22. Prove: If $L(f, a)$ exists, then f is bounded in some neighborhood of a; i.e., $(\exists \delta)(\exists b)\, \forall x \in N(a, \delta) \cap \text{Dom}\, f,\, |f(x)| \le b$.

23. Prove: If a is an accumulation point of Dom f and $(\exists c)(\exists \phi)$ $\forall x \in N(a, \phi(\epsilon)) \cap \text{Dom}\, f,\, |f(x) - l| < c\epsilon$, then $L(f, a) = l$.

24. Prove: If $L(f, a) = l$, if $L(h, a) = l$ and if $(\exists \delta)\, \forall x \in N'(a, \delta)$, $f(x)$, $g(x)$, and $h(x)$ exist and $f(x) \le g(x) \le h(x)$, then $L(g, a) = l$.

25. Prove: If $L(f, a) = l$ and if $l > 0$, then there exists a δ such that $\forall x \in N'(a, \delta) \cap \text{Dom}\, f,\, f(x) > 0$.

26. Prove: If $L(f, a) = l$ and if $l < 0$, then there exists a δ such that $\forall x \in N'(a, \delta) \cap \text{Dom}\, f,\, f(x) < 0$.

27. Prove: If $L(f, a) = l$ and $l \ne 0$, then $(\exists \delta)\, \forall x \in N'(a, \delta) \cap$ Dom $f,\, |f(x)| > \dfrac{|l|}{2}.$

6.1 Basic Limit Properties

From the examples and exercises of the last section we see that a direct appeal to the definition of limit frequently involves us in a lengthy and sometimes tedious sequence of computations. We now wish to consider properties of limits that may enable us to avoid a direct appeal to the definition and hence avoid the usual computations that are involved. The first such property that we will consider involves the binary operations of function addition and function multiplication as defined in Section 5.0.

Theorem 6.10. *If $L(f, a) = l_1$, if $L(g, a) = l_2$, and if a is an accumulation point of* Dom $f \cap$ Dom g, *then*

$$1) \ L(f + g, a) = l_1 + l_2.$$
$$2) \ L(fg, a) = l_1 l_2.$$

Proof. 1) Since $L(f, a) = l_1$ and $L(g, a) = l_2$, there exist convergence tests ϕ_1 and ϕ_2 such that

$$\forall x \in N'(a, \phi_1(\epsilon)) \cap \text{Dom} f, \quad |f(x) - l_1| < \epsilon,$$
$$\forall x \in N'(a, \phi_2(\epsilon)) \cap \text{Dom} g, \quad |g(x) - l_2| < \epsilon.$$

Therefore if $\phi(\epsilon) = \min \{\phi_1(\epsilon), \phi_2(\epsilon)\}$ and if $x \in N'(a, \phi(\epsilon)) \cap \text{Dom} (f + g)$, then $x \in N'(a, \phi_1(\epsilon)) \cap \text{Dom} f$ and $x \in N'(a, \phi_2(\epsilon)) \cap \text{Dom} g$. Consequently

$$\begin{aligned} |(f + g)(x) - (l_1 + l_2)| &= |f(x) - l_1 + g(x) - l_2| \\ &\le |f(x) - l_1| + |g(x) - l_2| \\ &< \epsilon + \epsilon = 2\epsilon. \end{aligned}$$

From Exercise 23, page 195, it then follows that $L(f + g, a) = l_1 + l_2$.

2) Since $L(g, a) = l_2$ it follows that g is bounded in some neighborhood of a; that is, there exists a δ and a positive number b such that if $x \in N(a, \delta) \cap \text{Dom} g$, then $|g(x)| < b$. Therefore if $\phi(\epsilon) = \min \{\delta, \phi_1(\epsilon), \phi_2(\epsilon)\}$ and if $x \in N'(a, \phi(\epsilon)) \cap \text{Dom} (fg)$, then $x \in N(a, \delta) \cap \text{Dom} g$, $x \in N'(a, \phi_1(\epsilon)) \cap \text{Dom} f$, and $x \in N'(a, \phi_2(\epsilon)) \cap \text{Dom} g$. It then follows that

$$\begin{aligned} |(fg)(x) - l_1 l_2| = |f(x)g(x) - l_1 l_2| &= |f(x)g(x) - g(x)l_1 + g(x)l_1 - l_1 l_2| \\ &\le |g(x)| \, |f(x) - l_1| + |l_1| \, |g(x) - l_2| < b\epsilon + |l_1|\epsilon. \end{aligned}$$

and hence $L(fg, a) = l_1 l_2$.

Q.E.D.

From Theorem 6.10 we can easily deduce limit properties of large classes of functions as, for example, the polynomial functions.

Theorem 6.11. *If f is a polynomial function, then for each real number a we have that $L(f, a) = f(a)$, i.e.,*

$$\lim_{x \to a} \sum_{\alpha = 0}^{n} b_\alpha x^\alpha = \sum_{\alpha = 0}^{n} b_\alpha a^\alpha.$$

The proof is left to the reader.

One interesting consequence of Theorem 6.11 is

Theorem 6.12. *If $(\forall x) \sum_0^n a_\alpha x^\alpha = 0$, then $a_0 = 0$, $a_1 = 0, \ldots, a_n = 0$.*

Proof. (By strong induction.) If

$$M = \{m \in Z_0 \mid (m > n) \text{ or } (m \le n \text{ and } a_m = 0)\},$$

then $M \subseteq Z_0$. As our induction hypothesis we have that every nonnegative integer that is smaller than m is in M, and we wish to prove that $m \in M$. We consider two cases, $m > n$ and $m \le n$.

If $m > n$ then $m \in M$ by definition of M. If $m \le n$ and $a_0 = 0, \ldots,$ $a_{m-1} = 0$, then

$$\sum_{\alpha=0}^{n} a_\alpha x^\alpha = \sum_{\alpha=m}^{n} a_\alpha x^\alpha.$$

Therefore if

$$f(x) = \sum_{\alpha=0}^{n} a_\alpha x^\alpha,$$

then

$$\frac{f(x)}{x^m} = \sum_{\alpha=0}^{n-m} a_{\alpha+m} x^\alpha, \quad x \ne 0.$$

By Theorem 6.11

$$\operatorname*{Lim}_{x \to 0} \sum_{\alpha=0}^{n-m} a_{\alpha+m} x^\alpha = a_m,$$

that is,

$$\operatorname*{Lim}_{x \to 0} \frac{f(x)}{x^m} = a_m.$$

On the other hand, since

$$(\forall x) f(x) = 0,$$

it follows that if $x \ne 0$, then

$$\frac{f(x)}{x^m} = 0$$

and consequently

$$\operatorname*{Lim}_{x \to 0} \frac{f(x)}{x^m} = 0.$$

Therefore $a_m = 0$ and hence $m \in M$.

Q.E.D.

From Theorem 6.12 we can then deduce the *identity theorem for polynomials*:

Corollary 6.13. *If* $(\forall x) \sum_0^m a_\alpha x^\alpha = \sum_0^n b_\alpha x^\alpha$, *if* $a_m \ne 0$ *and* $b_n \ne 0$, *then* $m = n$ *and* $a_0 = b_0, a_1 = b_1, \ldots, a_n = b_n$.

The proof is left to the reader.

From Corollary 6.13 it follows that for each polynomial function f either $f(x) = 0$ for every x or there exists one and only one nonnegative integer n and one and only one finite sequence, $\{a_m\}_0^n$, such that $a_n \neq 0$ and for each x

$$f(x) = \sum_{\alpha = 0}^{n} a_\alpha x^\alpha.$$

The integer n we call the *degree* of f.

From the foregoing theorems we see that Theorem 6.10 provides a very convenient way of deducing limit properties of functions that are the sum or product of other functions whose limit properties are known. The following theorem can be used in a similar way to deduce limit properties of functions that are the difference or quotient of other functions whose limit properties are known.

Theorem 6.14.   *If $L(f, a) = l$, then 1) $L(-f, a) = -l$, and 2) $L(1/f, a) = 1/l$ provided $l \neq 0$.*

Proof.   1) Since $\mathrm{Dom}\, f = \mathrm{Dom}\, (-f)$, it follows that a is an accumulation point of $\mathrm{Dom}\, f$ if and only if it is an accumulation point of $\mathrm{Dom}\, (-f)$. Thus if $L(f, a) = l$, then a is an accumulation point of $\mathrm{Dom}\, f$ and hence of $\mathrm{Dom}\, (-f)$. Furthermore there exists a convergence test ϕ with the property that if $x \in N'(a, \phi(\epsilon)) \cap \mathrm{Dom}\, f$ then $|f(x) - l| < \epsilon$. Since

$$|(-f)(x) - (-l)| = |-[f(x) - l]| = |f(x) - l|$$

it follows that $L(-f, a) = -l$. (Why?)

2) If $l \neq 0$ then $|l| > 0$. Therefore if $\epsilon_1 = \phi(|l|/2)$ and if $x \in N'(a, \epsilon_1) \cap \mathrm{Dom}\, f$, then

$$|l| - |f(x)| \leq |f(x) - l| < \frac{|l|}{2},$$
$$\frac{|l|}{2} < |f(x)|.$$

From this we see that $f(x) \neq 0$ and hence $x \in \mathrm{Dom}\, 1/f$. Therefore since a is an accumulation point of $\mathrm{Dom}\, f$, it follows that a is an accumulation point of $\mathrm{Dom}\, 1/f$. Furthermore if $x \in N'(a, \epsilon_1) \cap \mathrm{Dom}\, 1/f$, we have that $x \in \mathrm{Dom}\, f$ and hence by the argument above

$$\frac{|l|}{2} < |f(x)|,$$
$$\frac{1}{|f(x)|} < \frac{2}{|l|},$$
$$\frac{1}{|f(x)l|} < \frac{2}{l^2}.$$

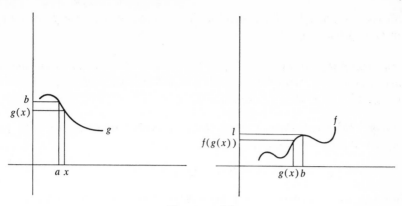

$$\text{FIGURE 6.2}$$

If $\psi(\epsilon) = \min \{\epsilon_1, \phi(\epsilon)\}$ and if $x \in N'(a, \psi(\epsilon)) \cap \text{Dom } 1/f$, then $x \in N'(a, \epsilon_1)$ $\cap \text{Dom } 1/f$ and $x \in N'(a, \phi(\epsilon)) \cap \text{Dom } f$. Consequently

$$\left| \frac{1}{f}(x) - \frac{1}{l} \right| = \left| \frac{1}{f(x)} - \frac{1}{l} \right| = \left| \frac{l - f(x)}{f(x)l} \right| = \frac{1}{|f(x)l|} |f(x) - l| < \frac{2\epsilon}{l^2}.$$

Therefore $L(1/f, a) = 1/l$.

$$\text{Q.E.D.}$$

Corollary 6.15. *If $L(f, a) = l_1$, if $L(g, a) = l_2$, and if a is an accumulation point of $\text{Dom } f \cap \text{Dom } g$, then*

1) $L(f - g, a) = l_1 - l_2$.
2) $L\left(\dfrac{f}{g}, a\right) = \dfrac{l_1}{l_2}$ *provided* $l_2 \neq 0$.

The proof is left to the reader.

Our next result deals with the limit properties of composite functions. Suppose that $h = f \circ g$, that $L(g, a) = b$ and $L(f, b) = l$. For x near a we then have that $g(x)$ is near b, and for $g(x)$ near b we should have that $f(g(x))$ is near l. It therefore seems reasonable that l is the limit of h at a. (See Figure 6.2) There is, however, one problem. By definition if $L(f, b) = l$ and if y is near b but different from b, then $f(y)$ is near l. If it should be the case that for x near a we have that $g(x) = b$, then we have no assurance that $f(g(x))$ is near l. Consider the following example.

If $(\forall x) g(x) = 0$, then $L(g, 1) = 0$. If

$$(\forall x) f(x) = \left[\!\!\left[\frac{1}{1 + x^2} \right]\!\!\right],$$

then $L(f, 0) = 0$. On the other hand, since $f(0) = 1$ it follows that $(\forall x) f \circ g(x) = 1$ and hence $L(f \circ g, 1) = 1$.

From this example we see that we must require that $g(x) \neq b$ for every x in Dom g that is near a.

Theorem 6.16. *If* $L(g, a) = b$, *if* $L(f, b) = l$, *if* a *is an accumulation point of* Dom $f \circ g$, *and if there exists a* δ *such that for each* x *in* $N'(a, \delta) \cap$ Dom g, $g(x) \neq b$, *then* $L(f \circ g, a) = l$.

Proof. Since $L(f, b) = l$, there exists a convergence test ϕ_1 with the property that if $x \in N'(b, \phi_1(\epsilon)) \cap$ Dom f, then

$$|f(x) - l| < \epsilon.$$

Since $L(g, a) = b$, there exists a convergence test ϕ_2 with the property that if $x \in N'(a, \phi_2(\epsilon)) \cap$ Dom g, then

$$|g(x) - b| < \epsilon.$$

In particular, since $\phi_1(\epsilon)$ is positive, if $\epsilon_1 = \phi_1(\epsilon)$ and if $x \in N'(a, \phi_2(\epsilon_1)) \cap$ Dom g, then

$$|g(x) - b| < \phi_1(\epsilon);$$

that is, $g(x) \in N(b, \phi_1(\epsilon))$. Consequently if $\phi(\epsilon) = \min \{(\phi_2 \circ \phi_1)(\epsilon), \delta\}$ and if $x \in N'(a, \phi(\epsilon)) \cap$ Dom $f \circ g$, then $x \in$ Dom g, $g(x) \in$ Dom f and $g(x) \neq b$. It then follows that $x \in N'(a, \phi_2(\phi_1(\epsilon))) \cap$ Dom g; hence $g(x) \in N'(b, \phi_1(\epsilon)) \cap$ Dom f and

$$|(f \circ g)(x) - l| = |f(g(x)) - l| < \epsilon.$$

$$\text{Q.E.D.}$$

Example. Since $\text{Lim}_{x \to 1} (x + 2) = 3$ and $\text{Lim}_{x \to 3} \sqrt{x} = \sqrt{3}$, we conclude that $\text{Lim}_{x \to 1} \sqrt{x + 2} = \sqrt{3}$.

As in the case of sequences it is sometimes important to know that a limit exists even though we may have no additional information about the limit. We now wish to prove two existence theorems which we shall refer to as the Cauchy criterion and the Stoltz criterion, respectively.

Theorem 6.17 (Cauchy's Convergence Criterion for Limits). $L(f, a)$ *exists iff* a *is an accumulation point of* Dom f *and there exists a convergence test* ϕ *with the property that for each* ϵ *and each* x *and* y *in* $N'(a, \phi(\epsilon)) \cap$ Dom f

$$|f(x) - f(y)| < \epsilon.$$

Proof. If $L(f, a)$ exists, then a is an accumulation point of Dom f and there exists a number l and a convergence test ϕ_1 with the property that

$$(\forall \epsilon) \, \forall x \in N'(a, \phi_1(\epsilon)) \cap \text{Dom } f, \quad |f(x) - l| < \epsilon.$$

Therefore if $\phi(\epsilon) = \phi_1(\epsilon/2)$, if $x \in N'(a, \phi(\epsilon)) \cap \mathrm{Dom}\, f$, and if $y \in N'(a, \phi(\epsilon))$ $\cap \mathrm{Dom}\, f$, then

$$|f(x) - f(y)| = |f(x) - l + l - f(y)| \leq |f(x) - l| + |f(y) - l|$$
$$< \frac{\epsilon}{2} + \frac{\epsilon}{2} = \epsilon.$$

Conversely if there exists a convergence test ϕ with the property that for each ϵ and each x and y in $N'(a, \phi(\epsilon)) \cap \mathrm{Dom}\, f$

$$|f(x) - f(y)| < \epsilon,$$

then in particular, since a is an accumulation point of $\mathrm{Dom}\, f$, it follows that there exists an element y in $N'(a, \phi(1)) \cap \mathrm{Dom}\, f$. Consequently

$$\forall x \in N'(a, \phi(1)) \cap \mathrm{Dom}\, f, \quad |f(x) - f(y)| < 1.$$

But $|f(x)| - |f(y)| \leq |f(x) - f(y)|$. Therefore

$$|f(x)| \leq 1 + |f(y)|.$$

From this we see that if $\delta = \phi(1)$, then f is bounded in $N(a, \delta)$, i.e.,

$$(\exists b) \; \forall x \in N(a, \delta) \cap \mathrm{Dom}\, f, \quad |f(x)| \leq b.$$

Then for each n greater than $1/\delta$ it follows that

$$\left\{ f(x) \mid x \in N'\left(a, \frac{1}{n}\right) \cap \mathrm{Dom}\, f \right\}$$

is bounded and, since a is an accumulation point of $\mathrm{Dom}\, f$, nonempty. Therefore if $m = [\![1/\delta]\!] + 1$ and if

$$y_n = \sup\left\{ f(x) \mid x \in N'\left(a, \frac{1}{n}\right) \cap \mathrm{Dom}\, f \right\}, \quad n \geq m,$$

then $\{y_n\}_m$ is a monotone decreasing sequence that is bounded below (why?) and hence it converges.

If

$$\mathrm{Lim}_{n \to \infty} y_n = l,$$

then there exists a convergence test ϕ_1 with the property that

$$\text{if } n > \phi_1(\epsilon), \text{ then } |y_n - l| < \epsilon.$$

Furthermore since $y_n > l - \epsilon$, $n \geq 1/\delta$ and since

$$y_n = \sup\left\{ f(x) \mid x \in N'\left(a, \frac{1}{n}\right) \cap \mathrm{Dom}\, f \right\},$$

it follows that there exists an x' in $N'(a, 1/n) \cap \mathrm{Dom}\, f$ such that

$$l - \epsilon < f(x') \leq y_n \leq l + \epsilon,$$

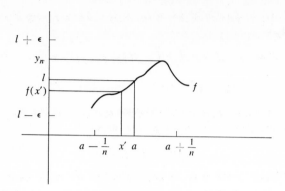

FIGURE 6.3

that is,

$$\forall n > \phi_1(\epsilon), \quad \exists x' \in N'\left(a, \frac{1}{n}\right) \cap \text{Dom} f, \quad |f(x') - l| < \epsilon.$$

(See Figure 6.3.) Therefore, if

$$x \in N'(a, \phi(\epsilon)) \cap \text{Dom} f$$

then there exists an integer n such that

$$n > \phi_1(\epsilon) \text{ and } n > \frac{1}{\phi(\epsilon)}.$$

Since $1/n < \phi(\epsilon)$ it follows that $N(a, 1/n) \subseteq N(a, \phi(\epsilon))$. Furthermore we know that there exists an x' in $N'(a, 1/n) \cap \text{Dom} f$ for which

$$|f(x') - l| < \epsilon.$$

But since x and x' are both in $N'(a, \phi(\epsilon)) \cap \text{Dom} f$ it follows that

$$|f(x) - f(x')| < \epsilon.$$

We then conclude that

$$|f(x) - l| = |f(x) - f(x') + f(x') - l| \le |f(x) - f(x')| + |f(x') - l|$$
$$< \epsilon + \epsilon = 2\epsilon.$$

Q.E.D.

It is interesting to note that a somewhat simpler proof can be provided for Theorem 6.17 by using Theorem 5.81, which for its proof requires the axiom of choice.

Second Proof of Theorem 6.17. If $L(f, a)$ exists, the proof is as before. For the converse we argue that if a is an accumulation point of Dom f, then by Theorem 5.81 there exists a sequence of elements of Dom f, $\{x_n\}_k$, that converges to a and for which $x_n \neq a$, $n \geq k$. Since $\{x_n\}_k$ converges to a, there exists a convergence test ϕ_1 with the property that

$$\text{if } n > \phi_1(\epsilon), \text{ then } |x_n - a| < \epsilon.$$

In particular, since $\phi(\epsilon)$ is positive, it follows that

$$\text{if } n > \phi_1(\phi(\epsilon)), \text{ then } x_n \in N'(a, \phi(\epsilon)) \cap \text{Dom } f.$$

Therefore if m and n are each greater than $\phi_1(\phi(\epsilon))$, then x_m and x_n are each in $N'(a, \phi(\epsilon)) \cap \text{Dom } f$ and hence

$$|f(x_m) - f(x_n)| < \epsilon.$$

From the Cauchy criterion for sequences it then follows that $\{f(x_n)\}_k$ converges; that is, there exist a number l and a convergence test ϕ_2 with the property that

$$\text{if } n > \phi_2(\epsilon), \text{ then } |f(x_n) - l| < \epsilon.$$

Furthermore for each ϵ there exists as integer n_1 such that $n_1 > \phi_1(\phi(\epsilon))$ and $n_1 > \phi_2(\epsilon)$. It then follows that

$$x_{n_1} \in N'(a, \phi(\epsilon)) \cap \text{Dom } f \text{ and } |f(x_{n_1}) - l| < \epsilon.$$

Since $x_{n_1} \in N'(a, \phi(\epsilon)) \cap \text{Dom } f$, it then follows that for each $x \in N'(a, \phi(\epsilon)) \cap \text{Dom } f$

$$|f(x) - f(x_{n_1})| < \epsilon$$

and hence

$$|f(x) - l| = |f(x) - f(x_{n_1}) + f(x_{n_1}) - l|$$
$$\leq |f(x) - f(x_{n_1})| + |f(x_{n_1}) - l| < \epsilon + \epsilon = 2\epsilon.$$

Therefore $L(f, a) = l$.

Q.E.D.

The Cauchy criterion for limits is a very plausible result. In intuitive terms it simply asserts that in order for each number in a certain collection to lie near a particular number it is necessary and sufficient that pairwise the numbers in that collection must lie near each other. As a consequence of the Cauchy criterion we then have the following useful result, whose proof we leave to the reader.

Theorem 6.18. *$L(f, a)$ does not exist if for some ϵ and every δ there exist numbers x and y in $N'(a, \delta) \cap \text{Dom } f$ such that*

$$|f(x) - f(y)| \geq \epsilon.$$

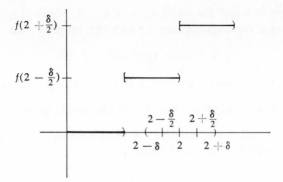

FIGURE 6.4

Example. If $f(x) = [\![x]\!]$, then $L(f, n)$ does not exist, because if $\epsilon = 1$ then for each δ we have that $n + (\delta/2) \in N'(n, \delta) \cap \text{Dom } f$, $n - (\delta/2) \in N'(n, \delta) \cap \text{Dom } f$ and

$$\left| f\left(n + \frac{\delta}{2}\right) - f\left(n - \frac{\delta}{2}\right) \right| \geq 1.$$

(See Figure 6.4.)

Another interesting and useful result is the Stolz criterion, whose proof we also leave to the reader.

Theorem 6.19 (Stolz Criterion). $L(f, a) = l$ *iff* a *is an accumulation point of* Dom f *and for each sequence* $\{x_n\}_k$, *of elements of* Dom f,

$$\text{if } \lim_{n \to \infty} x_n = a, \text{ then } \lim_{n \to \infty} f(x_n) = l.$$

EXERCISES

In Exercises 1–6 apply the results of this section to 'evaluate' (i.e., provide an equivalent name for) the given limits or prove that the limit does not exist.

1. $\lim\limits_{x \to 1} (x^3 + 6x)$.

2. $\lim\limits_{x \to 2} \dfrac{x^2 + 1}{x^2 - 1}$.

3. $\lim\limits_{x \to -1} \dfrac{x + 4}{x + 1}$.

4. $\lim\limits_{x \to 1} \left(\dfrac{x}{x - 1} - \dfrac{1}{x - 1} \right)$.

5. $\lim\limits_{x \to 1} \left(\dfrac{x}{x + 1} + \dfrac{1}{x + 1} \right)$.

6. $\lim\limits_{x \to 0} \dfrac{x(x + 1)}{x(x + 2)}$.

In Exercises 7–12 determine the values of 'a' for which the given limit exists and evaluate the limit for each a for which it does exist.

7. $\lim\limits_{x \to a} (x^3 + 6x)$.

8. $\lim\limits_{x \to a} \dfrac{x^2 + 1}{x^2 - 1}$.

9. $\lim\limits_{x \to a} \dfrac{x + 4}{x + 1}$.

10. $\lim\limits_{x \to a} \left(\dfrac{x}{x - 1} - \dfrac{1}{x - 1} \right)$.

11. $\operatorname*{Lim}_{x \to a} \left(\dfrac{x}{x + 1} + \dfrac{1}{x + 1} \right).$ **12.** $\operatorname*{Lim}_{x \to a} \dfrac{x(x + 1)}{x(x + 2)}.$

13. Prove: If $f(x) = x^2$ Rat x, then $L(f, a)$ exists iff $a = 0$.

14. Prove: If $f(x) = \left[\!\!\left[\dfrac{1}{1 + x^2} \right]\!\!\right]$, then $(\forall a) L(f, a)$ exists.

15. Prove: If $f(x) = \dfrac{1}{x}$, then $L(f, 0)$ does not exist.

16. Prove: If $f(x) = [\![x]\!]$, then $L(f, a)$ exists iff $a \notin Z$.

17. Prove: If $f(x) = \{x\}$, then $L(f, a)$ exists for all a.

18. Prove: If f is a rational function, then $\forall a \in \operatorname{Dom} f, L(f, a) = f(a)$.

19. Is it true that if $f = g + h$ and if any two of the three functions f, g, and h have a limit at a, then the third does and in each case $L(f, a) = L(g, a) + L(h, a)$?

20. Is it true that if $f = gh$ and if any two of the three functions f, g, and h have a limit at a, then the third does and in each case $L(f, a) = L(g, a)L(h, a)$?

21. Prove: If $f(x) = x^2 + [\![x]\!]$, then f does not have a limit at 0. Graph f on $[-1, 1]$.

22. Consider the figure consisting of straight line segments connecting $(1/2n, 1)$ to each of the two points $(1/(2n + 1), 0)$ and $(1/(2n - 1), 0)$ for each positive integer n. This figure is the graph of some function f. Give a formula for computing the value of f on $(0, 1]$ and prove that $L(f, 0)$ does not exist.

23. Consider the figure consisting of straight line segments connecting $(1/2n, 1/2n)$ to each of the two points $(1/(2n + 1), 0)$ and $(1/(2n - 1), 0)$ for each positive integer n. This is the graph of some function f. Give a formula for computing the values of f on $(0, 1]$ and prove that $L(f, 0)$ exists.

24. Prove: If $L(f_\alpha, a) = l_\alpha$, $\alpha = 1, 2, \ldots, n$, then $L(\sum_1^n f_\alpha, a) = \sum_1^n l_\alpha$; that is, if $L(f_\alpha, a)$ exists for $\alpha = 1, 2, \ldots, n$, then $L(\sum_1^n f_\alpha, a)$ exists and

$$\operatorname*{Lim}_{x \to a} \sum_{\alpha = 1}^{n} f_\alpha(x) = \sum_{\alpha = 1}^{n} \operatorname*{Lim}_{x \to a} f_\alpha(x).$$

25. Prove: If $L(f_\alpha, a)$ exists for $\alpha = 1, 2, \ldots, n$, then $L(\prod_1^n f_\alpha, a)$ exists and

$$\operatorname*{Lim}_{x \to a} \prod_{\alpha = 1}^{n} f_\alpha(x) = \prod_{\alpha = 1}^{n} \operatorname*{Lim}_{x \to a} f_\alpha(x).$$

6.2 Continuity

In Section 6.1 we defined $L(f, a)$ in such a way that its existence does not depend upon $f(a)$. If $L(f, a) = l$, then for each x near a, but different from

a, we have that $f(x)$ is near l. It is, of course, necessary that a be an accumulation point of Dom f, but $f(a)$ need not exist and if it does exist it need not be near l.

We now wish to consider a property that is very closely related to the limit property. It too is a property that a function f either has or does not have at a particular point a.

Definition 6.20. f is *continuous* at a iff $a \in$ Dom f and there exists a convergence test ϕ such that

$$(\forall \epsilon) \, \forall x \in N(a, \phi(\epsilon)) \cap \text{Dom} f, \quad |f(x)) - f(a)| < \epsilon.$$

f is *discontinuous* at a iff f is not continuous at a.

From the definition we see that if a is an accumulation point of Dom f, then f is continuous at a if and only if $f(a)$ exists, $L(f, a)$ exists, and $L(f, a) = f(a)$. Thus, for example, the constant functions are continuous everywhere,[1] for if

$$(\forall x) \, f(x) = c$$

then, as was proved earlier,

$$(\forall a) \, L(f, a) = c$$

but $f(a) = c$ and hence $L(f, a) = f(a)$. It is easily proved that the identity function is continuous everywhere and the Rat function is discontinuous everywhere.

From Definition 6.20 we also see that if a is not an accumulation point of Dom f, then f is continuous at a if and only if $a \in$ Dom f—that is, f is continuous at each isolated point of its domain. This may not seem to be consistent with the reader's intuitive notion of continuity. We urge its acceptance, however, as a matter of convenience. The following result illustrates its value.

Theorem 6.21.   *If g is continuous at a and if f is continuous at $g(a)$, then $f \circ g$ is continuous at a.*

Proof.   If f is continuous at $g(a)$, then there exists a convergence test ϕ_1 such that

$$\forall x \in N(g(a), \phi_1(\epsilon)) \cap \text{Dom} f, \quad |f(x) - f(g(a))| < \epsilon.$$

If g is continuous at a, then there exists a convergence test ϕ_2 such that

$$\forall x \in N(a, \phi_2(\epsilon)) \cap \text{Dom} g, \quad |g(x) - g(a)| < \epsilon.$$

---

[1] 'Everywhere' means *at each real number.*

Therefore if $\phi = \phi_2 \circ \phi_1$ and if $x \in N(a, \phi(\epsilon)) \cap \text{Dom} f \circ g$, then $x \in \text{Dom} g$, $g(x) \in \text{Dom} f$, and $x \in N(a, \phi_2(\phi_1(\epsilon))) \cap \text{Dom} g$. Consequently

$$|g(x) - g(a)| < \phi_1(\epsilon).$$

But since $g(x) \in \text{Dom} f$, it follows that $g(x) \in N(g(a), \phi_1(\epsilon)) \cap \text{Dom} f$ and hence

$$|(f \circ g)(x) - (f \circ g)(a)| = |f(g(x)) - f(g(a))| < \epsilon.$$

Q.E.D.

If we were to insist that functions are continuous only at points in their domain that are accumulation points of their domain, then Theorem 6.21 would have to have the additional hypothesis that a be an accumulation point of $\text{Dom} f \circ g$. As proof of this note that if g and f are defined by

$$g(x) = x, \quad x \text{ rational},$$
$$f(x) = x, \quad x \text{ irrational or } x = 0,$$

then g is continuous at 0, f is continuous at $g(0)$, 0 is an accumulation point of $\text{Dom} g$, $g(0)$ is an accumulation point of $\text{Dom} f$, but 0 is an isolated point of $\text{Dom} f \circ g$; indeed $f \circ g = \{(0, 0)\}$.

We have defined continuity in such a way that a given function either is or is not continuous at a given point. We are, however, interested in functions that are continuous on sets. It would seem reasonable to define the phrase 'f is continuous on S' to mean that f is continuous at each point of S. There are, however, contexts in which this definition is too restrictive. For example, if S is closed and a is a boundary point of S, then the continuity of f at a may depend upon the behavior of f at points near a but not in S. For certain uses we prefer the continuity of f on S to depend only on the values f assumes in S. We therefore choose to define the continuity of f on S in terms of the *restriction* of f to S.

Definition 6.22. g is the *restriction* of f to S iff $\text{Dom} g = (S \cap \text{Dom} f)$ and $\forall x \in (S \cap \text{Dom} f)$, $g(x) = f(x)$.

Definition 6.23. f is continuous *on* S iff $S \subseteq \text{Dom} f$ and the restriction of f to S is continuous at each point of S.

Example. The largest integer function is continuous on $[0, 1)$ in spite of the fact that it is discontinuous at 0.

Example. The Rat function is continuous on the set of rational numbers, it is continuous on the set of irrational numbers, and it is discontinuous everywhere.

Definition 6.24. f is a *continuous function*, or simply continuous, iff f is continuous on $\text{Dom} f$.

The constant functions, the identity function and numerous other functions defined earlier are continuous functions. Since most of the elementary continuity properties are easily deduced from limit properties already proved, we leave them as exercises.

EXERCISES

1. Prove: The absolute value function is a continuous function.

2. Prove: The nth root functions are continuous functions.

3. Prove: The largest integer function is continuous at a iff $a \notin Z$.

4. Prove: The distance to integer function is a continuous function.

In Exercises 5–11 determine where the function is continuous and where it is discontinuous. Prove your assertions.

5. $f(x) = x^2 - x$. **6.** $f(x) = 2x^3 + 3x$.

7. $f(x) = x|x|$. **8.** $f(x) = \dfrac{1}{x - 2}$, $x \neq 2$.

9. $f(x) = x^2 \operatorname{Rat}(x)$. **10.** $f(x) = x[\![2x]\!]$.

11. $f(x) = 0$, if x is irrational.
$\quad\quad\quad = 1/n$, if $x = m/n$, $n > 0$ and m and n are relatively prime.

12. Prove: If f is continuous at a, if $a \in \operatorname{Dom} g$, and if

$$(\exists \delta)\ \forall x \in N(a, \delta) \cap \operatorname{Dom} g, \quad g(x) = f(x),$$

then g is continuous at a.

13. Prove: If $g \subseteq f$, if $a \in \operatorname{Dom} g$, and if f is continuous at a, then g is continuous at a.

14. Prove: If f and g are each continuous at a, then $f + g$ and $f - g$ are continuous at a.

15. Prove: If each of the functions f_α, $\alpha = 1, 2, \ldots, n$ are continuous at a, then $\sum_1^n f_\alpha$ is continuous at a.

16. Prove: If f and g are each continuous at a, then fg is continuous at a.

17. Prove: If each of the functions f_α, $\alpha = 1, 2, \ldots, n$ are continuous at a, then $\prod_1^n f_\alpha$ is continuous at a.

18. Prove: Polynomial functions are continuous functions.

19. Prove: If f and g are continuous at a and if $g(a) \neq 0$, then f/g is continuous at a.

20. Prove: Rational functions are continuous functions.

21. Consider the figure consisting of straight line segments connecting $(n, 1)$ to each of the points $(n - 1 + 1/(n - 1), 0)$ and $(n + 1/n, 0)$ for every integer n greater than 2. This is the graph of some function f. Give a formula for computing the values of f on $[2\frac{1}{2}, \infty)$ and prove that f is a continuous function.

22. Prove: That the function defined in Exercise 23, page 205, is continuous on $(0, 1]$ and that if we adjoin to it the ordered pair $(0, 0)$ we obtain a function that is continuous on $[0, 1]$.

23. Prove that the function defined in Exercise 22, page 205, is continuous on $(0, 1]$ and that there is no ordered pair that can be adjoined to produce a function that is continuous on $[0, 1]$.

24. Prove: If S is an open subset of Dom f, then f is continuous on S iff f is continuous at each point of S.

25. Prove: If f and g are each continuous on S, then $f + g, f - g$, and fg are each continuous on S.

26. Prove: f is continuous on S iff $S \subseteq$ Dom f and $\forall a \in S$, $(\exists \phi)(\forall \epsilon) \, \forall x \in N(a, \phi(\epsilon)) \cap S, \, |f(x) - f(a)| < \epsilon$.

27. Prove: If f is continuous at a and if $f(a) > 0$, then

$$(\exists \delta) \, \forall x \in N(a, \delta) \cap \text{Dom} f, \, f(x) > 0.$$

28. Prove: If f is continuous at a and if $f(a) < 0$, then

$$(\exists \delta) \, \forall x \in N(a, \delta) \cap \text{Dom} f, \, f(x) < 0.$$

6.3 Right and Left Continuity, Right and Left Limits, and Limits at Infinity

Note that if f is continuous on $[a, b]$, then the condition for f to be continuous at a is fulfilled for x near a but larger than a and the condition for f to be continuous at b is fulfilled for x near b but smaller than b. It is frequently helpful to have this much information about a function, and it seems reasonable to say under such circumstances that f is *continuous on the right at a* and *continuous on the left at b*.

Definition 6.30. f is *continuous on the right* at a iff the restriction of f to $[a, \infty)$ is continuous at a.

f is *continuous on the left* at a iff the restriction of f to $(-\infty, 0]$ is continuous at a.

Example. The largest integer function is continuous on the right at 1 but not continuous on the left at 1.

The notion of right and left continuity suggests the following notion of right and left limits.

Definition 6.31. $L_+(f, a) = l$ iff $L(g, a) = l$ where g is the restriction of f to $[a, \infty)$. $L_-(f, a) = l$ iff $L(g, a) = l$ where g is the restriction of f to $(-\infty, a]$.

The symbol '$L_+(f, a)$' is read the *right limit of f at a*; '$L_-(f, a)$' is read the *left limit of f at a*.

From Definition 6.31 we see that if f is continuous on the right at a, then a is an isolated point of the domain of the restriction of f to $[a, \infty)$, or $f(a)$

exists, $L_+(f, a)$ exists, and $L_+(f, a) = f(a)$. Similarly if f is continuous on the left at a then a is an isolated point of the restriction of f to $(-\infty, a]$, or $f(a)$ exists, $L_-(f, a)$ exists, and $L_-(f, a) = f(a)$.

Another limit notion of interest is that of a *limit at infinity*, which we define in the following way.

Definition 6.32. $L_\infty(f) = l$ iff Dom f is unbounded above and there exists a convergence test ϕ with the property that

$$(\forall \epsilon)\ \forall x \in \text{Dom } f, \text{ if } x > \phi(\epsilon) \text{ then } |f(x) - l| < \epsilon.$$

$L_{-\infty}(f) = l$ iff Dom f is unbounded below and there exists a convergence test ϕ with the property that

$$(\forall \epsilon)\ \forall x \in \text{Dom } f, \text{ if } x < -\phi(\epsilon), \text{ then } |f(x) - l| < \epsilon.$$

Definition 6.33.
$$\text{Lim}_{x \to a^+}\ f(x) = L_+(f, a).$$
$$\text{Lim}_{x \to a^-}\ f(x) = L_-(f, a).$$
$$\text{Lim}_{x \to \infty}\ f(x) = L_\infty(f).$$
$$\text{Lim}_{x \to -\infty}\ f(x) = L_{-\infty}(f).$$

Since right and left limits are ordinary limits of restricted functions, their basic properties can be deduced from limit properties already established. We now wish to prove a result that will enable us to infer the properties of limits at infinity from right and left limits at 0.

Theorem 6.34.
1) $\displaystyle \text{Lim}_{x \to \infty} f(x) = l$ iff $\displaystyle \text{Lim}_{x \to 0^+} f\left(\frac{1}{x}\right) = l.$

2) $\displaystyle \text{Lim}_{x \to -\infty} f(x) = l$ iff $\displaystyle \text{Lim}_{x \to 0^-} f\left(\frac{1}{x}\right) = l.$

Proof. 1) If $g(x) = f(1/x)$ and if

$$\text{Lim}_{x \to \infty} f(x) = l,$$

then there exists a convergence test ϕ with the property that if $x \in \text{Dom } f$ and if $x > \phi(\epsilon)$, then

$$|f(x) - l| < \epsilon.$$

Therefore if

$$\psi(\epsilon) = \frac{1}{\phi(\epsilon)},$$

if $x \in \text{Dom } g$, and if $0 < x < \psi(\epsilon)$, then $(1/x) > \phi(\epsilon)$. Furthermore, since $x \in \text{Dom } g$, it follows that $(1/x) \in \text{Dom } f$. (Why?) Therefore

$$\left| f\left(\frac{1}{x}\right) - l \right| < \epsilon$$

and hence

$$\text{Lim}_{x \to 0^+} f\left(\frac{1}{x}\right) = l.$$

Conversely, if

$$\text{Lim}_{x \to 0^+} f\left(\frac{1}{x}\right) = l,$$

then there exists a convergence test ϕ with the property that if $x \in \text{Dom } g$ and $0 < x < \phi(\epsilon)$, then

$$\left| f\left(\frac{1}{x}\right) - l \right| < \epsilon.$$

Thus if

$$\psi(\epsilon) = \frac{1}{\phi(\epsilon)},$$

if $x \in \text{Dom } f$, and if $x > \psi(\epsilon)$, then $0 < (1/x) < \phi(\epsilon)$ and $(1/x) \in \text{Dom } g$. Therefore

$$| f(x) - l | < \epsilon$$

and hence

$$\text{Lim}_{x \to \infty} f(x) = l.$$

2) The proof is similar to that above and is left to the reader.

The notion of a limit at infinity is a natural generalization of the notion of the limit of a sequence. In view of the role that monotonicity played in the theory of sequences it seems reasonable that a similar property would enable us to infer useful results concerning limits at infinity.

Definition 6.35. If $S \subseteq \text{Dom } f$ and 'x' and 'y' are variables on S, then
1) f is *monotone increasing* on S iff $x < y$ implies $f(x) \leq f(y)$.
2) f is *strictly monotone increasing* on S iff $x < y$ implies $f(x) < f(y)$.
3) f is *monotone decreasing* on S iff $x < y$ implies $f(x) \geq f(y)$.
4) f is *strictly monotone decreasing* on S iff $x < y$ implies $f(x) > f(y)$.
5) f is *monotone* on S iff f is monotone increasing on S or monotone decreasing on S.
6) f is *strictly monotone* on S iff f is strictly monotone increasing on S or strictly monotone decreasing on S.

Definition 6.36.

1) f is *monotone increasing* iff f is monotone increasing on Dom f.

2) f is *strictly monotone increasing* iff f is strictly monotone increasing on Dom f.

3) f is *monotone decreasing* iff f is monotone decreasing on Dom f.

4) f is *strictly monotone decreasing* iff f is strictly monotone decreasing on Dom f.

5) f is *monotone* iff f is monotone on Dom f.

6) f is *strictly monotone* iff f is strictly monotone on Dom f.

The consequences of Definitions 6.35 and 6.36 we leave to the reader to prove.

EXERCISES

1. Prove: f is continuous at a iff f is continuous on the right at a and continuous on the left at a.

2. Prove: $\lim\limits_{x \to \infty} \dfrac{1}{x} = 0$.

In Exercises 3–7 prove or disprove the given assertion.

3. If $L_+(f, a) = l_1$ and $L_+(g, a) = l_2$, then $L_+(f + g, a) = l_1 + l_2$.

4. If $L_+(f, a) = l_1$ and $L_+(g, a) = l_2$, then $L_+(fg, a) = l_1 l_2$.

5. If $L_+(g, a) = b$ and $L_+(f, b) = l$ and if for some δ we have that $\forall x \in N(a, \delta)$, $g(x) \neq b$, then $L_+(f \circ g, a) = l$.

6. If $L_\infty(f) = l_1$ and $L_\infty(g) = l_2$, then $L_\infty(f + g) = l_1 + l_2$.

7. If $L_\infty(f) = l_1$ and $L_\infty(g) = l_2$, then $L_\infty(fg) = l_1 l_2$.

8. Prove: A monotone increasing function has a limit at infinity iff it is bounded above but its domain is unbounded above.

9. Investigate the right and left limits at 0 of f if $f(x) = x^2 + 1 + [\![1 + x]\!] \operatorname{Rat}(x)$.

10. Consider the figure consisting of straight line segments connecting $(n, 1/n)$ to each of the points $(n - 1 + 1/(n - 1), 0)$ and $(n + 1/n, 0)$ for all integers n greater than 2. This is the graph of some function f. Give a formula for computing the values of f on $[2\frac{1}{2}, \infty)$ and prove that $L_\infty(f)$ exists.

11. Prove: The function defined in Exercise 21, page 208, does not have a limit at infinity.

6.4 Continuity and Uniform Continuity

In an earlier discussion we pointed out that there are problems of interest in which it is important to know that a given set has a maximum or a minimum. At that point we proved that every nonempty set has a maximum and a minimum if it is closed and bounded. While this result is of importance, it simply transfers the problem of proving the existence of a maximum or minimum to the problem of proving that the given set is closed and bounded. We now wish to show that continuity provides one method of proving a given set to be closed and bounded.

Let us recall from Chapter 3 the definition that

$$f[S] = \{ f(x) \mid x \in S \cap \text{Dom } f \}.$$

We will now prove

Theorem 6.40.   *If S is closed and bounded and if f is continuous on S, then f[S] is also closed and bounded.*

First Proof.   To prove that $f[S]$ is closed it is sufficient to prove that it contains all of its accumulation points. If y is an accumulation point of $f[S]$ then for each positive integer n

$$N\left(y, \frac{1}{n}\right) \cap f[S] \neq \varnothing.$$

Therefore $\{ x \in S \mid f(x) \in N(y, 1/n) \}$ is not empty, and being a subset of S, it is bounded. If

$$x_n = \sup \left\{ x \in S \mid f(x) \in N\left(y, \frac{1}{n}\right) \right\}, \quad n \geq 1,$$

then since S is closed, it follows that $x_n \in S$, $n \geq 1$. Thus $\{x_n\}_1$ is a bounded sequence of elements of S. It therefore has a convergent subsequence $\{x_{m_n}\}_1$. If

$$\text{Lim}_{n \to \infty} x_{m_n} = a,$$

then, since S is closed, $a \in S$. Furthermore by the Stolz criterion it follows, since f is continuous on S, that

$$\text{Lim}_{n \to \infty} f(x_{m_n}) = f(a).$$

On the other hand, it is easily proved that for each positive integer n

$$f(x_n) \in \overline{N\left(y, \frac{1}{n}\right)}.$$

Indeed if for some positive integer n

$$f(x_n) \notin \overline{N\left(y, \frac{1}{n}\right)}$$

it would then follow that for some ϵ_1

$$N(f(x_n), \epsilon_1) \cap \overline{N\left(y, \frac{1}{n}\right)} = \varnothing.$$

Since $x_n \in S$ and f is continuous on S, there exists a convergence test ϕ such that if $x \in N(x_n, \phi(\epsilon)) \cap S$ then

$$|f(x) - f(x_n)| < \epsilon.$$

In particular since

$$x_n = \sup \left\{ x \in S \mid f(x) \in N\left(y, \frac{1}{n}\right) \right\},$$

it follows that there exists an x in

$$\left\{ x \in S \mid f(x) \in N\left(y, \frac{1}{n}\right) \right\}$$

such that $x_n - \phi(\epsilon_1) < x \leq x_n$. Therefore $x \in N(x_n, \phi(\epsilon_1)) \cap S$ and hence

$$|f(x) - f(x_n)| < \epsilon_1.$$

Then $f(x) \in N(f(x_n), \epsilon_1)$ and since

$$N(f(x_n), \epsilon_1) \cap \overline{N\left(y, \frac{1}{n}\right)} = \varnothing$$

it follows that

$$f(x) \notin N\left(y, \frac{1}{n}\right).$$

This is a contradiction that forces us to conclude that for each positive integer n

$$f(x_n) \in \overline{N\left(y, \frac{1}{n}\right)}.$$

Consequently

$$\operatorname*{Lim}_{n \to \infty} f(x_n) = y.$$

(Why?) Since every subsequence of $\{f(x_n)\}_1$ must also converge to y, it follows that

$$\operatorname*{Lim}_{n \to \infty} f(x_{m_n}) = y.$$

Therefore $y = f(x)$ and hence $y \in f[S]$.

We will prove by contradiction that $f[S]$ is bounded. If $f[S]$ is not bounded, then for each positive integer n there exists an x in S for which

$$|f(x)| > n.$$

It then follows that $\{x \in S \mid |f(x)| > n\}$ is nonempty and bounded. If

$$x_n = \sup \{x \in S \mid |f(x)| > n\}, \quad n \geq 1,$$

then $\{x_n\}_1$ is a bounded sequence of elements of S, (why?) and hence it has a convergent subsequence $\{x_{m_n}\}_1$. If

$$\operatorname*{Lim}_{n \to \infty} x_{m_n} = a$$

then $a \in S$. Since f is continuous on S there exists a convergence test ϕ such that

$$\text{if } x \in N(a, \phi(\epsilon)) \cap S, \text{ then } |f(x) - f(a)| < \epsilon.$$

In particular if $x \in N(a, \phi(1)) \cap S$, then $|f(x) - f(a)| < 1$. Since $|f(x)| - |f(a)| \leq |f(x) - f(a)|$ it then follows that

$$|f(x)| < |f(a)| + 1.$$

Since $\{x_{m_n}\}_1$ converges to a, it follows that there exists an integer n such that $m_n > |f(a)| + 1$ and $x_{m_n} \in N(a, \phi(1))$. We then have the contradiction that

$$|f(x_{m_n})| < |f(a)| + 1 \text{ and } |f(x_{m_n})| > m_n.$$

Q.E.D.

By appealing to the axiom of choice and the Heine-Borel Theorem we obtain the following interesting proof of Theorem 6.40.

Second Proof. To prove that $f[S]$ is closed, it is sufficient to prove that it contains all of its accumulation points. If y is an accumulation point of $f[S]$, then from Theorem 5.80 it follows that there exists a sequence, $\{y_n\}_1$, of elements of $f[S]$ that converges to y, that is,

$$\lim_{n \to \infty} y_n = y.$$

But since $y_n \in f[S]$, $n \geq 1$, it follows that for each positive integer n there exists an x in S for which

$$y_n = f(x).$$

From the axiom of choice it then follows that there exists a sequence $\{x_n\}_1$ of elements of S for which

$$y_n = f(x_n).$$

(Why?) Since S is bounded it follows that $\{x_n\}_1$ is a bounded sequence. It therefore has a convergent subsequence $\{x_{m_n}\}_1$. If

$$\lim_{n \to \infty} x_{m_n} = a$$

then $a \in S$. Since f is continuous on S, it then follows from the Stolz criterion that

$$\lim_{n \to \infty} f(x_{m_n}) = f(a).$$

On the other hand, since $y_n = f(x_n)$ and since $\{y_n\}_1$ converges to y, it follows that $\{f(x_n)\}_1$ must also converge to y. But since $\{f(x_n)\}_1$ converges to y, each subsequence of $\{f(x_n)\}_1$ must also converge to y. In particular, we must have that

$$\lim_{n \to \infty} f(x_{m_n}) = y.$$

Therefore $y = f(a)$ and hence $y \in f[S]$.

To prove that $f[S]$ is bounded, recall that for each x in S the restriction of f to S is continuous at x; hence the restriction is bounded in some neighborhood of x, i.e.,

$$(\exists b)(\exists \delta) \; \forall x \in N(x, \delta) \cap S, \quad |f(x)| < b.$$

Therefore if $\mathscr{C} = \{N(x, \delta) \mid \delta > 0, \; x \in S,$ and the restriction of f to S is bounded in $N(x, \delta)\}$, then $\mathscr{C}$ is an open covering for S. Since S is closed and bounded it follows from the Heine-Borel theorem that $\mathscr{C}$ contains a finite subcover:

$$\{N(a_1, \delta_1), \; N(a_2, \delta_2), \; \ldots, \; N(a_n, \delta_n)\}.$$

But by definition of $\mathscr{C}$ we have that f is bounded in $N(a_\alpha, \delta_\alpha)$, $\alpha = 1, 2, \ldots, n$; that is, there exist numbers $b_1, b_2, \ldots, b_n$ such that

$$|f(x)| < b_\alpha \text{ if } x \in N(a_\alpha, \delta_\alpha) \cap S.$$

If $b = \max \{b_1, b_2, \ldots, b_n\}$, then since for each x in S there exists an α for which

$$x \in N(a_\alpha, \delta_\alpha)$$

it follows that

$$|f(x)| < b$$

and hence $f[S]$ is bounded.

Q.E.D.

From Theorem 6.40 it follows that if f is continuous on a closed and bounded nonempty set S, then $\min f[S]$ and $\max f[S]$ exist. Indeed if S is a closed and bounded interval, then f not only assumes on S a minimal value and a maximal value but also all values in between. The proof follows easily from

Theorem 6.41. *If f is continuous on $[a, b]$ and* 1) $f(a) < 0 < f(b)$ *or* 2) $f(b) < 0 < f(a)$, *then for some c in $[a, b]$ we have that $f(c) = 0$.*

Proof. If $f(a) < 0 < f(b)$ and if $M = \{x \in [a, b] \mid f(x) \le 0\}$, then since $f(a) < 0$, it follows that $M \ne \varnothing$. Since $M \subseteq [a, b]$ it follows that M is bounded. Then M has a supremum c. Furthermore $c \in [a, b]$. We will prove that $f(c) = 0$. The proof is by contradiction.

If $f(c) > 0$, then since the restriction of f to $[a, b]$ is continuous at c there exists a δ such that

$$\forall x \in N(c, \delta) \cap [a, b], \quad f(x) > 0.$$

(See Exercise 27, page 209.) But this means that $N(c, \delta)$ contains no elements of M. This contradicts the fact that $c = \sup M$.

On the other hand, if $f(c) < 0$, there exists a δ such that

$$\forall x \in N(c, \delta) \cap [a, b], \quad f(x) < 0.$$

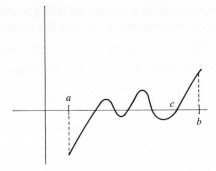

FIGURE 6.5

(See Exercise 28, page 209.) Since $c < b$ (why?), this means that c is not an upper bound for M, which again contradicts the fact that $c = \sup M$. Since we must have that $f(c) < 0$ or $f(c) = 0$ or $f(c) > 0$, we conclude that $f(c) = 0$.

If $f(b) < 0 < f(a)$, then we note that $-f$ is continuous on $[a, b]$ and $(-f)(a) < 0 < (-f)(b)$. By the argument above it then follows that for some c in $[a, b]$ we have that $(-f)(c) = 0$. But $(-f)(c) = -(f(c))$. Since $-(f(c)) = 0$ we conclude that $f(c) = 0$.

Q.E.D.

Theorem 6.41 asserts that a function that is continuous on a closed interval, that has a negative value at one end point and a positive value at the other end point must be zero somewhere in between. The beauty of this simple and obvious result is marred by the fact that its statement and proof are fragmented into cases. The reader may be interested in knowing that this theorem can be stated and proved without an appeal to cases. This we will show by a statement and proof that is marred only by its lack of simplicity.

A convenient way to specify that f has a negative value at one end point of $[a, b]$ and a positive value at the other end point without specifying which, is to specify that $f(a)f(b) < 0$. It is therefore sufficient to prove that if f is continuous on $[a, b]$ and if $f(a)f(b) < 0$, then there is a number c in $[a, b]$ for which $f(c) = 0$.

Second Proof of Theorem 6.41. If

$$M = \{x \in [a, b] \mid f(x)f(a) \geq 0\}$$

then since $f(a)f(a) \geq 0$ it follows that $M \neq \varnothing$. Furthermore, M is bounded. Therefore M has a supremum c and $c \in [a, b]$. We will now prove that $f(c) = 0$. The proof is by contradiction.

If

$$g(x) = f^2(a)f(c)f(x), \quad x \in [a, b],$$

then since f is continuous on $[a, b]$ it follows that g is continuous on $[a, b]$. Therefore there exists a convergence test ϕ with the property that

$$\forall x \in N(c, \phi(\epsilon)) \cap [a, b], \quad |g(x) - g(c)| < \epsilon.$$

In particular if $f(c) \neq 0$, then it follows that for every x in

$$N\left(c, \phi\left(\frac{f^2(a)f^2(c)}{2}\right)\right) \cap [a, b]$$

we have that $|g(x) - g(c)| < \frac{1}{2}f^2(a)f^2(c)$, that is,

$$-\tfrac{1}{2}f^2(a)f^2(c) < f^2(a)f(c)f(x) - f^2(a)f^2(c),$$
$$\tfrac{1}{2}f^2(a)f^2(c) < [f(c)f(a)][f(x)f(a)].$$

This means that $f(c)f(a)$ and $f(x)f(a)$ each have the same sign. Therefore $x \in M$ if and only if $c \in M$. But this is true for each x in $N(c, \phi(f^2(a)f^2(c)/2))$ $\cap [a, b]$. Since this contradicts the fact that $c = \sup M$, we are forced to conclude that $f(c) = 0$.

$$\text{Q.E.D.}$$

Let us now consider some interesting consequences of Theorem 6.41.

Theorem 6.42. *There exists an nth root of a if* 1) *n is a positive odd integer or* 2) *n is a positive even integer and a is positive.*

Proof. If $f(x) = x^n - a$ with $a > 0$, then $f(0) < 0$, because $f(0) = -a$, and $f(a + 1) > 0$, because $(a + 1)^n > a$. Furthermore f is continuous on $[0, a + 1]$. Therefore there exists a number c in $[0, a + 1]$ for which $f(c) = 0$ and hence $c^n = a$. If $f(x) = x^n - a$ with $a < 0$ and n odd, then $f(a - 1) < 0$ and $f(0) > 0$. Therefore for some c in $[a - 1, 0]$ we have that $f(c) = 0$ and hence $c^n = a$.

$$\text{Q.E.D.}$$

The reader may wish to compare the very simple proof of Theorem 6.42 with the lengthy and involved argument given in Chapter 4.

Theorem 6.43 (Fixed Point Theorem). *If f is continuous on $[a, b]$ and maps $[a, b]$ onto $[a, b]$, then for some x in $[a, b]$ we have that $f(x) = x$.*

Proof. If $g(x) = f(x) - x$, then $g(a) \geq 0$ and $g(b) \leq 0$. If $g(a) = 0$, then $f(a) = a$. If $g(b) = 0$, then $f(b) = b$. If $g(b) < 0 < g(a)$, then since g is continuous on $[a, b]$, there exists a c in $[a, b]$ for which $g(c) = 0$ and hence $f(c) = c$.

$$\text{Q.E.D.}$$

Theorem 6.44 (The Intermediate Value Theorem). *If f is continuous on $[a, b]$, then for each y such that $\inf f[a, b] \leq y \leq \sup f[a, b]$ there exists an x in $[a, b]$ for which $f(x) = y$; i.e., if f is continuous on $[a, b]$ then f maps $[a, b]$ onto a closed and bounded interval.*

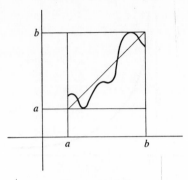

FIGURE 6.6

Proof. Since f is continuous on $[a, b]$, it follows that $f[a, b]$ is closed and bounded. Since $f[a, b]$ is also nonempty, it follows that both $\inf f[a, b]$ and $\sup f[a, b]$ exist. Furthermore if $c = \inf f[a, b]$, there exists an x_1 in $[a, b]$ for which $f(x_1) = c$. If $d = \sup f[a, b]$, then there exists an x_2 in $[a, b]$ for which $f(x_2) = d$.

If $c < y < d$ and if $g(x) = f(x) - y$, $x \in [a, b]$, then $g(x_1) < 0$ and $g(x_2) > 0$. Therefore between x_1 and x_2 there is an x for which $g(x) = 0$ and hence $f(x) = y$. It then follows that f maps $[a, b]$ onto $[c, d]$.

Q.E.D.

We turn now to another important property of continuity, the property of *uniform continuity*. We defined the phrase 'f is continuous on S' to mean that the restriction of f to S is continuous at each point of S. That is to say, f is continuous on S iff $S \subseteq \operatorname{Dom} f$ and

$$\forall x \in S, (\exists \phi) \quad \forall y \in S, \text{ if } |y - x| < \phi(\epsilon), \text{ then } |f(y) - f(x)| < \epsilon.$$

Thus if f is continuous on S, then for each x in S there exists a convergence test ϕ_x with the prescribed property. In general there is no reason to believe that the same convergence test will work for two different points in S. There are, however, functions f and sets S for which one convergence test does work for each x in S. That is $S \subseteq \operatorname{Dom} f$ and

$$(\exists \phi) \forall x \in S, \quad \forall y \in S, \text{ if } |y - x| < \phi(\epsilon), \text{ then } |f(y) - f(x)| < \epsilon.$$

Such a function is said to be *uniformly continuous on S*.

Definition 6.45. f is *uniformly continuous on S* iff there exists a convergence test ϕ with the property that for each x and y in S

$$\text{if } |y - x| < \phi(\epsilon) \text{ then } |f(y) - f(x)| < \epsilon.$$

We leave to the reader the proof of the following results.

Theorem 6.46. *If f is uniformly continuous on S, then f is continuous on S.*

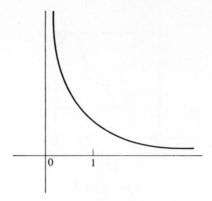

FIGURE 6.7

Theorem 6.47. *If $S \subseteq \operatorname{Dom} f$ then f is not uniformly continuous on S iff*
$(\exists \epsilon)(\forall \delta)\ \exists x \in S,\ \exists y \in S,\ |x - y| < \delta\ and\ |f(x) - f(y)| \geq \epsilon.$

From Theorem 6.46 we see that uniform continuity on S implies continuity on S. Uniform continuity on S is, however, more than just continuity on S as the following examples illustrate.

Example. If $S = (0, 1)$ and if

$$f(x) = \frac{1}{x}, \quad x \neq 0,$$

then f is continuous on S but f is not uniformly continuous on S. Indeed if $\epsilon = 1$ then for each δ we have that if $x = \min \{\frac{1}{2}, \delta\}$, and if $y = x/(1 + x)$ then $x \in (0, 1)$, $y \in (0, 1)$,

$$|x - y| = \left| x - \frac{x}{1 + x} \right| = x\,\frac{x}{1 + x} < x < \delta.$$

But

$$|f(x) - f(y)| = \left| \frac{1}{x} - \frac{1 + x}{x} \right| = 1.$$

From Theorem 6.47 it then follows that f is not uniformly continuous on $(0, 1)$. From Figure 6.7 we see that the difficulty is that near zero we can find numbers x and y as close together as we please, but such that $|f(x) - f(y)|$ is as large as we please.

From this observation we might be led to conjecture that f is not uniformly continuous on $(0, 1)$ because it is not bounded on $(0, 1)$. This, however, is not quite the source of difficulty. It is not the unboundedness but rather the fact that there are subintervals, $[x, y]$, in $(0, 1)$ which are as small as one pleases but on which the curve is so steep that $|f(x) - f(y)|$ does not

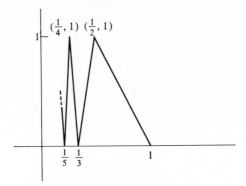

FIGURE 6.8

have to be small. Such subintervals can exist even with bounded functions as the following example illustrates.

Example. If $S = (0, 1)$ and if f is the function of Exercise 22, page 205, whose graph is the broken line curve of Figure 6.8, then f is bounded and continuous on $(0, 1)$ but not uniformly continuous, for if $\epsilon = 1$ then for each δ there exists an integer n such that $1/n < \delta$ and hence

$$\left|\frac{1}{n} - \frac{1}{n + 1}\right| < \delta \text{ but } \left|f\left(\frac{1}{n}\right) - f\left(\frac{1}{n + 1}\right)\right| = 1.$$

Note, that in this example and the preceding one we must move closer and closer to the origin for smaller and smaller values of δ in order to find intervals on which the property of uniform continuity is violated. Moreover, such intervals would not exist if the function were continuous at 0. This observation might lead us to conjecture that continuity on a closed set implies uniform continuity. But this conjecture is also false, as the following example shows.

Example. If $S = [2\frac{1}{2}, \infty)$ and if f is the function of Exercise 21, page 208, whose graph is the broken line curve of Figure 6.9, then again f is bounded and continuous on S but not uniformly continuous. (Why?)

This example depends upon having an unbounded set S. We then arrive at a final and correct conjecture—namely, continuity on a closed and bounded set implies uniform continuity.

Theorem 6.48. *If S is closed and bounded and if f is continuous on S, then f is uniformly continuous on S.*

Proof. (By contradiction.) If f were not uniformly continuous on S, then for some ϵ_1 it would be true that for every δ there is an x and y in S such that

$$|x - y| < \delta \text{ and } \epsilon_1 \le |f(x) - f(y)|.$$

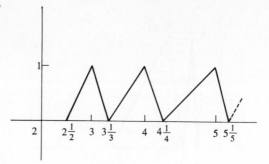

FIGURE 6.9

In particular, for each positive integer n if $\delta = 1/n$ then there exists an x and y in S such that

$$|x - y| < \frac{1}{n} \text{ and } |f(x) - f(y)| \geq \epsilon_1.$$

Thus if

$$A_n = \left\{ x \in S \mid \exists y \in S, \ |x - y| < \frac{1}{n}, \text{ and } |f(x) - f(y)| \geq \epsilon_1 \right\}, \quad n \geq 1,$$

then A_n is nonempty and bounded. If

$$x_n = \sup A_n, \quad n \geq 1,$$

then $\{x_n\}_1$ is a bounded sequence of elements of S, and hence the limit superior of $\{x_n\}_1$ exists. If

$$\overline{\lim_{n \to \infty}} \, x_n = a$$

then $a \in S$. (Why?) Furthermore since f is continuous at a there exists a convergence test ϕ such that

$$\forall x \in N(a, \phi(\epsilon)) \cap S, \quad |f(x) - f(a)| < \epsilon.$$

In particular we have that

$$\forall x \in N\left(a, \phi\left(\frac{\epsilon_1}{2}\right)\right) \cap S, \quad |f(x) - f(a)| < \frac{\epsilon_1}{2}.$$

Since

$$\overline{\lim_{n \to \infty}} \, x_n = a$$

it follows that there exists an integer n_1 that is greater than $4/\phi(\epsilon_1/2)$ for which

$$x_{n_1} \in N\left(a, \tfrac{1}{4}\phi\left(\frac{\epsilon_1}{2}\right)\right).$$

Since

$$x_{n_1} = \sup A_{n_1}$$

it follows that there exists an x in A_{n_1} such that

$$x_{n_1} - \tfrac{1}{4}\phi\!\left(\tfrac{\epsilon_1}{2}\right) < x \le x_{n_1}.$$

Furthermore since $x \in A_{n_1}$ there is a y in S such that

$$|x - y| < \frac{1}{n_1} \text{ and } |f(x) - f(y)| \ge \epsilon_1.$$

But since $1/n_1 < \tfrac{1}{4}\phi(\epsilon_1/2)$ it follows that

$$y \in N\!\left(x, \tfrac{1}{4}\phi\!\left(\tfrac{\epsilon_1}{2}\right)\right),$$
$$x \in N\!\left(x_{n_1}, \tfrac{1}{4}\phi\!\left(\tfrac{\epsilon_1}{2}\right)\right).$$

Therefore

$$y \in N\!\left(x_{n_1}, \tfrac{1}{2}\phi\!\left(\tfrac{\epsilon_1}{2}\right)\right).$$

But since

$$N\!\left(x_{n_1}, \tfrac{1}{4}\phi\!\left(\tfrac{\epsilon_1}{2}\right)\right) \subseteq N\!\left(x_{n_1}, \tfrac{1}{2}\phi\!\left(\tfrac{\epsilon_1}{2}\right)\right)$$

we have that

$$x \in N\!\left(x_{n_1}, \tfrac{1}{2}\phi\!\left(\tfrac{\epsilon_1}{2}\right)\right).$$

We also have that

$$x_{n_1} \in N\!\left(a, \tfrac{1}{2}\phi\!\left(\tfrac{\epsilon_1}{2}\right)\right)$$

from which it follows that

$$x \in N\!\left(a, \phi\!\left(\tfrac{\epsilon_1}{2}\right)\right),$$
$$y \in N\!\left(a, \phi\!\left(\tfrac{\epsilon_1}{2}\right)\right),$$

and hence

$$\begin{aligned}
|f(x) - f(y)| &= |f(x) - f(a) + f(a) - f(y)| \\
&\le |f(x) - f(a)| + |f(y) - f(a)| \\
&\le \frac{\epsilon_1}{2} + \frac{\epsilon_1}{2} = \epsilon_1.
\end{aligned}$$

This is a contradiction that forces us to conclude that f is uniformly continuous on S.

Q.E.D.

Second Proof.   Since f is continuous on S, it follows that for each x in S there exists a convergence test ϕ such that

$$\forall y \in N\!\left(x, \phi\!\left(\tfrac{\epsilon}{2}\right)\right) \cap S, \quad |f(y) - f(x)| < \frac{\epsilon}{2}.$$

From this it follows for each ϵ that if

$$\mathcal{C}_\epsilon = \left\{ N(x, \delta) \mid \delta > 0,\, x \in S,\, \text{and } \forall y \in N(x, \delta) \cap S,\, |f(y) - f(x)| < \frac{\epsilon}{2} \right\}$$

then $\mathcal{C}_\epsilon$ is an open covering of S. Since S is closed and bounded it follows, from the Heine-Borel theorem that $\mathcal{C}_\epsilon$ contains a finite subcovering

$$\{ N(x_1, \delta_1), \ldots, N(x_n, \delta_n) \}.$$

Furthermore from Theorem 5.82 it follows that there exists a number δ with the property that for each x and y in S if $|x - y| < \delta$ then for some integer m with $1 \le m \le n$

$$x \in N(x_m, \delta_m) \text{ and } y \in N(x_m, \delta_m). \cdot$$

Therefore

$$|f(x) - f(y)| = |f(x) - f(x_m) + f(x_m) - f(y)| \le |f(x) - f(x_m)|$$
$$+ |f(y) - f(x_m)| < \frac{\epsilon}{2} + \frac{\epsilon}{2} = \epsilon.$$

From this it follows that if

$$A_\epsilon = \{ S \mid \forall x \in S,\, \forall y \in S,\, \text{if } |x - y| < \delta \text{ then } |f(x) - f(y)| < \epsilon \}$$

then A_ϵ is not empty. If A_ϵ is bounded above, then $\sup A_\epsilon$ exists. We then define ψ by

$$\psi(\epsilon) = \tfrac{1}{2} \sup A_\epsilon \quad \text{if } A_\epsilon \text{ is bounded},$$
$$\psi(\epsilon) = 1 \qquad\qquad \text{if } A_\epsilon \text{ is unbounded}.$$

It then follows that for each x and y in S if $|x - y| < \psi(\epsilon)$ then there exists a δ in A_ϵ for which $|x - y| < \delta$ and hence $|f(x) - f(y)| < \epsilon$. Therefore f is uniformly continuous on S.

$$\text{Q.E.D.}$$

EXERCISES

1. Prove: If f is continuous on $[a, b]$, then f is one-to-one on $[a, b]$ iff f is strictly monotone on $[a, b]$.

2. Prove: If f is continuous and one-to-one on $[a, b]$, then f^{-1} is continuous on $f[a, b]$.

3. Prove: The inverse of a strictly monotone function is strictly monotone.

4. Prove: The function f defined by

$$f(x) = x \qquad x \in [0, 1] \qquad x \text{ rational}$$
$$= 2 - x \qquad x \in [1, 2] \qquad x \text{ irrational}$$

is continuous at each point of its domain, it is one-to-one, but its inverse is not continuous on its domain. Why doesn't this contradict the result of Exercise 2?

5. Prove: If f is uniformly continuous on S, and if $g \subset f$, then g is uniformly continuous on $S \cap \text{Dom } g$.

6.5 The Trigonometric Functions

In the introductory section of Chapter 5 we defined several special functions. Notably absent from the list of functions that we defined there are the trigonometric functions. The reason for their exclusion is that we do not, at this point, have the means to define them; more precisely we do not have the means to define them in the way that we wish them to be defined.

Let us recall that intuitively we understand the sine and cosine to be functions that map the set of real numbers into itself and so defined that if 'θ' is a real variable and if beginning with the point $(1, 0)$ and measuring counterclockwise we measure along the unit circle (see Figure 6.10) an arc of length θ, then the coordinates of the other end point of this arc will be $(\cos \theta, \sin \theta)$. Therefore in order to define the sine and cosine functions it is sufficient to have a function f which maps real numbers θ onto ordered pairs of real numbers (x, y) in such a way that $x^2 + y^2 = 1$ and (x, y) and $(1, 0)$ are end points of an arc of the unit circle whose length is θ. The basic problem is that of defining length. This we will do later. We will also prove that such a function f exists. It is plausible that such a function is continuous in the sense that if ϕ is a real number near θ, then $f(\phi)$ is a point on the unit circle near $f(\theta)$. Therefore if we define sin and cos by

$$\sin \theta = y \text{ and } \cos \theta = x \text{ iff } (x, y) = f(\theta)$$

it will then follow that sin and cos are continuous functions with the property that

$$\sin^2 \theta + \cos^2 \theta = 1.$$

Since the existence of the function f will not be proved until Chapter 8, we choose to postulate the existence of the two trigonometric functions sin

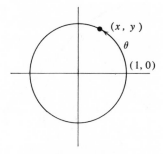

FIGURE 6.10

and cos as functions defined and continuous on the set of real numbers, which have the following properties.

1) $\cos 0 = 1$, $\sin \pi/2 = 1$.
2) $\sin (\theta - \phi) = \sin \theta \cos \phi - \cos \theta \sin \phi$.
3) $\cos (\theta - \phi) = \cos \theta \cos \phi + \sin \theta \sin \phi$.
4) $\displaystyle \lim_{\theta \to 0} \frac{\sin \theta}{\theta} = 1$.

Definition 6.50. $\tan = \dfrac{\sin}{\cos}$. $\cot = \dfrac{\cos}{\sin}$.

$\sec = \dfrac{1}{\cos}$. $\csc = \dfrac{1}{\sin}$.

From our earlier experiences with the trigonometric functions the properties 1–3 are, we hope, reasonable ones. Property 4, however, may not seem obvious to the reader. For it we offer the following heuristic argument. (See Figure 6.11.)

The area of the triangle OAB is less than the area of the sector of the circle OAC, which is in turn less than the area of the triangle OAD where AD is tangent to the circle at A. If AC is an arc of the unit circle of length θ, then AB is of length $\sin \theta$, OB is of length $\cos \theta$, AD is of length $\tan \theta$, and OA is of length 1. Therefore, the area of the triangle OAB is $\frac{1}{2} \sin \theta \cos \theta$, the area of the sector OAC is $\theta/2$, and the area of the triangle OAD is $\frac{1}{2} \tan \theta$. We then have that

$$\tfrac{1}{2} \sin \theta \cos \theta \le \tfrac{1}{2}\theta \text{ and } \tfrac{1}{2}\theta \le \tfrac{1}{2} \tan \theta.$$

Since $\cos 0 = 1$ and cos is continuous, it follows that there exists a δ such that for each θ in $N(0, \delta)$, $\cos \theta > 0$. Thus for sufficiently small θ we have that $\cos \theta$ is positive; hence, from the above inequalities,

$$\theta \cos \theta \le \sin \theta \le \frac{\theta}{\cos \theta}.$$

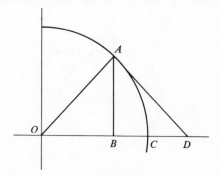

FIGURE 6.11

From this we see that

$$\text{if } \theta > 0, \text{ then } \cos \theta \leq \frac{\sin \theta}{\theta} \leq \frac{1}{\cos \theta},$$

and

$$\text{if } \theta < 0, \text{ then } \frac{1}{\cos \theta} \leq \frac{\sin \theta}{\theta} \leq \cos \theta.$$

Again since $\cos 0 = 1$ and since $\cos$ is continuous at 0, it follows that $\underset{\theta \to 0}{\text{Lim}} \cos \theta = 1$. We then have that

$$1 \leq \underset{\theta \to 0^+}{\text{Lim}} \frac{\sin \theta}{\theta} \leq 1,$$

$$1 \leq \underset{\theta \to 0^-}{\text{Lim}} \frac{\sin \theta}{\theta} \leq 1,$$

$$\underset{\theta \to 0}{\text{Lim}} \frac{\sin \theta}{\theta} = 1.$$

EXERCISES

1. $\sin 0 = 0$.
2. $\sin^2 \theta + \cos^2 \theta = 1$.
3. $\tan^2 \theta + 1 = \sec^2 \theta$.
4. $\cot^2 \theta + 1 = \csc^2 \theta$.
5. $\cos \pi/2 = 0$.
6. $\sin (-\theta) = -\sin \theta$.
7. $\cos (-\theta) = \cos \theta$.
8. $\sin (\theta + \phi) = \sin \theta \cos \phi + \cos \theta \sin \theta$.
9. $\cos (\theta + \phi) = \cos \theta \cos \phi - \sin \theta \sin \phi$.
10. $\sin 2\theta = 2 \sin \theta \cos \theta$.
11. $\cos 2\theta = \cos^2 \theta - \sin^2 \theta$.
12. $\sin (\theta + \pi/2) = \cos \theta$.
13. $\sin \pi = 0$, $\cos \pi = -1$.
14. $\sin 3\pi/2 = -1$, $\cos 3\pi/2 = 0$.
15. $\sin 2\pi = 0$, $\cos 2\pi = 1$.
16. $\sin (\theta + 2\pi) = \sin \theta$.
17. $\cos (\theta + 2\pi) = \cos \theta$.

6.6 Parameterization

From the material of the last section we see that the trigonometric functions provide an interesting means of describing the unit circle. By the unit circle we mean the graph of the relation

$$\{(x, y) \mid x^2 + y^2 = 1\}.$$

This relation can also be described as

$$\{(\cos \theta, \sin \theta) \mid \theta \in [0, 2\pi]\}.$$

This observation suggests a very interesting possibility for the study of relations in general. If A is a relation and if there exist functions f and g and a set S for which $S \subseteq \operatorname{Dom} f \cap \operatorname{Dom} g$ and

$$A = \{(g(x), f(x)) \mid x \in S\}$$

then it seems reasonable to hope that we may be able to deduce interesting things about the relation A from known properties of the functions f and g.

Such a description of a relation A we will call a *parameterization* of A. It is clear that in general a relation does not have a unique parameterization. For example,

$$\{ (\cos \theta, \sin \theta) \mid \theta \in [0, 2\pi] \} = \{ (\sin (\theta + \pi/2), \cos (\theta - \pi/2)) \mid \theta \in [0, 2\pi] \}.$$

We will now prove the somewhat surprising result that every relation on the real numbers has at least one parameterization.

Theorem 6.60. *For each relation A if $A \subseteq R \times R$ then there exist functions f and g and a set S such that $S \subseteq \operatorname{Dom} f \cap \operatorname{Dom} g$, $A = \{ (g(x), f(x)) \mid x \in S \}$, and if $F(x) = (g(x), f(x))$, $x \in S$ then F maps S one-to-one onto A.*

Analysis. The proof consists of showing that from any pair of real numbers (y, z) we can obtain a third number x by "interweaving" the decimal expansion for y and z as illustrated by the following example:

$$y = .333 \cdots$$
$$z = .222 \cdots$$
$$x = .3232 \cdots.$$

We then define S as the set of all numbers x that can be obtained in this way from pairs (y, z) in A, and we define f and g by

$$g(x) = y, \quad f(x) = z.$$

The single valuedness of f and g and the one-to-oneness for F are a consequence of the fact that every real number has a unique nonterminating decimal expansion. Therefore x is uniquely determined by y and z, and conversely y and z are uniquely determined by an appropriately chosen x. We must guard against the choice of certain types of numbers x as, for example,

$$.10101 \cdots$$

which upon "dissection" gives one nonterminating decimal

$$.111 \cdots$$

and one terminating, and hence unacceptable, decimal

$$.000 \cdots.$$

Proof. If $A \subseteq R \times R$ and if $(y, z) \in A$, then y and z each have a unique nonterminating decimal representation. That is, there exist sequences of integers $\{a_m\}_{-n}$ and $\{b_m\}_{-n}$ such that $n \geq 0, 0 \leq a_m \leq 9, 0 \leq b_m \leq 9$; each sequence has an infinite subsequence of positive terms,

$$y = \sum_{\alpha = -n}^{\infty} \frac{a_\alpha}{10^\alpha} \text{ and } z = \sum_{\alpha = -n}^{\infty} \frac{b_\alpha}{10^\alpha}.$$

Therefore if

$$x = \sum_{\alpha = -2n}^{\infty} \frac{c_\alpha}{10^\alpha} \quad \text{where } c_{2\alpha} = a_\alpha, \quad \alpha \geq -n,$$

$$c_{2\alpha + 1} = b_\alpha, \quad \alpha \geq -n,$$

then since the decimal expansions for y and z are nonterminating, x has a nonterminating expansion with the additional property that for each integer k there exist integers s and t such that $s > k$, $t > k$, $c_{2s} \neq 0$ and $c_{2t+1} \neq 0$. Therefore if

$$S = \left\{ x \mid \text{there exists a sequence of integer } \{c_m\}_{-2n} \text{ such that} \right.$$

$n > 0, 0 \leq c_m \leq 9$; for each integer k there exist integers s and t such that $s > k, t > k, c_{2s} \neq 0, c_{2t+1} \neq 0$, and

$$\left. \left(\sum_{\alpha = -n}^{\infty} \frac{c_{2\alpha}}{10^\alpha}, \sum_{\alpha = -n}^{\infty} \frac{c_{2\alpha + 1}}{10^\alpha} \right) \in A \right\}$$

then it follows that for each (y, z) in A there exists one and only one x in S, as described, for which

$$y = \sum_{\alpha = -n}^{\infty} \frac{c_{2\alpha}}{10^\alpha} \text{ and } z = \sum_{\alpha = -n}^{\infty} \frac{c_{2\alpha + 1}}{10^\alpha}.$$

We then define f and g in the obvious way, namely

$$g(x) = y \text{ and } f(x) = z, \quad x \in S.$$

We then have that

$$A = \{ (g(x), f(x)) \mid x \in S \}.$$

Finally, if

$$F(x) = (g(x), f(x)), \quad x \in S,$$

then clearly F maps S onto A. That F is one-to-one is easily proved. Indeed if $F(x) = F(x')$ it follows that $f(x) = f(x')$ and $g(x) = g(x')$. Therefore if

$$x = \sum_{\alpha = -2n}^{\infty} \frac{c_\alpha}{10^\alpha} \text{ and } x' = \sum_{\alpha = -2n}^{\infty} \frac{c'_\alpha}{10^\alpha}$$

then

$$\sum_{\alpha=-n}^{\infty} \frac{c_{2\alpha}}{10^{\alpha}} = \sum_{\alpha=-n}^{\infty} \frac{c'_{2\alpha}}{10^{\alpha}} \quad \text{and} \quad \sum_{\alpha=-n}^{\infty} \frac{c_{2\alpha+1}}{10^{\alpha}} = \sum_{\alpha=-n}^{\infty} \frac{c'_{2\alpha+1}}{10^{\alpha}}.$$

From the uniqueness theorem for decimal representations it follows that

$$c_{2\alpha} = c'_{2\alpha}, \quad \alpha \geq -n,$$
$$c_{2\alpha+1} = c'_{2\alpha+1}, \quad \alpha \geq -n.$$

Therefore $x = x'$ and F is one-to-one.

Q.E.D.

Theorem 6.60 is an existence theorem that assures us that every relation has a parameterization. It, however, offers no practical method for obtaining one. The functions f and g that occur in the proof are very complicated functions defined on a very peculiar set S. Note, however, that the set of real numbers can be mapped one-to-one onto any closed and bounded interval $[a, b]$. From this it follows that every relation has a parameterization with $S \subseteq [a, b]$. If S can also be mapped one-to-one onto the set of real numbers then it follows that the relation has a parameterization for which $S = [a, b]$. We will be interested in relations for which this is the case. Hereafter when we speak of a parameterization of a relation A we will mean that there exists an interval $[a, b]$ and there exist functions f and g each defined on $[a, b]$ for which

$$A = \{\, (g(x), f(x)) \mid x \in [a, b] \,\}.$$

The existence of such a parameterization suggests a natural extension of the notion of continuity to relations. A relation A is continuous if there exists an interval $[a, b]$ and there exist functions f and g each defined on $[a, b]$ for which

$$A = \{\, (g(x), f(x)) \mid x \in [a, b] \,\}$$

and for each y in $[a, b]$ and each x in $[a, b]$ if x is near y then $(g(x), f(x))$ is near $(g(y), f(y))$ in the sense that

$$\sqrt{[g(x) - g(y)]^2 + [f(x) - f(y)]^2}$$

is small. This in turn means that

$$[g(x) - g(y)]^2 + [f(x) - f(y)]^2$$

must be small, which means that $f(x)$ must be near $f(y)$ and $g(x)$ must be near $g(y)$. That is, f and g must be continuous at y. Conversely if f and g are continuous at y, then $(g(x), f(x))$ can be compelled to lie as close to $(g(y), f(y))$ as we please by restricting x to a sufficiently small neighborhood of y.

Definition 6.61. The *relation A is continuous* iff there exists an interval $[a, b]$ and there exist functions f and g each continuous on $[a, b]$ such that

$$A = \{ (g(x), f(x)) \mid x \in [a, b] \}.$$

The graph of a continuous relation we will call a *continuous curve*.

Those continuous curves that are of greatest interest to us in the material ahead are the *simple curves*. In simple language a simple curve is one that is not self-intersecting except possibly for the end points. If the end points coincide, we then have a *simple closed curve*.

Example. The unit circle is a simple closed curve because

$$\{ (x, y) \mid x^2 + y^2 = 1 \} = \{ (\cos 2\pi\theta, \sin 2\pi\theta) \mid \theta \in [0, 1] \}.$$

Here $g(\theta) = \cos 2\pi\theta$ and $f(\theta) = \sin 2\pi\theta$. Both f and g are continuous on $[0, 1]$. Furthermore $g(0) = g(1)$, $f(0) = f(1)$, and for each θ and ϕ in $(0, 1)$, if $(g(\theta), f(\theta)) = (g(\phi), f(\phi))$ then $\theta = \phi$.

Example. The graph of every function f that is continuous on $[a, b]$ is a continuous curve, since if $g(x) = x$, $x \in [a, b]$ we have that

$$f = \{ (g(x), f(x)) \mid x \in [a, b] \}.$$

⋆6.7 The Schröder-Bernstein Theorem

This section is intended for the reader who is particularly interested in set theory. It may be omitted without loss of continuity. We wish to direct attention to one particular implication of Theorem 6.60, specifically that since $R \times R$ is a relation on R there exists a function that maps $R \times R$ one-to-one onto a subset of R. From this fact it then follows by a very ingenious argument that $R \times R$ can be mapped one-to-one onto R. The proof goes in the following way.

From Theorem 6.60 there exists a set of real numbers S and a function F such that

$$F : R \times R \xrightarrow[\text{onto}]{1-1} S.$$

If $S = R$ then F is the desired function. If $S \neq R$ then we note that if we define G by

$$G(x) = (x, 0)$$

then G maps R one-to-one onto a subset of $R \times R$. Thus F maps $R \times R$ one-to-one onto a subset of R, and G maps R one-to-one onto a subset of $R \times R$. From these two functions we will define a third function H that maps R one-to-one onto $R \times R$. For the definition of H we require a sequence of subsets of R

$$A_0, A_1, \ldots$$

and a sequence of subsets of $R \times R$

$$B_1, \ B_2, \ \ldots,$$

which we define inductively in the following way:

$$A_0 = R - S,$$
$$B_{n+1} = \{G(x) \mid x \in A_n\},$$
$$A_{n+1} = \{F(z) \mid z \in B_n\}.$$

If

$$A = \bigcup_{\alpha=0}^{\infty} A_\alpha,$$

$$B = \bigcup_{\alpha=1}^{\infty} B_\alpha,$$

then $A \subseteq R$ and $B \subseteq R \times R$. We now prove

Lemma 1. 1) $x \in A$ *iff* $G(x) \in B$.
              2) $z \in (R \times R) - B$ *iff* $F(z) \in (R - A)$.

Proof. 1) If $x \in A$ then for some integer n we have that $x \in A_n$. Therefore $G(x) \in B_{n+1}$ and hence $G(x) \in B$. Conversely if $y \in B$, then for some n
we have that $y \in B_n$. Therefore there is an x in A_{n-1} such that $y = G(x)$.
Consequently $x \in A$.

2) The proof is left to the reader.

We now define H by

$$H(x) = G(x) \ \text{if} \ x \in A,$$
$$H(x) = F^{-1}(x) \ \text{if} \ x \in R - A.$$

That H is single valued follows from the fact that G and F^{-1} are single
valued. Note that H is so defined that $\text{Dom } H = R$ and $\text{Ran } H \subseteq R \times R$.
Furthermore if $z \in R \times R$ then $z \in B$ or $z \in (R \times R) - B$. If $z \in B$,
then there is an x in A for which $z = G(x)$. (Why?) Hence $H(x) = z$. If
$z \in (R \times R) - B$ then, by Lemma 1, $F(z) \in R - A$ and $H(F(z)) =
F^{-1}(F(z)) = z$. Therefore H maps R onto $R \times R$. To prove that H is
one-to-one we observe that if

$$H(x) = H(y)$$

then x and y are both in A or both in $R - A$ for if $x \in A$ and $y \in R - A$,
then $H(x) = G(x)$ and $H(y) = F^{-1}(y)$. But, by Lemma 1, $G(x) \in B$ and
$F^{-1}(y) \in (R \times R) - B$ therefore $G(x) \neq F^{-1}(y)$, that is, $H(x) \neq H(y)$. This
is a contradiction that forces us to conclude that x and y are both in A or
both in $R - A$. If $x \in A$ and $y \in A$, then $H(x) = G(x)$ and $H(y) = G(y)$.
Consequently since $H(x) = H(y)$ we have that $G(x) = G(y)$. But G is one-
to-one. Therefore $x = y$. Similarly if $x \in R - A$ and $y \in R - A$, then

$H(x) = F^{-1}(x)$ and $H(y) = F^{-1}(y)$. Since $H(x) = H(y)$ we conclude that $F^{-1}(x) = F^{-1}(y)$. But F^{-1} is also one-to-one. Therefore $x = y$. Thus

$$H: R \xrightarrow[\text{onto}]{1-1} R \times R.$$

The argument that has been used above can be used to prove a more general result.

Theorem 6.70 (Schröder-Bernstein).[1]   *If A can be mapped one-to-one onto a subset of B and if B can be mapped one-to-one onto a subset of A, then A can be mapped one-to-one onto B.*

We leave the proof to the reader and return to our discussion of the real numbers.

The fact that the points in the plane are no more numerous than the points on a line is another surprising result of set theory. In 1890 Peano proved an even more startling result. He proved that the set of points in a closed square

$$\{ (x, y) \mid 0 \le x \le 1 \text{ and } 0 \le y \le 1 \}$$

is a continuous curve; i.e., there exist functions f and g each defined and continuous on $[0, 1]$ such that

$$\{ (x, y) \mid 0 \le x \le 1 \text{ and } 0 \le y \le 1 \} = \{ (g(x), f(x)) \mid x \in [0, 1] \}.$$

Thus the continuous curves which we introduced in the last section include, in addition to those curves we intuitively accept as continuous curves, other things that we do not intuitively accept as 'curves'.[2] We may, however, take some comfort in the fact that Peano's so-called space filling curves are not simple curves. The simple curves give every indication of being what we intuitively wish a curve to be.

---

[1] This result was conjectured by Cantor and is also referred to as the Cantor-Bernstein theorem.

[2] For a further discussion of this very interesting topic we refer the reader to Lefschetz, *Introduction to Topology* (Princeton, New Jersey: Princeton University Press, 1949, pp. 5–8).

CHAPTER 7

The Derivative

7.0 Introduction

The next class of functions that we wish to study are the so-called differentiable functions, which we define in the following way.

Definition 7.00. f is *differentiable at* x iff $x \in \text{Dom } f$ and

$$\text{Lim}_{z \to x} \frac{f(z) - f(x)}{z - x}$$

exists. f is *differentiable on* S iff $S \subseteq \text{Dom } f$ and the restriction of f to S is differentiable at each point of S. f is *differentiable* iff f is differentiable on $\text{Dom } f$.

Definition 7.01. g is the *derivative* of f iff $\text{Dom } g = \{x \mid f \text{ is differentiable at } x\}$ and for each x in $\text{Dom } g$

$$g(x) = \text{Lim}_{z \to x} \frac{f(z) - f(x)}{z - x}.$$

The derivative of f we will denote by 'f''.

Example. The constant functions are differentiable everywhere. Indeed if $f(x) = c$ for each x, then for each x

$$\text{Lim}_{z \to x} \frac{f(z) - f(x)}{z - x} = \text{Lim}_{z \to x} \frac{c - c}{z - x} = 0.$$

Therefore f is differentiable everywhere, and $f'(x) = 0$ for each x.

Example. The identity function is differentiable everywhere. If $f(x) = x$ for each x then

$$\text{Lim}_{z \to x} \frac{f(z) - f(x)}{z - x} = \text{Lim}_{z \to x} \frac{z - x}{z - x} = 1.$$

Therefore f is differentiable everywhere and $f'(x) = 1$ for each x.

Example. The absolute value function is differentiable everywhere except at 0. If $f(x) = |x|$ and if $x > 0$ then there exists a δ such that if $z \in N(x, \delta)$ then $|z| = z$. Therefore

$$\lim_{z \to x} \frac{f(z) - f(x)}{z - x} = \lim_{z \to x} \frac{z - x}{z - x} = 1.$$

If $x < 0$, then there exists a δ such that if $z \in N(x, \delta)$, then $|z| = -z$. Therefore

$$\lim_{z \to x} \frac{f(z) - f(x)}{z - x} = \lim_{z \to x} \frac{-z + x}{z - x} = -1.$$

If $x = 0$, then since

$$\lim_{z \to 0^+} \frac{f(z) - f(0)}{z - 0} = \lim_{z \to 0^+} \frac{z}{z} = 1$$

and

$$\lim_{z \to 0^-} \frac{f(z) - f(0)}{z - 0} = \lim_{z \to 0^-} \frac{-z}{z} = -1,$$

it follows that

$$\lim_{z \to 0} \frac{f(z) - f(0)}{z - 0}$$

does not exist. Thus f is differentiable everywhere except at 0.

Example. The sine function is differentiable everywhere. From the identity

$$\sin z - \sin x = 2 \cos \frac{z + x}{2} \sin \frac{z - x}{2}$$

it follows that if $z \neq x$, then

$$\frac{\sin z - \sin x}{z - x} = \cos \frac{z + x}{2} \frac{\sin \frac{z - x}{2}}{\frac{z - x}{2}}.$$

Since cos is continuous

$$\lim_{z \to x} \cos \frac{z + x}{2} = \cos x.$$

Since

$$\lim_{z \to x} \frac{z - x}{2} = 0 \text{ and } \lim_{z \to 0} \frac{\sin z}{z} = 1,$$

it follows that

$$\lim_{z \to x} \frac{\sin \frac{z - x}{2}}{\frac{z - x}{2}} = 1.$$

Therefore

$$\operatorname*{Lim}_{z \to x} \frac{\sin z - \sin x}{z - x} = \cos x.$$

Consequently sin is differentiable everywhere and $\sin' x = \cos x$ for each x.

7.1 The Elementary Properties of Derivatives

Our first theorem asserts the not very surprising fact that in order for a function to be differentiable at a point it must be continuous at that point.

Theorem 7.10. *If f is differentiable at x, then f is continuous at x.*

Proof. If f is differentiable at x, then $x \in \operatorname{Dom} f$ and x is an accumulation point of $\operatorname{Dom} f$. (Why?) Furthermore since

$$\operatorname*{Lim}_{z \to x} \frac{f(z) - f(x)}{z - x} = f'(x) \quad \text{and} \quad \operatorname*{Lim}_{z \to x} (z - x) = 0$$

it follows that

$$\operatorname*{Lim}_{z \to x} \frac{f(z) - f(x)}{z - x} (z - x) = 0.$$

But if $z \neq x$, then

$$f(z) - f(x) = \frac{f(z) - f(x)}{z - x} (z - x).$$

Therefore

$$\operatorname*{Lim}_{z \to x} [f(z) - f(x)] = 0$$

and hence

$$\operatorname*{Lim}_{z \to x} f(z) = f(x)$$

Q.E.D.

The following result is of great value in that it enables us to determine the derivative of certain functions without a direct appeal to the definition.

Theorem 7.11. *If f and g are each differentiable at x and if x is an accumulation point of $\operatorname{Dom} f \cap \operatorname{Dom} g$, then $f + g$, $f - g$, and fg are each differentiable at x and*

1) $(f + g)'(x) = f'(x) + g'(x).$
2) $(f - g)'(x) = f'(x) - g'(x).$
3) $(fg)'(x) = f'(x)g(x) + f(x)g'(x).$

Furthermore if $g(x) \neq 0$, then f/g is differentiable at x and

4) $(f/g)'(x) = \dfrac{g(x)f'(x) - f(x)g'(x)}{g^2(x)}.$

Proof. 1) If $z \neq x$, then

$$\frac{(f + g)(z) - (f + g)(x)}{z - x} = \frac{f(z) - f(x)}{z - x} + \frac{g(z) - g(x)}{z - x}.$$

Since f and g are each differentiable at x

$$\operatorname*{Lim}_{z \to x} \frac{f(z) - f(x)}{z - x} = f'(x) \quad \text{and} \quad \operatorname*{Lim}_{z \to x} \frac{g(z) - g(x)}{z - x} = g'(x).$$

Therefore, since x is also an accumulation point of Dom $(f + g)$,

$$\operatorname*{Lim}_{z \to x} \frac{(f + g)(z) - (f + g)(x)}{z - x} = f'(x) + g'(x).$$

2) The proof is left to the reader.

3) If $z \neq x$, then

$$\frac{(fg)(z) - (fg)(x)}{z - x} = \frac{f(z)g(z) - f(x)g(z) + f(x)g(z) - f(x)g(x)}{z - x}$$

$$= \frac{f(z) - f(x)}{z - x} g(z) + f(x) \frac{g(z) - g(x)}{z - x}.$$

Since f and g are differentiable at x,

$$\operatorname*{Lim}_{z \to x} \frac{f(z) - f(x)}{z - x} = f'(x) \quad \text{and} \quad \operatorname*{Lim}_{z \to x} \frac{g(z) - g(x)}{z - x} = g'(x).$$

Furthermore, g is continuous at x and hence

$$\operatorname*{Lim}_{z \to x} g(z) = g(x).$$

Since x is an accumulation point of Dom (fg), it follows that

$$\operatorname*{Lim}_{z \to x} \frac{(fg)(z) - (fg)(x)}{z - x} = f'(x)g(x) + f(x)g'(x).$$

4) If $g(x) \neq 0$, then since g is continuous at x, there exists a δ such that if $z \in N'(x, \delta) \cap$ Dom g then $g(z) \neq 0$. Therefore

$$\frac{(f/g)(z) - (f/g)(x)}{z - x} = \frac{f(z)g(x) - f(x)g(z)}{(z - x)g(z)g(x)}$$

$$= \frac{f(z)g(x) - f(x)g(x) + f(x)g(x) - f(x)g(z)}{(z - x)g(z)g(x)}$$

$$= \frac{1}{g(z)g(x)} \left(g(x)\frac{f(z) - f(x)}{z - x} - f(x)\frac{g(z) - g(x)}{z - x} \right)$$

Since f and g are differentiable at x and since x is an accumulation point of Dom (f/g), it follows that

$$\operatorname*{Lim}_{z \to x} \frac{(f/g)(z) - (f/g)(x)}{z - x} = \frac{g(x)f'(x) - f(x)g'(x)}{g^2(x)}.$$

Q.E.D.

Example. The reciprocal function is differentiable everywhere except at 0. If $f(x) = 1/x$, $x \neq 0$, then f is the quotient of a constant function and the identity function. Therefore by 4) if $x \neq 0$ then $f'(x) = -1/x^2$.

Example. If $f(x) = x \sin x$, then f is differentiable everywhere and $f'(x) = x \cos x + \sin x$.

Theorem 7.12 (The Chain Rule). *If g is differentiable at x, if f is differentiable at $g(x)$, and if x is an accumulation point of Dom $(f \circ g)$, then $f \circ g$ is differentiable at x and*

$$(f \circ g)'(x) = (f' \circ g)(x)g'(x).$$

Proof. Since f is differentiable at $g(x)$,

$$\operatorname*{Lim}_{z \to g(x)} \frac{f(z) - f(g(x))}{z - g(x)} = f'(g(x)).$$

Therefore if we define h by

$$h(y) = \frac{f(y) - f(g(x))}{y - g(x)}, \quad y \in \operatorname{Dom} f, \quad y \neq g(x),$$
$$h(y) = f'(g(x)), \qquad\qquad y = g(x),$$

then it follows that h is continuous at $g(x)$. Furthermore, if $y \neq g(x)$, we have that

$$f(y) - f(g(x)) = h(y)[y - g(x)].$$

In particular, if $z \in \operatorname{Dom} (f \circ g)$ and if $y = g(z)$,

$$f(g(z)) - f(g(x)) = h(g(z))[g(z) - g(x)].$$

Therefore, if $z \neq x$, then

$$\frac{(f \circ g)(z) - (f \circ g)(x)}{z - x} = (h \circ g)(z)\left(\frac{g(z) - g(x)}{z - x}\right).$$

Since g is differentiable at x,

$$\operatorname*{Lim}_{z \to x} \frac{g(z) - g(x)}{z - x} = g'(x).$$

Furthermore g is continuous at x. Since h is continuous at $g(x)$

$$\operatorname*{Lim}_{z \to x} (h \circ g)(z) = h(g(x)) = (f' \circ g)(x).$$

Therefore

$$\operatorname*{Lim}_{z \to x} \frac{(f \circ g)(z) - (f \circ g)(x)}{z - x} = (f' \circ g)(x)g'(x).$$

Q.E.D.

Example. If $f(x) = \sin 1/x$, $x \neq 0$, then f is the composite of the sine function and the reciprocal function. Therefore $f'(x) = (-1/x^2) \cos 1/x$, $x \neq 0$.

From the chain rule we obtain an interesting result in the event that f and g are inverses. In this case $(f \circ g)(x) = x$ if $x \in \text{Dom } g$. If x is also an accumulation point of Dom g, then

$$(f \circ g)'(x) = 1.$$

Furthermore, if g is differentiable at x and if f is differentiable at $g(x)$, then

$$(f \circ g)'(x) = (f' \circ g)(x)g'(x).$$

Therefore

$$(f' \circ g)(x)g'(x) = 1.$$

From this it follows that $g'(x) \neq 0$, and hence

$$(f' \circ g)(x) = \frac{1}{g'(x)}.$$

A more general result is easily proved.

Theorem 7.13. *If g is differentiable at x, if $g'(x) \neq 0$, if there exists a δ such that g is continuous and one-to-one on $N(x, \delta)$, and if f is the inverse of the restriction of g to $N(x, \delta)$, then f is differentiable at $g(x)$ and*

$$(f' \circ g)(x) = \frac{1}{g'(x)}.$$

Proof. Since g is differentiable at x,

$$\operatorname*{Lim}_{z \to x} \frac{g(z) - g(x)}{z - x} = g'(x).$$

Since $g'(x) = 0$,

$$\operatorname*{Lim}_{z \to x} \frac{z - x}{g(z) - g(x)} = \frac{1}{g'(x)}.$$

Therefore there exists a convergence test ϕ_1 with the property that if $z \in N'(x, \phi_1(\epsilon)) \cap N(x, \delta)$, then

$$\left| \frac{z - x}{g(z) - g(x)} - \frac{1}{g'(x)} \right| < \epsilon.$$

Since g is continuous on $N(x, \delta)$ it follows that f is continuous at $g(x)$ (see Exercise 2, page 224). Therefore there exists a convergence test ϕ_2 with the property that if $y \in N'(g(x), \phi_2(\epsilon)) \cap \text{Dom } f$, then

$$|f(y) - f(g(x))| < \epsilon.$$

In particular, if $y \in N'(g(x), (\phi_2 \circ \phi_1)(\epsilon)) \cap \mathrm{Dom}\, f$, then
$$|f(y) - f(g(x))| < \phi_1(\epsilon).$$
Since $f(g(x)) = x$ it follows that $f(y) \in N(x, \phi_1(\epsilon)) \cap N(x, \delta)$ and hence
$$\left| \frac{f(y) - f(g(x))}{y - g(x)} - \frac{1}{g'(x)} \right| = \left| \frac{f(y) - x}{g(f(y)) - g(x)} \right| < \epsilon,$$
that is, $(f' \circ g)(x) = 1/g'(x)$.

Q.E.D.

From Theorem 7.13 it follows that subject to the hypotheses of the theorem

$$f'(x) = \frac{1}{(g' \circ f)(x)}.$$

Example. If $f(x) = \sqrt{x}$, $x \geq 0$ and if $g(x) = x^2$, $x \geq 0$, then f and g are inverses. Since $g'(x) = 2x$ it follows that if $x \neq 0$, then $f'(x) = 1/(2\sqrt{x})$.

Example. $\cos x = \sin(\pi/2 - x)$ therefore
$$\cos' x = \sin'(\pi/2 - x)(-1) = -\cos(\pi/2 - x) = -\sin x.$$

As useful as the results of this section are, they do not completely replace the definition of the derivative. Consider, for example, the function f defined by
$$f(x) = x^2 \, \mathrm{Rat}\,(x).$$
Since the Rat function is discontinuous everywhere it is not differentiable anywhere. In spite of this, f is differentiable at the origin, for since the Rat function is bounded, it follows that
$$\mathrm{Lim}_{x \to 0} \frac{f(x) - f(0)}{x - 0} = \mathrm{Lim}_{x \to 0} \frac{x^2 \, \mathrm{Rat}\,(x)}{x} = \mathrm{Lim}_{x \to 0} x \, \mathrm{Rat}\,(x) = 0.$$
Therefore $f'(0) = 0$. It is also interesting to note that f is not differentiable at any other point.

The derivative of a function f provides us with interesting and useful information about f. The derivative of f', which we denote by f'' and call the second derivative of f, also provides information about f. So do the derivatives of all orders which we define recursively in the following way.

Definition 7.14. $f^{(0)} = f$.
$$f^{(n+1)} = (f^{(n)})'.$$
The symbol ' $f^{(n)}$ ' is read the *nth derivative of f* or the *derivative of f of order n*.

Example. If $n \geq 0$, then $\sin^{(4n)} x = \sin x$, $\sin^{(4n+1)}x = \cos x$, $\sin^{(4n+2)}x = -\sin x$, $\sin^{(4n+3)}x = -\cos x$.

EXERCISES

1. Prove: If $F = \sum_1^n f_\alpha$, if x is an accumulation point of Dom F, and if each f_α is differentiable at x, then F is differentiable at x and $F'(x) = \sum_1^n f'_\alpha(x)$.

2. Prove: If f is differentiable at x and $F = cf$, then F is differentiable at x and $F'(x) = cf'(x)$.

3. Prove: If $f(x) = x^n$, $n \geq 1$, then f is differentiable everywhere and $f'(x) = nx^{n-1}$.

4. Prove: Polynomial functions are differentiable everywhere. If $f(x) = \sum_0^n a_\alpha x^\alpha$, then $f'(x) = \sum_1^n \alpha a_\alpha x^{\alpha-1}$.

5. Prove: If $g(x) = f(a) + f'(a)(x - a) + \cdots + \dfrac{f^{(n)}(a)}{n!} (x - a)^n$, then $g^{(m)}(a) = f^{(m)}(a)$, $m = 0, 1, \ldots, n$.

6. Prove: Rational functions are differentiable at each point in their domain.

7. Prove: If $f(x) = x^n$, $n \leq -1$, $x \neq 0$, then f is differentiable everywhere except at 0 and $f'(x) = nx^{n-1}$.

8. Prove: If $f(x) = x^{1/n}$, $n \geq 2$ with $x \geq 0$ if n is even, then f is differentiable at each point of Dom f except at 0 and $f'(x) = x^{1/n-1}/n$.

9. Prove: If $F = f^n$ and f is differentiable at x, then F is differentiable at x and $F'(x) = nf^{n-1}(x)f'(x)$.

10. Prove: If $F = \prod_1^n f_\alpha$, if x is an accumulation point of Dom F, and if each f_α is differentiable at x, then F is differentiable at x. Furthermore if $F(x) \neq 0$, then

$$\frac{F'(x)}{F(x)} = \sum_{\alpha=1}^n \frac{f'_\alpha(x)}{f_\alpha(x)}.$$

11. Prove: If f is differentiable at x and if for some $N(x, \delta)$ the restriction of g to $N(x, \delta)$ and the restriction of f to $N(x, \delta)$ are equal, then g is differentiable at x and $g'(x) = f'(x)$.

In Exercises 12–20 find f'.

12. $f(x) = \tan x$.   **13.** $f(x) = \cot x$.   **14.** $f(x) = \sec x$.

15. $f(x) = \csc x$.   **16.** $f(x) = [\![x]\!]$.   **17.** $f(x) = \{x\}$.

18. $f(x) = x^2 \sin \dfrac{1}{x}$, $x \neq 0$, $f(0) = 0$.

19. $f(x) = \sin^2 x$.   **20.** $f(x) = \sin x^2$.

In Exercises 21–23 find $f^{(n)}$

21. $f(x) = \dfrac{1}{x}$.   **22.** $f(x) = \sqrt{x}$.   **23.** $f(x) = x^{10} + x + 1$.

24. Give an example of functions f and g each defined everywhere and not differentiable anywhere but for which $f + g$ is differentiable everywhere.

25. Give an example of functions f and g each defined everywhere and not differentiable anywhere but for which fg is differentiable everywhere.

7.2 Applications—Maxima and Minima

In the chapter on continuity we established that a function that is continuous on a closed and bounded set has both a maximum and a minimum value. The differential calculus provides a very useful method for determining these values. This method requires that we be able to identify the points at which functions have *local maxima* and *local minima*.

Definition 7.20.   1) f has a *local maximum* at a iff $a \in \operatorname{Dom} f$ and there exists a δ such that

$$\forall x \in N(a, \delta) \cap \operatorname{Dom} f, \quad f(x) \le f(a).$$

2) f has a *local minimum* at a iff $a \in \operatorname{Dom} f$ and there exists a δ such that

$$\forall x \in N(a, \delta) \cap \operatorname{Dom} f, \quad f(x) \ge f(a).$$

A function can have both a local maximum and a local minimum at the same point. For example, the constant functions have both a local maximum and a local minimum at every point. It should also be observed that there exist functions defined everywhere that do not have a local maximum or a local minimum anywhere, as, for example, the identity function.

Theorem 7.21.   1) *If $S \subseteq \operatorname{Dom} f$ and if there exists an a in S for which $f(a) = \max f[S]$, then a is a local maximum of the restriction of f to S.*
   2) *If $S \subseteq \operatorname{Dom} f$ and if there exists an a in S for which $f(a) = \min f[S]$, then a is a local minimum of the restriction of f to S.*

The proof is left to the reader.

If f is continuous on a closed and bounded set S, then we know that $f[S]$ has both a maximum and a minimum. Theorem 7.21 assures us that the points at which the maximum value is assumed are among the local maximum points of the restriction of f to S, and the points at which the minimum value is assumed are among the local minimum points of the restriction of f to S.

To aid us in locating the local maximum and local minimum points we introduce the following definition.

Definition 7.22.   1) f is *increasing at a* iff f is continuous at a and there exists a δ such that

$$\forall x \in N(a, \delta) \cap \operatorname{Dom} f, \, f(x) < f(a) \text{ if } x < a, \text{ and } f(x) > f(a) \text{ if } x > a.$$

2) f is *decreasing at a* iff f is continuous at a and there exists a δ such that

$\forall x \in N(a, \delta) \cap \mathrm{Dom}\, f$, $f(x) > f(a)$ if $x < a$, and $f(x) < f(a)$ if $x > a$.

The Rat function is discontinuous everywhere and hence at each point it is neither increasing nor decreasing. The constant functions are continuous everywhere but are also neither increasing nor decreasing at each point. The identity function is increasing everywhere.

A function can be increasing or decreasing at a local maximum or a local minimum. For example, if f is defined on $[0, 1]$ by $f(x) = x$, then f is increasing at 1 and 1 is a local maximum. This is possible because there are no points in $\mathrm{Dom}\, f$ near 1 and to the right of 1.

Theorem 7.23. *If a is an accumulation point of* $\mathrm{Dom}\, f \cap [a, \infty)$ *and an accumulation point of* $(-\infty, a] \cap \mathrm{Dom}\, f$, *and if f is either increasing at a or decreasing at a, then f does not have a local maximum or a local minimum at a.*

The proof is left to the reader.

Theorem 7.24. *If f is differentiable at a, then f is increasing at a if* $f'(a) > 0$ *and f is decreasing at a if* $f'(a) < 0$.

Proof. Since f is differentiable at a it follows that f is continuous at a. Furthermore

$$\lim_{x \to a} \frac{f(x) - f(a)}{x - a} = f'(a).$$

Therefore if $f'(a) > 0$, then there exists a δ such that if $x \in N'(a, \delta) \cap \mathrm{Dom}\, f$ then

$$\frac{f(x) - f(a)}{x - a} > 0.$$

From this we see that $f(x) - f(a)$ and $x - a$ are either both positive or both negative; that is, if $x > a$ then $f(x) > f(a)$ and if $x < a$ then $f(x) < f(a)$. Therefore f is increasing at a.

If $f'(a) < 0$ then there exists a δ such that if $x \in N'(a, \delta) \cap \mathrm{Dom}\, f$, then

$$\frac{f(x) - f(a)}{x - a} < 0.$$

From this it follows that if $x < a$ then $f(x) > f(a)$, and if $x > a$ then $f(x) < f(a)$. Therefore f is decreasing at a.

Q.E.D.

From Theorem 7.23 and 7.24 we obtain the following result whose proof we leave to the reader.

Theorem 7.25. *If a is an accumulation point of* $\mathrm{Dom}\, f \cap [a, \infty)$ *and an accumulation point of* $(-\infty, a] \cap \mathrm{Dom}\, f$, *if f is differentiable at a, and if f has a local maximum or a local minimum at a, then* $f'(a) = 0$.

The theorems that we have proved are very general ones. Let us illustrate their application with functions that are continuous on closed and bounded intervals.

If f is continuous on a closed and bounded interval S, then $\max f[S]$ and $\min f[S]$ each exist. Furthermore the maximum and minimum values can only be assumed at an end point of S or at an interior point of S which is a zero of f' or at an interior point of S at which f is not differentiable.

Example. If $S = [-1, 2]$ and f is defined by

$$f(x) = 4x^3 - 3x^2 - 6x$$

then

$$f'(x) = 12x^2 - 6x - 6 = 6(2x^2 - x - 1) = 6(2x + 1)(x - 1)$$

and f' is zero only at $-\frac{1}{2}$ and 1. Since f is continuous on S it has both a maximum and a minimum value on S. Since f is differentiable at each point on S, the maximum-minimum values can only be assumed at a boundary point, -1 or 2, or at a point where f' is zero, i.e., $-\frac{1}{2}$ or 1. The problem has, therefore, been reduced to that of finding the maximum and minimum of

$$\{f(-1),\ f(-\tfrac{1}{2}),\ f(1),\ f(2)\}.$$

Since $f(-1) = -1$, $f(-\frac{1}{2}) = -\frac{7}{4}$, $f(1) = -5$, and $f(2) = 8$, we conclude that $\max f[S] = 8$, this value being assumed only at the boundary point 2, and $\min f[S] = -5$, this value being assumed only at the interior point 1.

Example. If $S = [-2, 3]$ and if f is defined by

$$f(x) = |x^2 - 1|$$

then f is differentiable everywhere except at 1 and -1. Furthermore f' is zero only at 0. Thus the max-min values can occur only at one or more of the five points -2, -1, 0, 1, 3. Since

$$\{f(-2),\ f(-1),\ f(0),\ f(1),\ f(3)\} = \{3,\ 0,\ 1,\ 0,\ 8\}$$

we conclude that $\max f[S] = 8$, this value being assumed only at the boundary point 3, while $\min f[S] = 0$, this value being assumed only at the two interior points -1, and 1.

The results of this section are of interest for other reasons than their use in max-min problems. We illustrate with the following interesting results.

Theorem 7.26. *If f is differentiable on (a, b) and if f' has no zeros in (a, b), then f is strictly monotone on (a, b).*

Proof. (By contradiction.) If f were not strictly monotone on (a, b), then there would exist numbers x, y, and z in (a, b) with $x < y < z$, for which we would have 1) $f(x) \leq f(y)$ and $f(z) \leq f(y)$ or 2) $f(x) \geq f(y)$ and $f(z) \geq f(y)$. If 1) holds, then f must have a local maximum at an interior point of $[x, z]$ and f' must be zero at such a point. If 2) holds, then f has a local minimum at an interior point of $[x, z]$ and f' must be zero at such a point. Thus in either case f' has a zero on (a, b). This is a contradiction from which we conclude that f is strictly monotone on (a, b).

Q.E.D.

Theorem 7.27 (Darboux). *If f is differentiable on [a, b] and if d is a number between f'(a) and f'(b), then there exists a c in [a, b] for which f'(c) = d.*

Proof. If $f'(a) < d < f'(b)$ and if $g(x) = f(x) - d(x - a)$, $x \in [a, b]$, then g is differentiable on $[a, b]$. Therefore g is continuous on $[a, b]$, and hence it assumes a maximum and a minimum value on $[a, b]$. Since $g'(x) = f'(x) - d$ and since $f'(a) - d < 0$, it follows that g is decreasing at a. Therefore g does not assume its minimum value at a. Furthermore since $f'(b) - d > 0$, it follows that g is increasing at b, and hence g does not assume its minimum value at b. From this it follows that g must assume its minimum value at some point c in (a, b). Since c is an interior point of (a, b) and since c is a local minimum of g, it follows that $g'(c) = 0$. Therefore $f'(c) = d$.

If $f'(b) < d < f'(a)$, the argument is similar and is left to the reader.

EXERCISES

Find the maximum and minimum values assumed on [0, 3] by the functions in Exercises 1–6.

1. $f(x) = (x - 1)^2 + 1$.   2. $f(x) = x^3 - \frac{5}{2}x^2 + 1$.
3. $f(x) = x^{[x]}$.   4. $f(x) = 1 + 2(x - 3)^{1/3}$.
5. $f(x) = \dfrac{x^2 + x + 1}{x^2 - x - 1}$.   6. $f(x) = x^2 + \dfrac{1}{x^2}$.

7.3 Applications—Curve Sketching

It is sometimes claimed that a continuous function is one whose graph can be drawn without lifting the pencil. This notion of a continuous function is, however, much too restrictive, as we will now show. We offer the following as an example of a continuous function whose graph cannot be drawn.

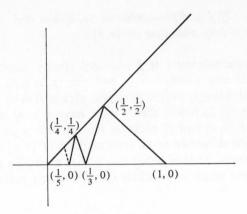

$(\frac{1}{2}, \frac{1}{2})$

$(\frac{1}{4}, \frac{1}{4})$

$(\frac{1}{5}, 0)$ $(\frac{1}{3}, 0)$ $(1, 0)$

FIGURE 7.1

Example.   Consider the curve consisting of straight line segments connecting $(1/2n, 1/2n)$ to each of the two points $(1/(2n + 1), 0)$ and $(1/(2n - 1), 0)$ for all positive integers n. This is the graph of a function that is continuous on $(0, 1]$. Furthermore if we adjoin to this function the ordered pair $(0, 0)$, we obtain a function f that is continuous on $[0, 1]$. (See Exercise 22, page 208.) If, beginning at $(1, 0)$, we attempt to draw its graph without lifting our pencil we find that after drawing a few line segments we have not arrived at the origin, and indeed we entertain little hope of ever getting there. (See Figure 7.1.) The problem is that there always remain infinitely many line segments to be drawn. We, of course, give up and attempt to conceal our frustration by saying "and so on."

If, on the other hand, we start at the origin, then we are denied even the comfort of an "and so on," for we find that we do not know how to begin. Any motion made from the origin will be seriously misrepresentative of the curve. From our intuitive understanding of the motion of a pencil we see that a small arc drawn from the origin would imply the existence of a line that is tangent to the arc at the origin. It is easily shown that for the graph of the function f no such line exists at the origin.

The slope of a line through the origin and a nearby point $(x, f(x))$ on the curve is given by

$$\frac{f(x)}{x}.$$

By definition the tangent to the curve at the origin is the line through the origin whose slope is

$$\lim_{x \to 0^+} \frac{f(x)}{x}$$

provided, of course, this limit exists. But this limit does not exist, as we see from the Stolz criterion and the fact that

$$\lim_{n \to \infty} \frac{f\left(\frac{1}{2n}\right)}{\frac{1}{2n}} = 1 \quad \text{and} \quad \lim_{n \to \infty} \frac{f\left(\frac{1}{2n-1}\right)}{\frac{1}{2n-1}} = 0.$$

In general if x is an interior point of Dom f, then in order that we be able to sketch the graph of f at $(a, f(a))$ it is necessary that f be differentiable on the right at a and differentiable on the left at a in the sense of

Definition 7.30. 1) f is *differentiable on the right* at a iff $a \in$ Dom f and

$$\lim_{x \to a^+} \frac{f(x) - f(a)}{x - a}$$

exists.

2) f is *differentiable on the left* at a iff $a \in$ Dom f and

$$\lim_{x \to a^-} \frac{f(x) - f(a)}{x - a}$$

exists.

From the foregoing example we see that if a function f is continuous on $[a, b]$ and if its graph can be drawn without lifting the pencil, then f is more than continuous; it is differentiable on $[a, b]$ except possibly at a finite number of points. But even at these points f is differentiable on the right and differentiable on the left.

For the remainder of this section we will consider functions that are differentiable except possibly at a finite set of points in their domain. We know, of course, that a graph of such a function can be very useful. If we are content with a rough sketch we would probably plot a few points and then connect these points in some reasonable way. Of course, we would attempt to take into account the points of discontinuity. It is reasonable to ask if there is a "best" set of points to plot, in the sense that by connecting these points we obtain a picture that is most like the "true" picture. A partial answer is provided by the following observations.

If f is differentiable on (a, b) and f' has no zeros on that interval, then, by Theorem 7.26, it follows that f is strictly monotone on (a, b). Therefore if we locate all of the points at which f is not differentiable and all the points at which f' is zero, then the collection of all such points divides the real axis into intervals on which f is strictly monotone.

Example. If
$$f(x) = \tfrac{1}{10}(2x^3 - 3x^2 - 12x + 16)$$
then f is differentiable everywhere and
$$f'(x) = \tfrac{1}{10}(6x^2 - 6x - 12) = \tfrac{3}{5}(x - 2)(x + 1).$$

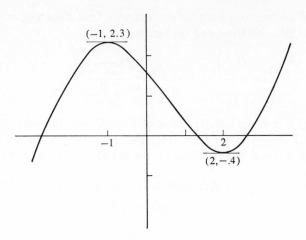

FIGURE 7.2

Since f' is zero at -1 and at 2, it follows that f is monotone on $(-\infty, -1)$, on $(-1, 2)$, and on $(2, \infty)$. Indeed, f is monotone increasing on $(-\infty, 1)$ and on $(2, \infty)$, and monotone decreasing on $(-1, 2)$. (Why?) Furthermore $f(-1) = 2.3$ and $f(2) = -.4$. Plotting the points $(-1, 2.3)$ and $(2, -.4)$ and connecting them in a "reasonable" way we obtain Figure 7.2.

Example. If

$$f(x) = \frac{x(x-1)}{x-2}, \quad x \neq 2,$$

then f is differentiable everywhere except at 2 and

$$f'(x) = \frac{x^2 - 4x + 2}{(x-2)^2}, \quad x \neq 2.$$

Therefore f' is zero at $2 + \sqrt{2}$ and at $2 - \sqrt{2}$. If $x < 2 - \sqrt{2}$, then $f'(x) > 0$. Therefore f is strictly monotone increasing on $(-\infty, 2 - \sqrt{2})$. If $2 - \sqrt{2} < x < 2$, then $f'(x) < 0$, and hence f is strictly monotone decreasing on $(2 - \sqrt{2}, 2)$. If $2 < x < 2 + \sqrt{2}$, then $f'(x) < 0$, and hence f is strictly monotone decreasing on $(2, 2 + \sqrt{2})$. If $x > 2 + \sqrt{2}$, then $f'(x) > 0$ and f is strictly monotone increasing on $(2 + \sqrt{2}, \infty)$. Since $f(2 - \sqrt{2}) = 3 - 2\sqrt{2}$ and $f(2 + \sqrt{2}) = 3 + 2\sqrt{2}$, we plot the points $(2 - \sqrt{2}, 3 - 2\sqrt{2})$ and $(2 + \sqrt{2}, 3 + 2\sqrt{2})$ and "connect" them obtaining Figure 7.3.

Other useful information can be obtained from f'' the derivative of f'. If f' is differentiable on (a, b) and if f'' has no zeros on this interval, then it follows that f' is strictly monotone on (a, b). Therefore the points at which f' is not differentiable and the points at which f'' is zero divide the

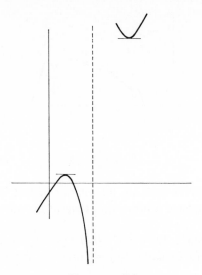

FIGURE 7.3

real axis into intervals on which f' is strictly monotone. On those intervals on which f' is monotone increasing, the graph of f is concave upward; on the intervals on which f' is monotone decreasing the graph of f is concave downward.

For the first example above we have that

$$f(x) = \tfrac{1}{10}(2x^3 - 3x^2 - 12x + 16),$$
$$f'(x) = \tfrac{1}{10}(6x^2 - 6x - 12),$$
$$f''(x) = \tfrac{1}{10}(12x - 6).$$

Since f' is differentiable everywhere and f'' is zero only at $\tfrac{1}{2}$, we have that the graph of f is concave downward on $(-\infty, \tfrac{1}{2})$ and concave upward on $(\tfrac{1}{2}, \infty)$. (Why?) Figure 7.2 can then be improved with this additional information and the fact that $f(\tfrac{1}{2}) = .95$ and $f'(\tfrac{1}{2}) = -1.35$.

EXERCISES

In Exercises 1–4 locate all local maximum and local minimum points and graph the function.

1. $f(x) = (x - 1)^2$.   **2.** $f(x) = |x^2 - 1|$.

3. $f(x) = \dfrac{x + 1}{x(x - 1)}$.   **4.** $f(x) = x^{2/3}(x - 5)$.

7.4 Rolle's Theorem and the Mean Value Theorem

Rolle's Theorem is a geometrically obvious result, illustrated in Figure 7.4. Geometrically, it asserts that the graph of a function that is continuous on

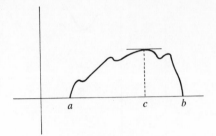

FIGURE 7.4

a closed interval, differentiable on the interior of that interval, and zero at each end point must have a horizontal tangent at some interior point c.

Theorem 7.40 (Rolle's Theorem). *If $a < b$, if f is continuous on $[a, b]$ and differentiable on (a, b), and if $f(a) = f(b) = 0$, then there exists a number c in (a, b) for which*

$$f'(c) = 0.$$

Proof. If $f(x) = 0$ for each x in $[a, b]$, then $f'(x) = 0$ for each x in (a, b). Since $a < b$, it follows that (a, b) is not empty. Therefore, there exists a number c in (a, b) for which $f'(c) = 0$.

If for some x in $[a, b]$, $f(x) \neq 0$ then $f(x) > 0$ or $f(x) < 0$. If $f(x) > 0$ then f being continuous on $[a, b]$ assumes a maximum value on $[a, b]$, and this value must be positive. That is, there exists a number c in $[a, b]$ for which $f(c)$ is the maximum value of f on $[a, b]$ and $f(c) > 0$. Since $f(a) = f(b) = 0$ it follows that $c \neq a$ and $c \neq b$, that is, $c \in (a, b)$. Furthermore since $f(c)$ is a maximum value for f on $[a, b]$, it follows that f has a local maximum at c. Since by hypothesis $f'(c)$ exists, it follows that $f'(c) = 0$.

If $f(x) < 0$, the argument is similar and is left for the reader.

From Rolle's Theorem we easily deduce a generalization known as the Mean Value Theorem. Geometrically the Mean Value Theorem asserts that the graph of a function that is continuous on a closed interval and differentiable on the open interval must have a tangent that is parallel to the secant as illustrated in Figure 7.5. The proof consists of an interesting application of Rolle's Theorem to the function that gives the "vertical" distance between the secant line and the curve.

Theorem 7.41 (Mean Value Theorem for Derivatives). *If $a < b$, if f is continuous on $[a, b]$ and differentiable on (a, b), then there exists a number c in (a, b) for which*

$$f'(c) = \frac{f(b) - f(a)}{b - a}$$

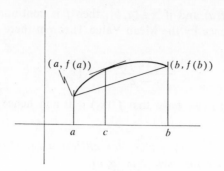

FIGURE 7.5

Proof. The function g defined on $[a, b]$ by

$$g(x) = f(x) - f(a) - [f(b) - f(a)] \frac{x - a}{b - a}$$

is continuous on $[a, b]$ and differentiable on (a, b). Furthermore, $g(a) = g(b) = 0$. Therefore by Rolle's theorem there is a number c in (a, b) for which $g'(c) = 0$. Since

$$g'(x) = f'(x) - \frac{f(b) - f(a)}{b - a}$$

it follows that

$$f'(c) = \frac{f(b) - f(a)}{b - a}.$$

Q.E.D.

One important application of the Mean Value Theorem concerns anti-derivatives.

Definition 7.42. f is an *antiderivative* of g iff $f' = g$. f is an antiderivative for g *on* S iff f is an antiderivative of the restriction of g to S.

Given a function f, its derivative f' is uniquely determined; that is, there is one and only one g such that $f' = g$. However, given a function g there may be many functions f such that $f' = g$. For example, all constant functions have the same derivative. Indeed if f is a constant function, then for each x, $f'(x) = 0$. Is the converse of this true? If for each x, $f'(x) = 0$, does it follow that f is a constant function? The answer is yes, as we can prove from the Mean Value Theorem.

Theorem 7.43. *If $f'(x) = 0$ for all x in $[a, b]$, then for some c we have $f(x) = c$ for each x in $[a, b]$.*

Proof. If $c = f(a)$ and if $x \in (a, b]$, then f is continuous and differentiable on $[a, x]$; hence by the Mean Value Theorem there is an x_1 in (a, x) such that

$$\frac{f(x) - f(a)}{x - a} = f'(x_1).$$

But since $x_1 \in (a, x)$, we have that $f'(x_1) = 0$ and hence $f(x) = f(a) = c$.
Q.E.D.

Corollary 7.44. *If* $f'(x) = g'(x)$ *for all* $x \in [a, b]$, *then for some* c *we have* $f(x) - g(x) = c$ *for each* x *in* $[a, b]$.

The proof is left to the reader.

Theorem 7.43 and its corollary provide information that is of great value in proving certain uniqueness theorems. Note, for example, that if in addition to the hypotheses of the corollary f and g have the same value at some point in $[a, b]$, that is, if for some y in $[a, b]$, $f(y) = g(y)$, then it follows that $c = 0$ and hence $f(x) = g(x)$ for each x in $[a, b]$. Thus Corollary 7.44 assures us that there exists at most one function whose domain is $[a, b]$ which has a specified derivative on $[a, b]$, and which has a specified value at a specified point in $[a, b]$, i.e., if Dom $g = [a, b]$, if $c \in [a, b]$, and if d is any real number, then there exists at most one function f such that Dom $f = [a, b]$, $f' = g$ and $f(c) = d$.

Let us review this argument in another context. Recall that the sine function has the interesting property that $\sin'' = -\sin$; that is, for each x

$$\sin'' (x) + \sin (x) = 0.$$

The cosine function also has this property—that is, for each x

$$\cos'' (x) + \cos (x) = 0.$$

Let us inquire about the class of all functions that possess this property. What can we infer about a function f which is everywhere twice differentiable and has the property that for each x

$$f''(x) + f(x) = 0?$$

Note that if f is such a function, then for each x

$$2f'(x)f''(x) + 2f(x)f'(x) = 0.$$

Furthermore if $F = (f')^2 + (f)^2$, then $F' = 2f'f'' + 2ff'$. Since $F'(x) = 0$ it follows from Theorem 7.43 that F is a constant function, that is, for some c and all x

$$[f'(x)]^2 + [f(x)]^2 = c.$$

Note that c is determined by the value of f and f' at any given point. Furthermore, if for each x, $f''(x) + f(x) = 0$ and $g''(x) + g(x) = 0$, it follows that $(f - g)''(x) + (f - g)(x) = 0$. Therefore for some c and each x

$$[f'(x) - g'(x)]^2 + [f(x) - g(x)]^2 = c.$$

If in addition we have that $f(0) = g(0)$ and $f'(0) = g'(0)$, it follows that $c = 0$. But the sum of two squares is zero iff each square is zero. Therefore for each x

$$f(x) = g(x).$$

Thus there is at most one function f that is twice differentiable everywhere, for which

$$f''(x) + f(x) = 0,$$

which has a specified value at the origin and whose first derivative has a specified value at the origin. That is, there exists at most one function f such that $f''(x) + f(x) = 0, f(0) = b$ and $f'(0) = a$. Note, however, that if

$$f(x) = a \sin x + b \cos x$$

then $f''(x) + f(x) = 0, f(0) = b$ and $f'(0) = a$. We have therefore proved

Theorem 7.45. *If f'' is defined everywhere and if $f''(x) + f(x) = 0$ for each x then*

$$f(x) = f'(0) \sin x + f(0) \cos x.$$

As a final illustration of the Mean Value Theorem we will consider the problem of the continuity of derivatives.

Early in this chapter we proved that if a function is differentiable at a point it is also continuous at that point. The requirement that a function be differentiable at a point is, however, stronger than the requirement that it be continuous at that point. This is illustrated by the example function on page 246, which is continuous at the origin but not differentiable there.

There are, of course, many other functions that behave as this example function does. Consider as an additional example f defined by

$$f(x) = x \sin \frac{1}{x}, \quad x \neq 0,$$
$$f(0) = 0.$$

Since

$$0 \le |f(x)| \le x$$

and since $\underset{x \to 0}{\text{Lim }} x = 0$ it follows that

$$\underset{x \to 0}{\text{Lim }} f(x) = 0 = f(0).$$

Thus f is continuous at 0; indeed f is continuous everywhere. As in the first example the question of the existence of $f'(0)$ is that of the existence of

$$\underset{x \to 0}{\text{Lim }} \frac{f(x)}{x}.$$

Since for $x \neq 0$ we have that $f(x) = x \sin (1/x)$, and since in every neighborhood of the origin there exist numbers x and y such that $\sin (1/x) = 1$ and $\sin (1/y) = 0$ it follows that

$$\left| \frac{f(x)}{x} - \frac{f(y)}{y} \right| = \left| \frac{x \sin \dfrac{1}{x}}{x} - \frac{y \sin \dfrac{1}{y}}{y} \right| = 1.$$

Therefore $f'(0)$ does not exist.

The family of functions defined by

$$f_n(x) = x^n \sin \frac{1}{x}, \quad x \neq 0,$$
$$f_n(0) = 0$$

is a very interesting one. The members of this family possess a curious variety of continuity properties. For example, f_0 is continuous and differentiable everywhere except at 0, where it is neither continuous nor differentiable. The function f_1 is continuous everywhere and differentiable everywhere except at 0. The function f_2 is continuous and differentiable everywhere, but f_2' is not continuous at 0. We leave the proof of these facts to the reader and turn our attention to the interesting question of how a *derived function* can be discontinuous. By a *derived function* we mean one that is the derivative of some other function.

In general a function f is discontinuous at a iff 1) $f(a)$ does not exist, or 2) $\text{Lim}_{x \to a} f(x)$ does not exist, or 3) $f(a)$ and $\text{Lim}_{x \to a} f(x)$ each exist but are not equal. If, however, f is a derivative, then we will show that 3) cannot hold.

Theorem 7.46. *If f is differentiable at each point in some $N(a, \delta)$ and if $\text{Lim}_{x \to a^+} f'(x)$ exists, then $\text{Lim}_{x \to a^+} f'(x) = f'(a)$. Furthermore if $\text{Lim}_{x \to a^-} f'(x)$ exists, then $\text{Lim}_{x \to a^+} f'(x) = f'(a)$.*

Proof. If $\text{Lim}_{x \to a^+} f'(x) = l$ and if $l \neq f'(a)$, then there exists a convergence test ϕ_1 such that if $x \in N(a, \phi(\epsilon)) \cap \text{Dom} f'$ and if $x > a$, then

$$|f'(x) - l| < \epsilon.$$

In particular, if $\epsilon_1 = \frac{1}{2}|f'(a) - l|$ and if $x \in N(a, \epsilon_1) \cap N(a, \delta)$, then

$$|f'(x) - l| < \frac{|f'(a) - l|}{2}.$$

Furthermore since

$$\text{Lim}_{x \to a^+} \frac{f(x) - f(a)}{x - a} = f'(a)$$

it follows that there exists a convergence text ϕ_2 such that if $x \in N(a, \phi_2(\epsilon)) \cap \text{Dom} f'$ and if $x > a$ then

$$\left| \frac{f(x) - f(a)}{x - a} - f'(a) \right| < \epsilon.$$

In particular if $x \in N(a, \epsilon_1) \cap N(a, \delta)$, then

$$\left| \frac{f(x) - f(a)}{x - a} - f'(a) \right| < \frac{|f'(a) - l|}{2}.$$

Therefore if $\delta_1 = \min \{\delta, \phi_1(\epsilon_1), \phi_2(\epsilon_1)\}$, then there is an x in $N(a, \delta_1) \cap$ Dom f' such that $x > a$. Since f is differentiable on $[a, x]$ it follows from the Mean Value Theorem that for some c in (a, x)

$$\frac{f(x) - f(a)}{x - a} = f'(c).$$

Since $c \in N(a, \phi_2(\epsilon_1)) \cap N(a, \delta)$ we then have that

$$
\begin{aligned}
|f'(a) - l| &= \left| f'(a) - \frac{f(x) - f(a)}{x - a} + f'(c) - l \right| \\
&< \left| f'(a) - \frac{f(x) - f(a)}{x - a} \right| + |f'(c) - l| \\
&= \frac{|f'(a) - l|}{2} + \frac{|f'(a) - l|}{2} = |f'(a) - l|.
\end{aligned}
$$

This is a contradiction that forces us to conclude that $f'(a) = l$.

The proof for the left limit is similar and is left to the reader.

EXERCISES

Describe the set of all antiderivatives for the functions in Exercises 1–6.

1. $f(x) = x$.   **2.** $f(x) = \sqrt{x}$.   **3.** $f(x) = x^2 + x$.

4. $f(x) = \sin x$.   **5.** $f(x) = x \sin x$.   **6.** $f(x) = \dfrac{x + 1}{x^3}$.

7. Prove: If f'' is defined everywhere and if for some nonzero number c we have that $f''(x) + cf(x) = 0$ for all x, then

$$f(x) = \frac{f'(0)}{\sqrt{c}} \sin (\sqrt{c}\, x) + f(0) \cos (\sqrt{c}\, x).$$

8. Use the Mean Value Theorem to prove that if $a < b$, if f is differentiable on (a, b), and if f' is positive valued on (a, b), then f is monotone strictly increasing on (a, b).

9. If $f(x) = [\![x]\!]$, $x \notin Z$, does f have a continuous antiderivative?

7.5 The Extended and the Generalized Law of the Mean

Suppose that we are given a function f, and for some reason it is important that we be able to compute the value of f at specified points. Suppose further that f is so defined that its values at the points of interest are difficult or even impossible to compute. It might be the case that for the purposes at hand we would be content to have an approximation to the function values provided these approximations are correct to a specified number of decimal places.

Suppose that the value of f at a certain point a can be easily computed, as is the case for the sine function at 0, $\pi/4$, $\pi/2$, etc. Can we provide an approximation to the value of f at points near a together with an estimate of the error of the approximation? We will show that for certain functions f such a local approximation can be given by polynomial functions and the error can be estimated.

Of all straight lines through a given point on a curve, the one that most nearly coincides with the curve at that point is the tangent line. This suggests that if we wish a local approximation of f at a by a first-degree polynomial function g, then f should be differentiable at a, and g should be defined so that $g(a) = f(a)$ and $g'(a) = f'(a)$, i.e.,

$$g(x) = f(a) + f'(a)(x - a).$$

We will now prove a result that will enable us to estimate the error involved in using $g(b)$ as an approximation to $f(b)$. To avoid the need for discussing separately the cases where $a < b$ and $b < a$ we introduce the following notation.

Definition 7.50. If $a \neq b$, then $\langle a, b \rangle = (a, b) \cup (b, a)$.

From the definition we see that $\langle a, b \rangle$ is a nonempty open interval. Indeed if $a < b$, then $\langle a, b \rangle = (a, b)$, and if $b < a$, then $\langle a, b \rangle = (b, a)$. The symbol '$\langle a, b \rangle$' we will read the *open interval with end points a and b*. Since $\langle a, b \rangle$ is an open interval, its closure $\overline{\langle a, b \rangle}$ is a closed interval— namely $[a, b]$ or $[b, a]$ according as $a < b$ or $b < a$.

Theorem 7.51. *If f' is continuous on $\overline{\langle a, b \rangle}$ and differentiable on $\langle a, b \rangle$, then there exists a c in $\langle a, b \rangle$ for which*

$$f(b) = f(a) + f'(a)(b - a) + \frac{f''(c)}{2}(b - a)^2.$$

Proof. If

$$F(x) = f(x) - g(x) - [f(b) - g(b)]\frac{(x - a)^2}{(b - a)^2}, \quad x \in \overline{\langle a, b \rangle},$$

where

$$g(x) = f(a) + f'(a)(x - a)$$

then F and F' are continuous on $\overline{\langle a, b \rangle}$, and F' is differentiable on $\langle a, b \rangle$. Furthermore, F has been defined in such a way that $F(b) = 0$, and since

$f(a) = g(a)$ we also have that $F(a) = 0$. From Rolle's Theorem it then follows that for some number b_1 in $\langle a, b \rangle$, $F'(b_1) = 0$. Since

$$F'(x) = f'(x) - g'(x) - [f(b) - g(b)] \frac{2(x - a)}{(b - a)^2}, \quad x \in \overline{\langle a, b \rangle}$$

and since $f'(a) = g'(a)$ we have that F' is continuous on $\overline{\langle a, b_1 \rangle}$, differentiable on $\langle a, b_1 \rangle$, $F'(a) = 0$, and $F'(b_1) = 0$. Therefore, applying Rolle's Theorem again, there exists a number c in $\langle a, b_1 \rangle$, and hence in $\langle a, b \rangle$, for which $F''(c) = 0$. Since

$$F''(x) = f''(x) - g''(x) - [f(b) - g(b)] \frac{2}{(b - a)^2}, \quad x \in \overline{\langle a, b \rangle},$$

and since $g''(c) = 0$ (why?) we have on solving for $f(b)$ that

$$f(b) = g(b) + \frac{f''(c)}{2} (b - a)^2.$$

Q.E.D.

It is customary to refer to $f(a) + f'(a)(b - a)$ as a first order approximation to $f(b)$ at a. From Theorem 7.51 we see that the error in a first order approximation is exactly $f''(c)(b - a)^2/2$ for some number c that is between a and b. In general the number c cannot be found, and if it is found $f''(c)$ may be difficult or impossible to compute. If, however, f'' is bounded on $\langle a, b \rangle$, then a bound on the error can be found.

Example. Since the sine function has a derivative that is continuous everywhere, since $\sin 0 = 0$ and $\sin' 0 = 1$, it follows that for each x the first order approximation to $\sin x$ at 0 is x and the error in this approximation is given by

$$\frac{\sin''(c)}{2} x^2$$

for some number c between 0 and x. Since $\sin'' = -\sin$ and since 1 is a bound for the sine function it follows that

$$\left| \frac{\sin''(c)}{2} x^2 \right| \leq \frac{x^2}{2}.$$

Therefore for each x in $N(0, \delta)$ the error in approximating $\sin x$ by x is not greater than $\delta^2/2$. For example if $\delta = .1$, then x is an approximation to $\sin x$ that is accurate to two decimal places. Indeed

$$|\sin x - x| \leq .005.$$

For first order approximations it is convenient to carry out the computations with the coordinate origin translated to $(a, f(a))$. The equation of the tangent line then becomes $y = f'(a)x$. It is, however, conventional to use the special symbols 'dx' and 'dy' as variables in the equation of the

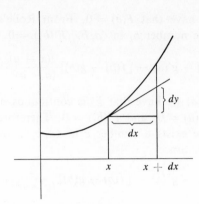

FIGURE 7.6

tangent line with the understanding that if $y = f(x)$ then $dy = f'(x)\,dx$. Thus for each assignment of values to the variables 'x' and 'dx'

$$f(x) + f'(x)\,dx$$

is an approximation to $f(x + dx)$. Furthermore the absolute value of the error in this approximation does not exceed $b(dx)^2/2$ where b is a bound for f'' on $\langle x, x + dx \rangle$.

Example. To obtain an approximation to $\sqrt{1.1}$ we note that if $f(x) = \sqrt{x}$ then $f'(x) = 1/(2\sqrt{x})$, $x \neq 0$. The nearest point at which f and f' can be easily evaluated is 1. The first order approximation to $\sqrt{x}$ at 1 is

$$1 + \frac{dx}{2}.$$

To obtain a bound on the error we note that

$$f''(x) = -\frac{1}{4\sqrt{x^3}}, \quad x \neq 0.$$

From this we see that if x is small, then $|f''(x)|$ will be large. We therefore wish to restrict x to a small neighborhood of 1. The neighborhood must, however, be large enough to contain 1.1. If $\delta = \frac{1}{9}$ then $1.1 \in N(1, \delta)$ and for each x in $N(1, \delta)$, $\frac{4}{9} < \frac{8}{9} = 1 - \frac{1}{9} < x$; $1/\sqrt{x} < \frac{2}{3}$; and

$$|f''(x)| \leq \frac{1}{4(2/3)^3} = \frac{27}{32}.$$

Therefore if $|dx| < \delta$ then the error in our approximation does not exceed $27(dx)^2/32$. In particular, if $dx = .1$ we have that 1.05 is an approximation to $\sqrt{1.1}$ that is correct to two decimal places. In fact

$$|\sqrt{1.1} - 1.05| < \tfrac{27}{6400}.$$

If in some context we wish local approximations to $f(x)$ of greater accuracy than those provided by a first order approximation, it is reasonable to ask about the error that results from approximating f by a polynomial g of degree n that, at a point a agrees with f not only in function value but also in the value of its first n derivatives, i.e.,

$$g(x) = f(a) + \frac{f'(a)}{1!}(x - a) + \cdots + \frac{f^{(n)}(a)}{n!}(x - a)^n.$$

One measure of the error involved in approximating $f(b)$ by $g(b)$ is given by the following theorem, which is known as the extended law of the mean or as Taylor's formula with remainder.

Theorem 7.52 (Taylor's Formula with Remainder). *If $f^{(n)}$ is continuous on $\overline{\langle a, b\rangle}$ and differentiable on $\langle a, b\rangle$, then there exists a c in $\langle a, b\rangle$ for which*

$$f(b) = f(a) + \frac{f'(a)}{1!}(b - a) + \cdots + \frac{f^{(n)}(a)}{n!}(b - a)^n + \frac{f^{(n+1)}(c)}{(n + 1)!}(b - a)^{n+1}$$

Proof. If

$$F(x) = f(x) - g(x) - [f(b) - g(a)]\frac{(x - a)^{n+1}}{(b - a)^{n+1}}, \quad x \in \overline{\langle a, b\rangle},$$

where

$$g(x) = f(a) + \frac{f'(a)}{1!}(x - a) + \cdots + \frac{f^{(n)}(a)}{n!}(x - a)^n,$$

then F and each of its first n derivatives are continuous on $\langle a, b\rangle$. Furthermore for each x in $\overline{\langle a, b\rangle}$

$$F^{(m)}(x) = f^{(m)}(x) - g^{(m)}(x)$$
$$- [f(b) - g(b)]\frac{(n + 1)n(n - 1)\cdots(n + 2 - m)(x - a)^{n+1-m}}{(b - a)^{n+1}},$$
$$m = 0, 1, \ldots, n.$$

Since $g^{(m)}(a) = f^{(m)}(a)$, $m = 0, 1, \ldots, n$ it follows that $F^{(m)}(a) = 0$, $m = 0, 1, \ldots, n$. We now wish to prove that if $1 \le m \le n + 1$ then there exists a number c between a and b for which $F^{(m)}(c) = 0$. This we prove inductively.

If $m = 1$ we have that $F(a) = 0$, $F(b) = 0$, F is continuous on $\overline{\langle a, b\rangle}$ and differentiable on $\langle a, b\rangle$. It then follows from Rolle's Theorem that there exists a number c in $\langle a, b\rangle$ for which $F^{(1)}(c) = 0$. As our induction hypothesis we have that $m < n + 1$ and there exists a number c in $\langle a, b\rangle$ for which $F^{(m)}(c) = 0$. We then have that $F^{(m)}(a) = 0$, $F^{(m)}(c) = 0$, $F^{(m)}$ is continuous on $\overline{\langle a, c\rangle}$ and differentiable on $\langle a, c\rangle$. Consequently there is a number d in $\langle a, c\rangle$, and hence in $\langle a, b\rangle$, for which $F^{(m+1)}(d) = 0$.

We have therefore proved that $F^{(m)}$ is zero at some point in $\langle a, b \rangle$ for $m = 1, 2, \ldots, n + 1$. In particular there is a number c in $\langle a, b \rangle$ for which $F^{(n+1)}(c) = 0$. Since

$$F^{(n+1)}(x) = f^{(n+1)}(x) - g^{(n+1)}(x) - [f(b) - g(b)] \frac{(n+1)!}{(b-a)^{n+1}}, \quad x \in \langle a, b \rangle$$

and since $g^{(n+1)}(c) = 0$ we have, on solving for $f(b)$, that

$$f(b) = g(b) + \frac{f^{(n+1)}(c)}{(n+1)!} (b-a)^{n+1}.$$

$$\text{Q.E.D.}$$

We refer to

$$f(a) + \frac{f'(a)}{1!} (b-a) + \cdots + \frac{f^{(n)}(a)}{n!} (b-a)^n$$

as an nth order approximation to $f(b)$ at a. From Theorem 7.52 we see that the error in such an approximation is exactly

$$\frac{f^{(n+1)}(c)}{(n+1)!} (b-a)^{n+1}.$$

As in the case of first order approximations a bound on the error can be obtained if $f^{(n+1)}$ is bounded on $\langle a, b \rangle$.

Example. Since $\sin^{(2n)}(0) = 0$ and $\sin^{(2n+1)}(0) = (-1)^n$, we have that for each x the $2n$th order approximation to $\sin x$ is

$$x - \frac{x^3}{3!} + \frac{x^5}{5!} - \cdots + (-1)^{n-1} \frac{x^{2n-1}}{(2n-1)!}$$

and the error is

$$\frac{\sin^{(2n+1)}(c)x^{2n+1}}{(2n+1)!}$$

for some c in $\langle 0, x \rangle$. Since

$$\left| \frac{\sin^{(2n+1)}(c)x^{2n+1}}{(2n+1)!} \right| \leq \frac{|x|^{2n+1}}{(2n+1)!}$$

it follows that for each x in $N(0, \delta)$ the error in approximating $\sin x$ by

$$x - \frac{x^3}{3!} + \frac{x^5}{5!} - \cdots + (-1)^{n-1} \frac{x^{2n-1}}{(2n-1)!}$$

does not exceed $\delta^{2n+1}/(2n+1)!$. For example if $\delta = .1$, then the error in a second order approximation does not exceed $\frac{1}{6000}$, and hence is accurate to three decimal places. The error in a fourth order approximation does not exceed $1/(10^5 \cdot 5!)$ and hence is accurate to seven decimal places.

The Mean Value Theorem can also be generalized in another useful way.

Theorem 7.53 (Cauchy's Generalized Law of the Mean). *If f and g are continuous on $[a, b]$ and differentiable on (a, b), then there is a number c in (a, b) for which*

$$f'(c)[g(b) - g(a)] = g'(c)[f(b) - f(a)].$$

If in addition $g(b) \neq g(a)$ and for each x in (a, b) we have that $f'(x)$ and $g'(x)$ are not both zero, then

$$\frac{f'(c)}{g'(c)} = \frac{f(b) - f(a)}{g(b) - g(a)}.$$

Proof. If F is defined on $[a, b]$ by

$$F(x) = [f(x) - f(a)][g(b) - g(a)] - [f(b) - f(a)][g(x) - g(a)]$$

then F is continuous on $[a, b]$ and differentiable on (a, b). Furthermore, $F(a) = F(b) = 0$. Therefore, by Rolle's Theorem there is a number c in (a, b) for which $F'(c) = 0$. Since

$$F'(x) = f'(x)[g(b) - g(a)] - g'(x)[f(b) - f(a)],$$

it follows that

$$f'(c)[g(b) - g(a)] = g'(c)[f(b) - f(a)].$$

If $g(b) \neq g(a)$ and if for each x in (a, b) we have that $f'(x)$ and $g'(x)$ are not both zero, then $g'(c) \neq 0$ and hence

$$\frac{f'(c)}{g'(c)} = \frac{f(b) - f(a)}{g(b) - g(a)}.$$

Q.E.D.

The Generalized Law of the Mean has an interesting geometrical interpretation when f and g are parameterizing functions for a simple continuous relation. If f and g are continuous on $[a, b]$ if

$$R = \{ (g(x), f(x)) \mid x \in [a, b] \}$$

and if $(g(x), f(x)) = (g(y), f(y))$ only if $x = y$, then R is a relation whose graph is a simple continuous curve. (See Figure 7.7.)

For each c in (a, b) we would define the tangent[1] to the curve at $(g(c), f(c))$ as the line through $(g(c), f(c))$ whose slope is

$$\underset{x \to c}{\mathrm{Lim}} \frac{f(x) - f(c)}{g(x) - g(c)}$$

---

[1] Before accepting this definition we should verify that the result does not depend upon the choice of parameterizing functions. This task we leave as a project for the reader.

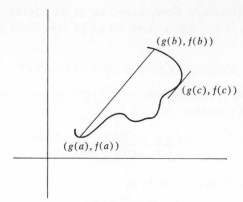

$(g(b), f(b))$

$(g(c), f(c))$

$(g(a), f(a))$

FIGURE 7.7

if this limit exists. If f and g are differentiable at c and if $g'(c) \neq 0$, then this limit does exist. Indeed

$$\operatorname*{Lim}_{x \to c} \frac{f(x) - f(c)}{g(x) - g(c)} = \operatorname*{Lim}_{x \to c} \frac{\dfrac{f(x) - f(c)}{x - c}}{\dfrac{g(x) - g(c)}{x - c}} = \frac{f'(c)}{g'(c)}.$$

If $g'(c) = 0$ and $f'(c) \neq 0$, then the tangent line is the vertical line through $(g(c), f(c))$.

If f and g are differentiable on (a, b) but not both zero at any point, then by the Generalized Law of the Mean we have that there is a c in (a, b) for which

$$f'(c)[g(b) - g(a)] = g'(c)[f(b) - f(a)].$$

If $g(b) = g(a)$ then $f(b) \neq f(a)$ and hence $g'(c) = 0$ and $f'(c) \neq 0$. Therefore, the chord through the point $(g(a), f(a))$ and $(g(b), f(b))$ is a vertical line and the tangent at $(g(c), f(c))$ is a vertical line. If $g(b) \neq g(a)$ then

$$\frac{f'(c)}{g'(c)} = \frac{f(b) - f(a)}{g(b) - g(a)}.$$

But this means that the tangent to the curve at $(g(c), f(c))$ is parallel to the chord through $(g(a), f(a))$ and $(g(b), f(b))$.

From the Generalized Law of the Mean we can deduce a useful result that was first stated by the Marquis de l'Hospital in 1696 and which is now known as l'Hospital's Rule. This rule gives conditions under which the limit of a quotient of two functions is the limit of the quotient of their derivatives.

Theorem 7.54 (L'Hospital's Rule). *If*
1) *f and g are each differentiable in some $N'(a, \delta_0)$,*
2) *$\forall x \in N'(a, \delta_0)$, $f'(x)$ and $g'(x)$ are not both zero,*

3) a is an accumulation point of Dom f/g,

4) $L(f, a) = L(g, a) = 0$ or $(\forall \epsilon)(\exists \delta_\epsilon)\forall x \in N(a, \delta_\epsilon) \cap \text{Dom } g, \; |g(x)| > \epsilon,$
and

5) $\displaystyle \lim_{x \to a} \frac{f'(x)}{g'(x)} = l,$

then $\displaystyle \lim_{x \to a} \frac{f(x)}{g(x)} = l.$

Proof Procedure. We will use the Generalized Law of the Mean to show that for each x and y in $N'(a, \delta_0)$, if $x < y < a$, there exists a c in (x, y) such that

$$\frac{f(x) - f(y)}{g(x) - g(y)} = \frac{f'(c)}{g'(c)}.$$

If $L(f, a) = 0$ and $L(g, a) = 0$ then for y close to a it follows that

$$\frac{f(x) - f(y)}{g(x) - g(y)}$$

is close to $f(x)/g(x)$; if in addition, x is sufficiently close to a, then $f'(c)/g'(c)$ will be near l and hence $f(x)/g(x)$ will be near l. This establishes that

$$\lim_{x \to a^-} \frac{f(x)}{g(x)} = l.$$

By a similar argument we can show that

$$\lim_{x \to a^+} \frac{f(x)}{g(x)} = l.$$

If, in addition, f and g are continuous at a, then the proof can be simplified; to gain insight into the basic argument we will first prove the result in this special case.

Proof. With the additional hypothesis that f and g are continuous at a it follows from hypothesis 4) that $f(a) = g(a) = 0$. Since, by hypothesis 5),

$$\lim_{x \to a} \frac{f'(x)}{g'(x)} = l$$

there exists a convergence test ϕ_1 for which

$$\left| \frac{f'(x)}{g'(x)} - l \right| < \epsilon.$$

if $x \in N(a, \phi_1(\epsilon)) \cap \text{Dom } f'/g'$.

By hypothesis 2), $f'(x)$ and $g'(x)$ are not both zero if $x \in N'(a, \delta_0)$. Therefore, if $\phi(\epsilon) = \min \{\delta_0, \phi_1(\epsilon)\}$ and if $x \in N'(a, \phi(\epsilon)) \cap \text{Dom } f/g$, then

$g(x) \neq 0$, and hence from the Generalized Law of the Mean there is a number c between a and x for which

$$\frac{f(x) - f(a)}{g(x) - g(a)} = \frac{f'(c)}{g'(c)}.$$

Since $f(a) = g(a) = 0$, and since $c \in N(a, \phi_1(\epsilon))$,

$$\frac{f(x)}{g(x)} = \frac{f(x) - f(a)}{g(x) - g(a)},$$

and hence

$$\left| \frac{f(x)}{g(x)} - l \right| = \left| \frac{f'(c)}{g'(c)} - l \right| < \epsilon.$$

Therefore

$$\lim_{x \to a} \frac{f(x)}{g(x)} = l.$$

Without the additional hypothesis that f and g are continuous at a, we modify the argument thus.

From hypotheses 3) and 4) it follows that g is not a constant function; indeed given any number w and any $N'(a, \delta)$ there exists a y in $N'(a, \delta) \cap \operatorname{Dom} f/g$ such that $w \neq g(y)$. Furthermore, if $L(f, a) = 0$ and $L(g, a) = 0$, then for each x in $\operatorname{Dom} f/g$

$$\lim_{y \to a} \frac{f(x) - f(y)}{g(x) - g(y)} = \frac{f(x)}{g(x)};$$

that is, there exists a convergence test ϕ_x with the property that if $y \in N'(a, \phi_x(\epsilon)) \cap \operatorname{Dom} f/g$, then

$$\left| \frac{f(x) - f(y)}{g(x) - g(y)} - \frac{f(x)}{g(x)} \right| < \epsilon.$$

Therefore if $\phi(\epsilon) = \min\{\delta_0, \phi_1(\epsilon)\}$, then for each x in $N'(a, \phi(\epsilon)) \cap \operatorname{Dom} f/g$ there exists a y in $N'(a, \phi_x(\epsilon)) \cap \operatorname{Dom} f/g$ for which $x < y < a$ or $a < y < x$, $g(x) \neq g(y)$, and

$$\left| \frac{f(x) - f(y)}{g(x) - g(y)} - \frac{f(x)}{g(x)} \right| < \epsilon.$$

By the Generalized Law of the Mean it then follows that there exists a number c lying between x and y for which

$$\frac{f(x) - f(y)}{g(x) - g(y)} = \frac{f'(c)}{g'(c)}.$$

Since $c \in N'(a, x)$ and $N'(a, x) \subseteq N'(a, \phi_1(\epsilon))$,

$$\left| \frac{f'(c)}{g'(c)} - l \right| < \epsilon.$$

Therefore

$$\left| \frac{f(x)}{g(x)} - l \right| = \left| \frac{f(x)}{g(x)} - \frac{f(x) - f(y)}{g(x) - g(y)} + \frac{f'(c)}{g'(c)} - l \right|$$

$$\leq \left| \frac{f(x)}{g(x)} - \frac{f(x) - f(y)}{g(x) - g(y)} \right| + \left| \frac{f'(c)}{g'(c)} - l \right| < \epsilon + \epsilon = 2\epsilon.$$

and hence

$$\operatorname*{Lim}_{x \to a} \frac{f(x)}{g(x)} = l.$$

If for each ϵ there exists a δ_ϵ with the property that for each x in $N'(a, \delta_\epsilon) \cap \operatorname{Dom} g$

$$|g(x)| > \epsilon,$$

then for each x in $N'(a, \delta_{1/\epsilon}) \cap \operatorname{Dom} g$

$$\frac{1}{|g(x)|} < \epsilon.$$

Furthermore, since a is an accumulation point of $\operatorname{Dom} f/g$, there exists a y in $N'(a, \phi_1(\epsilon)) \cap N'(a, \delta_0) \cap \operatorname{Dom} f/g$. If $\epsilon_1 = |g(y)|$, then for each x in $N'(a, \delta_{\epsilon_1}) \cap \operatorname{Dom} f/g$

$$|g(x)| > |g(y)|.$$

If in addition $y < x < a$ or $a < x < y$, then, by the Generalized Law of the Mean, there exists a number c lying between y and x for which

$$\frac{f(y) - f(x)}{g(y) - g(x)} = \frac{f'(c)}{g'(c)}.$$

Since $y \in N'(a, \phi_1(\epsilon))$, it follows that $c \in N'(a, \phi_1(\epsilon))$ and hence

$$\left| \frac{f(y) - f(x)}{g(y) - g(x)} - l \right| = \left| \frac{f'(c)}{g'(c)} - l \right| < \epsilon.$$

From this it follows that

$$l - \epsilon < \frac{\dfrac{f(x)}{g(x)} - \dfrac{f(y)}{g(x)}}{1 - \dfrac{g(y)}{g(x)}} < l + \epsilon.$$

Since $|g(y)| < |g(x)|$, $1 - g(y)/g(x) > 0$ and hence

$$(l - \epsilon)\left(1 - \frac{g(y)}{g(x)}\right) < \frac{f(x)}{g(x)} - \frac{f(y)}{g(x)} < (l + \epsilon)\left(1 - \frac{g(y)}{g(x)}\right)$$

But since

$$\operatorname*{Lim}_{x \to a} \frac{1}{|g(x)|} = 0,$$

it follows that if x is sufficiently near a, then (leaving the details to the reader)

$$l - 2\epsilon < (l - \epsilon)\left(1 - \frac{g(y)}{g(x)}\right) \text{ and } (l + \epsilon)\left(1 - \frac{g(y)}{g(x)}\right) < l + 2\epsilon$$

and hence

$$l - 2\epsilon < \frac{f(x)}{g(x)} - \frac{f(y)}{g(x)} < l + 2\epsilon$$

$$-\epsilon(|f(y)| + 2) < \frac{f(y)}{g(x)} - 2\epsilon < \frac{f(x)}{g(x)} - l < \frac{f(y)}{g(x)} + 2\epsilon < \epsilon(|f(y)| + 2),$$

that is,

$$\left|\frac{f(x)}{g(x)} - l\right| < \epsilon(|f(y)| + 2).$$

Thus if $y < a$,

$$\lim_{x \to a-} \frac{f(x)}{g(x)} = l$$

and if $y > a$,

$$\lim_{x \to a+} \frac{f(x)}{g(x)} = l.$$

Consequently

$$\lim_{x \to a} \frac{f(x)}{g(x)} = l.$$

Q.E.D.

Example. $\displaystyle\lim_{x \to 0} \frac{1 - \cos x}{x^2} = \lim_{x \to 0} \frac{\sin x}{2x} = \frac{1}{2}.$

EXERCISES

In Exercises 1–3 give an approximation that is accurate to five decimal places.

1. $\sqrt{5}$.　　　　　　**2.** $\sin .8$.　　　　　　**3.** $\sqrt[3]{2}$.

In Exercises 4–6 determine the limit.

4. $\displaystyle\lim_{x \to 0} \frac{1 - \cos^2 x}{x}$.　　**5.** $\displaystyle\lim_{x \to 0} \frac{x - \sin x}{x^2}$.　　**6.** $\displaystyle\lim_{x \to 0} \frac{1 - \cos^2 x}{\sqrt{x}}$.

7. Prove: If

1) f and g are each differentiable in some $N'(a, \delta)$,
2) $\forall x \in N'(a, \delta), f'(x)$ and $g'(x)$ are not both zero,
3) a is an accumulation point of Dom f/g,
4) $\displaystyle\lim_{x \to a} f(x) = \lim_{x \to a} g(x) = 0$　or　$(\forall\epsilon)(\exists\delta) \forall x \in N(a, \delta) \cap \text{Dom } f$, $|g(x)| > \epsilon$,
5) $(\forall\epsilon)(\exists\delta) \forall x \in N(a, \delta) \cap \text{Dom } f/g, \dfrac{f'(x)}{g'(x)} > \epsilon$,

then $(\forall\epsilon)(\exists\delta) \forall x \in N(a, \delta) \cap \text{Dom } f/g. \dfrac{f(x)}{g(x)} > \epsilon$.

CHAPTER **8**

The Riemann Integral

8.0 The Basic Concept

Historically integration had its origin in the problems of mensuration—to determine the length of a given curve, the area of a given surface, and the volume of a given solid. Reversing the historical order, let us first give a definition of the Riemann integral, and then we will ask why the definition given is a sensible one.

Throughout this chapter we will restrict our discussion primarily to functions that are bounded on some closed and bounded interval in the sense of

Definition 8.00. f is *bounded on* $[a, b]$ iff $[a, b] \subseteq \text{Dom} f$ and for some number d and each x in $[a, b]$ we have that $|f(x)| \leq d$.

Given an appropriate function f and an interval $[a, b]$, the Riemann integral of f on $[a, b]$ is a real number which we define in the following way. We first consider all possible subdivisions of $[a, b]$ into a finite number of closed subintervals, no two of which may have more than an end point in common. Any such collection of subintervals is completely determined by the set of end points of the subintervals, provided the order of the end points is known. We therefore introduce the following notation which will be used throughout this chapter. We will use the symbol

$$\{a_0, a_1, \ldots, a_n\}$$

to denote a set whose elements are ordered as indicated, i.e.,

$$a_0 < a_1 < \cdots < a_n.$$

Definition 8.01. N is a *subdivision* of $[a, b]$ iff N is a finite subset of $[a, b]$ and N contains both a and b. If $N = \{a_0, a_1, \ldots, a_n\}$, then

$$|N| = \max \{a_1 - a_0, a_2 - a_1, \ldots, a_n - a_{n-1}\}.$$

The symbol '$|N|$' is read the *norm of N*.

267

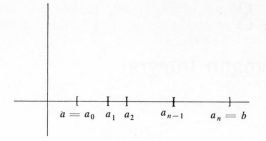

$$a = a_0 \quad a_1 \quad a_2 \qquad a_{n-1} \qquad a_n = b$$

FIGURE 8.1

If f is bounded on $[a, b]$, then for each subdivision $\{a_0, a_1, \ldots, a_n\}$ of $[a, b]$

$$\sum_{\alpha=1}^{n} (\sup f[a_{\alpha-1}, a_\alpha])(a_\alpha - a_{\alpha-1}) \text{ and } \sum_{\alpha=1}^{n} (\inf f[a_{\alpha-1}, a_\alpha])(a_\alpha - a_{\alpha-1})$$

each exist.

Definition 8.02. If f is *bounded* on $[a, b]$, if $N = \{a_0, \ldots, a_n\}$, and if N is a subdivision of $[a, b]$, then

$$\bar{S}_f(N) = \sum_{\alpha=1}^{n} (\sup f[a_{\alpha-1}, a_\alpha])(a_\alpha - a_{\alpha-1})$$

and

$$\underline{S}_f(N) = \sum_{\alpha=1}^{n} (\inf f[a_{\alpha-1}, a_\alpha])(a_\alpha - a_{\alpha-1}).$$

$\bar{S}_f(N)$ is an *upper Darboux sum* for f on $[a, b]$; $\underline{S}_f(N)$ is a *lower Darboux sum* for f on $[a, b]$.

We next consider the set of all upper Darboux sums for f on $[a, b]$ and the set of all lower Darboux sums for f on $[a, b]$.

Definition 8.03. If f is bounded on $[a, b]$ then

$$\mathscr{U}_f[a, b] = \{\bar{S}_f(N) \mid N \text{ is a subdivision of } [a, b]\};$$
$$\mathscr{L}_f[a, b] = \{\underline{S}_f(N) \mid N \text{ is a subdivision of } [a, b]\}.$$

Example. If $f(x) = 2$, $x \in [a, b]$, then for each subdivision N of $[a, b]$ we have, if $N = \{a_0, a_1, \ldots, a_n\}$, that $\sup f[a_{\alpha-1}, a_\alpha] = 2$, $\inf f[a_{\alpha-1}, a_\alpha] = 2$ and hence

$$\underline{S}_f(N) = \bar{S}_f(N) = \sum_{\alpha=1}^{n} 2(a_\alpha - a_{\alpha-1}) = 2 \sum_{\alpha=1}^{n} (a_\alpha - a_{\alpha-1}) = 2(b - a).$$

Therefore, $\mathscr{L}_f[a, b] = \mathscr{U}_f[a, b] = \{2(b - a)\}$.

Example. If $f(x) = \text{Rat}(x)$, $x \in [a, b]$, then for each subdivision N of $[a, b]$ it follows that if $N = \{a_0, a_1, \ldots, a_n\}$, then $\sup f[a_{\alpha-1}, a_\alpha] = 1$, $\inf f[a_{\alpha-1}, a_\alpha] = -1$ and hence

$$\bar{S}_f(N) = \sum_{\alpha=1}^{n} 1 \cdot (a_\alpha - a_{\alpha-1}) = b - a,$$

$$\underline{S}_f(N) = \sum_{\alpha=1}^{n} (-1)(a_\alpha - a_{\alpha-1}) = a - b.$$

Therefore $\mathscr{L}_f[a, b] = \{a - b\}$ and $\mathscr{U}_f[a, b] = \{b - a\}$.

Example. If $f(x) = x$, $x \in [a, b]$, then for each subdivision N of $[a, b]$ if $N = \{a_0, a_1, \ldots, a_n\}$, then $\sup f[a_{\alpha-1}, a_\alpha] = a_\alpha$ and $\inf f[a_{\alpha-1}, a_\alpha] = a_{\alpha-1}$. Therefore

$$\underline{S}_f(N) = \sum_{\alpha=1}^{n} a_{\alpha-1}(a_\alpha - a_{\alpha-1}) \text{ and } \bar{S}_f(N) = \sum_{\alpha=1}^{n} a_\alpha(a_\alpha - a_{\alpha-1}).$$

We next observe that if f is bounded on $[a, b]$, then for each subdivision N of $[a, b]$ we have, if $N = \{a_0, a_1, \ldots, a_n\}$, that

$$\begin{aligned}
\bar{S}_f(N) &= \sum_{\alpha=1}^{n} (\sup f[a_{\alpha-1}, a_\alpha])(a_\alpha - a_{\alpha-1}) \\
&\geq \sum_{\alpha=1}^{n} (\inf f[a_{\alpha-1}, a_\alpha])(a_\alpha - a_{\alpha-1}) \\
&\geq \sum_{\alpha=1}^{n} (\inf f[a, b])(a_\alpha - a_{\alpha-1}) = (\inf f[a, b])(b - a)
\end{aligned}$$

and

$$\begin{aligned}
\underline{S}_f(N) &= \sum_{\alpha=1}^{n} (\inf f[a_{\alpha-1}, a_\alpha])(a_\alpha - a_{\alpha-1}) \\
&\leq \sum_{\alpha=1}^{n} (\sup f[a_{\alpha-1}, a_\alpha])(a_\alpha - a_{\alpha-1}) \\
&\leq \sum_{\alpha=1}^{n} (\sup f[a, b])(a_\alpha - a_{\alpha-1}) = (\sup f[a, b])(b - a).
\end{aligned}$$

Therefore the set of lower sums is bounded above and the set of upper sums is bounded below. Consequently $\sup \mathscr{L}_f[a, b]$ and $\inf \mathscr{U}_f[a, b]$ each exist.

Definition 8.04. If f is bounded on $[a, b]$ then

$$\int_{\underline{a}}^{b} f = \sup \mathscr{L}_f[a, b] \text{ and } \overline{\int_a^b} f = \inf \mathscr{U}_f[a, b].$$

$\int_{\underline{a}}^{b} f$ is the *lower Darboux integral* of f on $[a, b]$ and $\overline{\int_a^b} f$ is the *upper Darboux integral* of f on $[a, b]$.

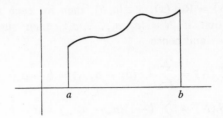

$$\text{FIGURE 8.2}$$

Example. If $f(x) = 2$, $x \in [a, b]$, then $\int_{\underline{a}}^{b} f = 2(b - a)$ and $\overline{\int}_{a}^{b} f = 2(b - a)$

$$\int_{\underline{a}}^{b} \text{Rat} = a - b \text{ and } \overline{\int}_{a}^{b} \text{Rat} = b - a.$$

From these examples we see that there are functions for which the upper integral and the lower integral are equal, and there are functions for which they are not equal. Those functions f for which the upper and lower integrals are equal are of special interest. Such functions are called (Riemann) integrable functions, and the common value of the upper and lower integrals is the (Riemann) integral of f on $[a, b]$.

Definition 8.05. f is (*Riemann*) *integrable* on $[a, b]$ iff f is bounded on $[a, b]$ and $\int_{\underline{a}}^{b} f = \overline{\int}_{a}^{b} f$. If f is integrable on $[a, b]$, then

$$\int_{a}^{b} f = \overline{\int}_{a}^{b} f.$$

From the examples above we see that if $f(x) = 2$, then f is integrable on every interval, $[a, b]$ and $\int_{a}^{b} f = 2(b - a)$. On the other hand the Rat function is not integrable on any interval, for while $\int_{\underline{a}}^{b} \text{Rat}$ and $\overline{\int}_{a}^{b} \text{Rat}$ each exist, they are not equal.

The integral of a given function over a given interval, if it exists, is a number. This number is completely determined by the function f, called the integrand of the integral; the left end-point of the interval a, called the lower limit of the integral; and the right end-point of the interval b, called the upper limit of the integral.

At this point let us consider some problems that illustrate why the Riemann integral is a useful and sensible concept. The arguments are intended to be heuristic and intuitive. Let us begin with the classical problem of determining "the area under a curve."

Consider a figure that is bounded by the curves whose equations are $y = f(x)$, $y = 0$, $x = a$, and $x = b$ where $a < b$ and f is a function that is bounded and nonnegative on $[a, b]$. (See Figure 8.2). To each such figure

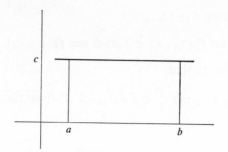

FIGURE 8.3

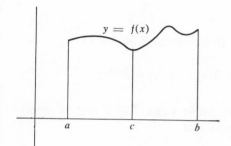
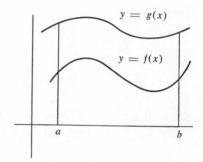

FIGURE 8.4

we wish to assign a number that we might reasonably call the area of the figure. Since the figure is uniquely determined by f, a, and b, we are seeking to define a mapping A which assigns to triples (f, a, b) a real number and which has certain useful properties. If f is a constant function then the figure is a rectangle. (See Figure 8.3.) For practical reasons we wish the area of a rectangle to be the product of its dimensions. We will therefore require that the mapping A have the property

$$P_1. \quad A(\bar{c}, a, b) = c(b - a)$$

where $\bar{c}$ denotes the constant function whose value is c everywhere, that is, $\bar{c}(x) = c$, for each x. We also wish the area of a figure to be equal to the sum of the areas of its parts in the following sense. (See Figure 8.4.)

$P_2.$ If $c \in (a, b)$ then $A(f, a, b) = A(f, a, c) + A(f, c, b)$.
$P_3.$ If for each x in $[a, b]$, $f(x) \le g(x)$, then $A(f, a, b) \le A(g, a, b)$.

From P_3 we can prove by induction that for each subdivision N of $[a, b]$ if $N = \{a_0, \ldots, a_n\}$, then

$$A(f, a, b) = \sum_{\alpha=1}^{n} A(f, a_{\alpha-1}, a_\alpha).$$

Furthermore for each x in $[a_{\alpha-1}, a_\alpha]$

$$\inf f[a_{\alpha-1}, a_\alpha] \leq f(x) \leq \sup f[a_{\alpha-1}, a_\alpha].$$

It then follows from P_3 that

$$A(\overline{\inf f[a_{\alpha-1}, a_\alpha]}, a_{\alpha-1}, a_\alpha) \leq A(f, a_{\alpha-1}, a_\alpha) \leq A(\overline{\sup f[a_{\alpha-1}, a_\alpha]}, a_{\alpha-1}, a_\alpha).$$

But from P_1

$$A(\overline{\inf f[a_{\alpha-1}, a_\alpha]}, a_{\alpha-1}, a_\alpha) = (\inf f[a_{\alpha-1}, a_\alpha])(a_\alpha - a_{\alpha-1}),$$
$$A(\overline{\sup f[a_{\alpha-1}, a_\alpha]}, a_{\alpha-1}, a_\alpha) = (\sup f[a_{\alpha-1}, a_\alpha])(a_\alpha - a_{\alpha-1}).$$

Therefore,

$$\underline{S}_f(N) = \sum_{\alpha=1}^{n} (\inf f[a_{\alpha-1}, a_\alpha])(a_\alpha - a_{\alpha-1}) \leq A(f, a, b)$$
$$\leq \sum_{\alpha=1}^{n} (\sup f[a_{\alpha-1}, a_\alpha])(a_\alpha - a_{\alpha-1}) = \bar{S}_f(N).$$

Since $A(f, a, b)$ is a lower bound for upper sums, $\bar{S}_f(N)$, and an upper bound for lower sums, $\underline{S}_f(N)$, it follows that

$$\underline{\int_a^b} f \leq A(f, a, b) \leq \overline{\int_a^b} f.$$

From this we see that if a mapping A exists having properties P_1–P_3 then for integrable functions

$$A(f, a, b) = \int_a^b f.$$

Conversely if $\int_a^b f$ can be shown to have the properties P_1–P_3, then for integrable functions we can define $A(f, a, b)$ as $\int_a^b f$.

As a second application of interest let us consider the problem of determining the work done by a force as it acts along a straight line. As in the case of area, our first problem is to decide what we mean by work.

If an object of weight w is raised vertically a short distance d, then the product wd is the work done in moving the object the given distance. This number is of interest because it is a measure of the amount of energy expended. There is, however, a simplifying assumption in this example—namely, that the given object weighs the same at each point of the path. For small distances this assumption introduces only a small error. Suppose, however, the object is to be raised from the surface of the earth to a point several hundreds of miles above the earth. The pull of gravity being greater at the surface of the earth, the object weighs more on the surface than it does several hundred miles in space. We are interested in how the total energy expended is related to the force exerted and the distance. Since for such problems the motion is along a straight line, let us assign coordinates and consider the distance to be determined by an interval $[a, b]$. Suppose further that the force at each point of $[a, b]$ is given by a function f. The work done is then determined by f, a, and b. We are, therefore, seeking to define a mapping W which associates with each triple (f, a, b) a real number and which has certain useful properties. From experience we know that for constant functions we wish the work to be the force times the distance. We also wish the work to be additive—that is, the work done in moving the object from a to b should be the work done in moving the object from a to any intermediate point c plus the work done in moving from c to b. Finally, we would agree that the greater the force exerted the more work is done. We, therefore, wish the mapping W to have the properties

P_1. $W(\bar{c}, a, b) = c(b - a)$.

P_2. If $c \in (a, b)$ then $W(f, a, b) = W(f, a, c) + W(f, c, b)$.

P_3. If for each x in $[a, b]$, $f(x) \leq g(x)$, then $W(f, a, b) \leq W(g, a, b)$

Note that these are the same properties that we wish to have for the area function. The work problem and the area problem are, therefore, mathematically the same. They differ only in the interpretation of the symbols. As in the case of area we can easily establish that if there exists a function W having the properties P_1–P_3, then

$$\underline{\int_a^b} f \leq W(f, a, b) \leq \overline{\int_a^b} f.$$

Thus if f is integrable on $[a, b]$, then

$$W(f, a, b) = \int_a^b f.$$

As a final example consider a particle that moves along a straight line and whose velocity at any instant of the time interval $[a, b]$ is given by a function f. What is the displacement of the particle at time b relative to its position at time a? We would agree that for a constant velocity the displacement should be the velocity times the time. Furthermore the displacement should be additive, and finally we wish the greater velocity to produce the greater displacement.

We, therefore, seek to define a mapping L which assigns to triples (f, a, b) a real number and which has the properties

P_1. $L(\bar{c}, a, b) = c(b - a)$.

P_2. If $c \in (a, b)$ then $L(f, a, b) = L(f, a, c) + L(f, c, b)$.

P_3. If for each x in $[a, b]$, $f(x) \leq g(x)$ then $L(f, a, b) \leq L(g, a, b)$.

This is again the same collection of properties that we required of the area function and the work function, and again the difference in the problem is only in the interpretation. The first property states that for constant velocity the displacement is the velocity times the time. The second states that displacement is additive, and the third asserts that the greater the velocity the greater the displacement. Computation as in the last two examples reveals that if there exists such a function L and if f is integrable on $[a, b]$, then

$$L(f, a, b) = \int_a^b f.$$

From these examples we see that the Riemann integral has many useful applications provided it has properties P_1–P_3, that is:

P_1. $\int_a^b \bar{c} = c(b - a)$.

P_2. If $c \in (a, b)$, if $\int_a^b f$, $\int_a^c f$, and $\int_c^b f$ exist then $\int_a^b f = \int_a^c f + \int_c^b f$.

P_3. If $\int_a^b f$ and $\int_a^b g$ exist and if for each x in $[a, b]$, $f(x) \leq g(x)$, then $\int_a^b f \leq \int_a^b g$.

For the proof of the property P_1 we note that if $f(x) = c$, $x \in [a, b]$, then for each subdivision N of $[a, b]$ we have, if $N = \{a_0, a_1, \ldots, a_n\}$, that $\sup f[a_{\alpha-1}, a_\alpha] = c$ and $\inf f[a_{\alpha-1}, a_\alpha] = c$. Therefore

$$\underline{S}_f(N) = \bar{S}_f(N) = \sum_{\alpha=1}^n c(a_\alpha - a_{\alpha-1}) = c(b - a).$$

Consequently $\mathscr{L}_f[a, b] = \mathscr{U}_f[a, b] = \{c(b - a)\}$ and hence $\underline{\int_a^b} f = \overline{\int_a^b} f = c(b - a)$.

We have then proved

Theorem 8.06. $\int_a^b \bar{c} = c(b - a)$.

The properties P_2 and P_3 are easily proved from the properties of supremums and infimums.

If $\int_a^c f$ and $\int_c^b f$ exist and if

$$A = \{\bar{S}_f(N) + \bar{S}_f(M) \mid N \text{ is a subdivision of } [a, c] \text{ and } M \text{ is a subdivision of } [c, b]\}$$

then $\inf A = \int_a^c f + \int_c^b f$. (Why?) Furthermore for each subdivision N of $[a, c]$ and each subdivision M of $[c, b]$, we have that $N \cup M$ is a subdivision of $[a, b]$ and $\bar{S}_f(N \cup M) = \bar{S}_f(N) + \bar{S}_f(M)$. (Why?) Therefore

$$A \subseteq \mathscr{U}_f[a, b]$$

and $\inf \mathscr{U}_f[a, b] \leq \inf A$, i.e., $\int_a^b f \leq \int_a^c f + \int_c^b f$. Similarly if

$$B = \{\underline{S}_f(N) + \underline{S}_f(M) \mid N \text{ is a subdivision of } [a, c] \text{ and } M \text{ is a subdivision of } [c, b]\}$$

then $\sup B = \int_a^c f + \int_c^b f$. Again for each subdivision N of $[a, c]$ and each subdivision M of $[c, b]$ we have that $N \cup M$ is a subdivision of $[a, b]$ and $\underline{S}_f(N \cup M) = \underline{S}_f(N) + \underline{S}_f(M)$. Therefore

$$B \subseteq \mathscr{L}_f[a, b],$$

hence $\sup B \leq \sup \mathscr{L}_f[a, b]$, i.e., $\int_a^c f + \int_c^b f \leq \int_a^b f$. We therefore have that

$$\int_a^c f + \int_c^b f \leq \int_a^b f \leq \int_a^c f + \int_c^b f$$

from which we conclude that $\int_a^b f = \int_a^c f + \int_c^b f$.

We have proved

Theorem 8.07. *If* $c \in (a, b)$ *if* $\int_a^c f$, $\int_c^b f$, *and* $\int_a^b f$ *exist, then* $\int_a^b f = \int_a^c f + \int_c^b f$.

The third property follows easily from the fact that if $f(x) \leq g(x)$ for each x in $[a, b]$, then for each subdivision N of $[a, b]$ we have, if $N = \{a_0, \ldots, a_n\}$, that

$$\sup f[a_{\alpha-1}, a_\alpha] \leq \sup g[a_{\alpha-1}, a_\alpha]$$

and hence

$$\bar{S}_f(N) = \sum_{\alpha=1}^n (\sup f[a_{\alpha-1}, a_\alpha])(a_\alpha - a_{\alpha-1})$$
$$\leq \sum_{\alpha=1}^n (\sup g[a_{\alpha-1}, a_\alpha])(a_\alpha - a_{\alpha-1}) = \bar{S}_g(N).$$

From this it follows that $\inf \mathscr{U}_f[a, b] \leq \inf \mathscr{U}_g[a, b]$. (Why?) Thus if $\int_a^b f$ and $\int_a^b g$ each exist, then $\int_a^b f \leq \int_a^b g$.

This we summarize as

Theorem 8.08. *If* $\int_a^b f$ *and* $\int_a^b g$ *exist and if* $f(x) \leq g(x)$ *for each* x *in* $[a, b]$, *then* $\int_a^b f \leq \int_a^b g$.

From Theorems 8.06–8.08 we see that the Riemann integral does have the properties we required in the area, work, and displacement problems. As we pointed out, when restricted to integrable functions these three problems are mathematically the same, differing only in interpretation. It is clearly, then, a matter of some importance to know which functions are integrable and which are not.

8.1 Existence Theorems

As the reader has surely noticed the results proved above have the defect of containing a very large "if"; if the integral exists, then such and such is the case. It is important that we have an existence theorem. We know, of course, that functions that are integrable on an interval must be bounded on that interval. We know also that while this condition is necessary it is not sufficient. There exist functions that are bounded on an interval that are not integrable on that interval. In this section we will investigate conditions that are sufficient to assure the existence of the integral. The basic sufficiency condition that we will prove in this section is that continuous functions are integrable. To prove this we must first establish that for functions f that are bounded on an interval $[a, b]$

$$\underline{\int_a^b} f \leq \overline{\int_a^b} f.$$

This follows easily from certain results about upper and lower Darboux sums, which we will prove as lemmas. For these results we must have the notion of a *refinement* of a subdivision. By a refinement of a subdivision N we mean a subdivision that contains all of the points in N and possibly others as well.

Definition 8.10. If N_1 and N_2 are subdivisions of $[a, b]$, then N_2 is a *refinement* of N_1 iff $N_1 \subseteq N_2$.

Lemma 1. *If f is bounded on $[a, b]$ and if $c \in (a, b)$ then*
1) $(\sup f[a, c])(c - a) + (\sup f[c, b])(b - c) \leq (\sup f[a, b])(b - a)$.
2) $(\inf f[a, c])(c - a) + (\inf f[c, b])(b - c) \geq (\inf f[a, b])(b - a)$.

Proof. 1) (See Figure 8.5.) Since

$$\sup f[a, c] \leq \sup f[a, b] \text{ and } \sup f[c, b] \leq \sup f[a, b]$$

we have that

$$(\sup f[a, c])(c - a) \leq (\sup f[a, b])(c - a)$$

and

$$(\sup f[c, b])(b - c) \leq (\sup f[a, b])(b - c).$$

Adding, we obtain

$$(\sup f[a, c])(c - a) + (\sup f[c, b])(b - c) \leq (\sup f[a, b])(b - a).$$

2) The proof is left to the reader.

Lemma 2. *If f is bounded on $[a, b]$, if N_1 is a subdivision of $[a, b]$, and if N is a refinement of N_1, then $\overline{S}_f(N) \leq \overline{S}_f(N_1)$ and $\underline{S}_f(N) \geq \underline{S}_f(N_1)$.*

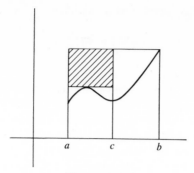

$$a \qquad c \qquad b$$

FIGURE 8.5

Proof. (By induction on the number p of points in N that are not in N_1.) If $p = 0$ then $N = N_1$ and hence $\bar{S}_f(N) = \bar{S}_f(N_1)$ and $\underline{S}_f(N) = \underline{S}_f(N_1)$. As our induction hypothesis we assume the result true for each refinement of N_1 with p additional points of subdivision. If N is a refinement of N_1 with $p + 1$ additional points, then there exists a c in N that is not in N_1. If $N_2 = N - \{c\}$ then N_2 is a refinement of N_1 with p additional points of subdivision and hence by the induction hypothesis $\bar{S}_f(N_2) \leq \bar{S}_f(N_1)$ and $\underline{S}_f(N_2) \geq \underline{S}_f(N_1)$. Furthermore if $N_2 = \{a_0, \ldots, a_n\}$ then there exists an integer k such that $a_k < c < a_{k+1}$ and hence $N = \{a_0, a_1, \ldots, a_k, c, a_{k+1}, \ldots, a_n\}$. By Lemma 1

$$(\sup f[a_k, c])(c - a_k) + (\sup f[c, a_{k+1}])(a_{k+1} - c)$$
$$\leq (\sup f[a_k, a_{k+1}])(a_{k+1} - a_k)$$

and

$$(\inf f[a_k, c])(c - a_k) + (\inf f[c, a_{k+1}])(a_{k+1} - c)$$
$$\geq (\inf f[a_k, a_{k+1}])(a_{k+1} - a_k).$$

Therefore $\bar{S}_f(N) \leq \bar{S}_f(N_2)$ and $\underline{S}_f(N) \geq \underline{S}_f(N_2)$. Since $\bar{S}_f(N_2) \leq \bar{S}_f(N_1)$ and $\underline{S}_f(N_2) \geq \underline{S}_f(N_1)$ we conclude that $\bar{S}_f(N) \leq \bar{S}_f(N_1)$ and $\underline{S}_f(N) \geq \underline{S}_f(N_1)$.

Q.E.D.

From Lemma 2 we see that upon refinement of the subdivision, upper sums, $\bar{S}_f(N)$, tend to shrink and lower sums, $\underline{S}_f(N)$, tend to grow.

Lemma 3. *If f is bounded on $[a, b]$, then for each subdivision N_1 and N_2 of $[a, b]$ we have that*

$$\underline{S}_f(N_1) \leq \bar{S}_f(N_2).$$

Proof. If N_1 and N_2 are subdivisions of $[a, b]$ and if $N = N_1 \cup N_2$, then N is a refinement of N_1 and a refinement of N_2. Since $\underline{S}_f(N) \leq \bar{S}_f(N)$ (why?) we have from Lemma 2 that

$$\underline{S}_f(N_1) \leq \underline{S}_f(N) \leq \bar{S}_f(N) \leq \bar{S}_f(N_2).$$

Q.E.D.

Theorem 8.11. *If f is bounded on* $[a, b]$, *then*

$$\underline{\int_a^b} f \le \overline{\int_a^b} f.$$

Proof. By Lemma 3 every upper sum $\overline{S}_f(N)$ is an upper bound for the set of lower sums. Therefore

$$\underline{\int_a^b} f \le \overline{\int_a^b} f.$$

(Why?)

Q.E.D.

From Theorem 8.11 we can prove a very general existence theorem, namely

Theorem 8.12. *If f is bounded on* $[a, b]$ *then f is integrable on* $[a, b]$ *iff for each* ϵ *there exists a subdivision N of* $[a, b]$ *for which*

$$\overline{S}_f(N) - \underline{S}_f(N) < \epsilon.$$

Proof. If for each ϵ there exists a subdivision N of $[a, b]$ for which

$$\overline{S}_f(N) - \underline{S}_f(N) < \epsilon,$$

then since

$$\underline{S}_f(N) \le \underline{\int_a^b} f \le \overline{\int_a^b} f \le \overline{S}_f(N)$$

we have that

$$0 \le \overline{\int_a^b} f - \underline{\int_a^b} f \le \overline{S}_f(N) - \underline{S}_f(N) < \epsilon.$$

Therefore

$$\underline{\int_a^b} f = \overline{\int_a^b} f$$

and hence f is integrable on $[a, b]$.

Conversely if f is integrable on $[a, b]$, then

$$\underline{\int_a^b} f = \overline{\int_a^b} f$$

and for each ϵ there exist subdivisions N_1 and N_2 for which

$$\overline{S}_f(N_1) < \overline{\int_a^b} f + \frac{\epsilon}{2}$$

$$\underline{S}_f(N_2) > \underline{\int_a^b} f - \frac{\epsilon}{2}.$$

Therefore if $N = N_1 \cup N_2$, then by Lemma 2

$$\bar{S}_f(N) - \underline{S}_f(N) \leq \bar{S}_f(N_1) - \underline{S}_f(N_2) < \int_a^b f + \frac{\epsilon}{2} - \int_a^b f + \frac{\epsilon}{2} = \epsilon.$$

Q.E.D.

Let us digress a moment to illustrate the use of Theorems 8.11 and 8.12.

Theorem 8.13.   *If f is integrable on $[a, b]$ then f is integrable on any sub-interval of $[a, b]$; i.e., if f is integrable on $[a, b]$ and if $a \leq c < d \leq b$, then f is integrable on $[c, d]$.*

Proof.   If f is integrable on $[a, b]$ then f is bounded on $[a, b]$. Therefore f is bounded on $[c, d]$. Furthermore for each ϵ there exists a subdivision N of $[a, b]$ for which

$$\bar{S}_f(N) - \underline{S}_f(N) < \epsilon.$$

If $N_1 = N \cup \{c, d\}$ then N_1 is a refinement of N and hence

$$\bar{S}_f(N_1) - \underline{S}_f(N_1) \leq \bar{S}_f(N) - \underline{S}_f(N) < \epsilon.$$

If $M = N_1 \cap [c, d]$ then M is a subdivision of $[c, d]$. Furthermore

$$\bar{S}_f(M) - \underline{S}_f(M) \leq \bar{S}_f(N_1) - \underline{S}_f(N_1).$$

(Why?) It then follows that

$$\bar{S}_f(M) - \underline{S}_f(M) < \epsilon$$

and hence f is integrable on $[c, d]$.

Q.E.D.

Theorem 8.14.   *If $a < c < b$ and if any two of $\int_a^b f$, $\int_a^c f$, and $\int_c^b f$ exist, then the third exists and*

$$\int_a^b f = \int_a^c f + \int_c^b f.$$

Proof.   From Theorem 8.07 the equality follows from the existence of the integrals. If f is integrable on $[a, b]$, then by Theorem 8.13 it is integrable on $[a, c]$ and on $[c, b]$. If f is integrable on $[a, c]$ and on $[c, b]$, then from Theorem 8.12 it follows that for each ϵ there exists a subdivision N_1 of $[a, c]$ and a subdivision N_2 of $[c, b]$ for which

$$\bar{S}_f(N_1) - \underline{S}_f(N_1) < \frac{\epsilon}{2} \text{ and } \bar{S}_f(N_2) - \underline{S}_f(N_2) < \frac{\epsilon}{2}.$$

Therefore if $N = N_1 \cup N_2$ then N is a subdivision of $[a, b]$ and

$$\bar{S}_f(N) - \underline{S}_f(N) = \bar{S}_f(N_1) + \bar{S}_f(N_2) - \underline{S}_f(N_1) - \underline{S}_f(N_2) < \epsilon.$$

Consequently f is integrable on $[a, b]$.

Q.E.D.

Theorem 8.15. *If f and g are each integrable on* $[a, b]$, *then* $f + g$ *is integrable on* $[a, b]$ *and*

$$\int_a^b (f + g) = \int_a^b f + \int_a^b g.$$

Proof. Since f and g are each integrable on $[a, b]$ it follows that f and g are bounded on $[a, b]$ hence $f + g$ is also bounded on $[a, b]$. Therefore $\int_a^b (f + g)$ and $\overline{\int_a^b} (f + g)$ each exist. Furthermore for each subdivision N of $[a, b]$, if $N = \{a_0, \ldots, a_n\}$, then

$$\sup (f + g)[a_{\alpha-1}, a_\alpha] \leq \sup f[a_{\alpha-1}, a_\alpha] + \sup g[a_{\alpha-1}, a_\alpha].$$

(Why?) Consequently,

$$\bar{S}_{f+g}(N) \leq \bar{S}_f(N) + \bar{S}_g(N).$$

From this it follows that $\overline{\int_a^b} (f + g) \leq \overline{\int_a^b} f + \overline{\int_a^b} g$, for otherwise we would have that

$$\overline{\int_a^b} f + \overline{\int_a^b} g < \overline{\int_a^b} (f + g).$$

Therefore if $\epsilon = \overline{\int_a^b} (f + g) - \overline{\int_a^b} f - \overline{\int_a^b} g$, then there exist subdivisions N_1 and N_2 of $[a, b]$ such that

$$\bar{S}_f(N_1) < \overline{\int_a^b} f + \frac{\epsilon}{2} \quad \text{and} \quad \bar{S}_g(N_2) < \overline{\int_a^b} g + \frac{\epsilon}{2}.$$

If $N = N_1 \cup N_2$ then

$$\bar{S}_{f+g}(N) \leq \bar{S}_f(N) + \bar{S}_g(N) \leq \bar{S}_f(N_1) + \bar{S}_g(N_1) < \overline{\int_a^b} f + \frac{\epsilon}{2} + \overline{\int_a^b} g + \frac{\epsilon}{2}$$

$$= \overline{\int_a^b} (f + g).$$

This is a contradiction that compels us to conclude that

$$\overline{\int_a^b} (f + g) \leq \overline{\int_a^b} f + \overline{\int_a^b} g.$$

In a similar way we can prove that

$$\underline{\int_a^b} f + \underline{\int_a^b} g \leq \underline{\int_a^b} (f + g).$$

However, since $\underline{\int_a^b} f = \overline{\int_a^b} f$ and $\underline{\int_a^b} g = \overline{\int_a^b} g$ and since

$$\underline{\int_a^b} f + \underline{\int_a^b} g \leq \underline{\int_a^b} (f + g) \leq \overline{\int_a^b} (f + g) \leq \overline{\int_a^b} f + \overline{\int_a^b} g,$$

we conclude that $f + g$ is integrable and

$$\int_a^b (f + g) = \int_a^b f + \int_a^b g.$$

Q.E.D.

Theorem 8.15 assures us that integration 'distributes' over function addition. As we will see later, this is a very useful property. So also is the following result, whose proof we leave to the reader.

Theorem 8.16. *If f is integrable on $[a, b]$, then for each c we have that cf is integrable on $[a, b]$ and*

$$\int_a^b cf = c \int_a^b f.$$

We now prove the very useful existence theorem which we announced at the beginning of this section.

Theorem 8.17. *If f is continuous on $[a, b]$, then f is integrable on $[a, b]$.*

Proof. If f is continuous on $[a, b]$, then it is bounded on $[a, b]$. Moreover it is uniformly continuous on $[a, b]$. Therefore $(\exists \phi)(\forall x)(\forall y)$ if $x \in [a, b]$, if $y \in [a, b]$, and if $|x - y| < \phi\left(\dfrac{\epsilon}{b - a}\right)$, then

$$|f(x) - f(y)| < \frac{\epsilon}{b - a}.$$

Consequently for each subdivision N of $[a, b]$ if $N = \{a_0, a_1, \ldots, a_n\}$ and if

$$|N| < \phi\left(\frac{\epsilon}{b - a}\right),$$

then since f is continuous on $[a_{\alpha-1}, a_\alpha]$, $\alpha = 1, \ldots, n$, there exists an x_α and a y_α in $[a_{\alpha-1}, a_\alpha]$ for which $f(x_\alpha) = \sup f[a_{\alpha-1}, a_\alpha]$, and $f(y_\alpha) = \inf f[a_{\alpha-1}, a_\alpha]$. Therefore

$$
\begin{aligned}
\bar{S}_f(N) - \underline{S}_f(N) &= \sum_{\alpha=1}^n (\sup f[a_{\alpha-1}, a_\alpha])(a_\alpha - a_{\alpha-1}) \\
&\quad - \sum_{\alpha=1}^n (\inf f[a_{\alpha-1}, a_\alpha])(a_\alpha - a_{\alpha-1}) \\
&= \sum_{\alpha=1}^n f(x_\alpha)(a_\alpha - a_{\alpha-1}) - \sum_{\alpha=1}^n f(y_\alpha)(a_\alpha - a_{\alpha-1}) \\
&= \sum_{\alpha=1}^n [f(x_\alpha) - f(y_\alpha)](a_\alpha - a_{\alpha-1}) \\
&= \sum_{\alpha=1}^n \frac{\epsilon}{b - a}(a_\alpha - a_{\alpha-1}) = \epsilon.
\end{aligned}
$$

Q.E.D.

Theorem 8.17 provides very useful information. For example, it assures us that since the constant functions are continuous everywhere they are integrable over every bounded inteval. The same is true of the polynomial functions.

There are, however, other interesting conditions that are sufficient to insure the existence of the integral—as, for example,

Theorem 8.18. *If f is bounded and monotone on* $[a, b]$, *then f is integrable on* $[a, b]$.

Proof. If f is monotone increasing, if $c = \inf f[a, b]$ and $d = \sup f[a, b]$, then for each ϵ there exists a subdivision $\{c_0, c_1, \ldots, c_n\}$ of $[c, d]$ with norm smaller than $\epsilon/(b - a)$. If $a_0 = a$ and

$$a_\alpha = \sup \{x \in [a, b] \mid f(x) \le c_\alpha\}, \quad \alpha = 1, 2, \ldots, n,$$

then $\{a_0, a_1, \ldots, a_n\}$ is a subdivision of $[a, b]$ with the property that

$$\forall x \in [a_{\alpha-1}, a_\alpha], \quad c_{\alpha-1} \le f(x) \le c_\alpha.$$

Therefore

$$\sup f[a_{\alpha-1}, a_\alpha] - \inf f[a_{\alpha-1}, a_\alpha] \le c_\alpha - c_{\alpha-1} < \frac{\epsilon}{b - a}.$$

Consequently

$$\bar{S}_f(N) - \underline{S}_f(N) = \sum_{\alpha=1}^{n} (\sup f[a_{\alpha-1}, a_\alpha] - \inf f[a_{\alpha-1}, a_\alpha])(a_\alpha - a_{\alpha-1})$$

$$\le \sum_{\alpha=1}^{n} \frac{\epsilon}{b - a}(a_\alpha - a_{\alpha-1})$$

$$= \epsilon.$$

From this it follows that f is integrable on $[a, b]$.

                                                                    Q.E.D.

Other interesting results we leave as exercises.

EXERCISES

1. Prove: If f and g are each integrable on $[a, b]$, then $f - g$ is integrable on $[a, b]$ and

$$\int_a^b (f - g) = \int_a^b f - \int_a^b g.$$

2. Prove: If f_α is integrable on $[a, b]$, $\alpha = 1, 2, \ldots, n$ then $\sum_1^n f_\alpha$ is integrable on $[a, b]$ and

$$\int_a^b \sum_{\alpha=1}^{n} f_\alpha = \sum_{\alpha=1}^{n} \int_a^b f_\alpha.$$

3. Prove: If $g(x) = f(x)$, $x \in \text{Dom} f$ and $f(x) \geq 0$,
$$g(x) = 0, \ x \in \text{Dom} f \text{ and } f(x) < 0,$$
and if $h(x) = f(x)$, $x \in \text{Dom} f$ and $f(x) < 0$,
$$h(x) = 0, \ x \in \text{Dom} f \text{ and } f(x) \geq 0,$$

then 1) f is integrable on $[a, b]$ iff g and h are each integrable on $[a, b]$, and 2) if g and h are integrable on $[a, b]$, then g^2, gh, and h^2 are each integrable on $[a, b]$. [Hint: $\bar{S}_g(N) - \underline{S}_g(N) \leq \bar{S}_f(N)$ and $\bar{S}_{g^2}(N) - \underline{S}_{g^2}(N) \leq (\sup g[a, b] + \inf g[a, b])(\bar{S}_g(N) - \underline{S}_g(N)).$]

4. Prove: If f is integrable on $[a, b]$, then f^2 is integrable on $[a, b]$. [Hint: Exercise 3.]

5. Prove: If f and g are each integrable on $[a, b]$, then fg is integrable on $[a, b]$. [Hint: $fg = (f + g)^2 - (f - g)^2$.]

6. Prove: If f is integrable on $[a, b]$, then $(\inf f[a, b])(b - a) \leq \int_a^b f \leq (\sup f[a, b])(b - a)$.

7. Prove: If f is integrable on $[a, b]$ and if c is a bound for f on $[a, b]$, then $\left| \int_a^b f \right| \leq c(b - a)$.

8. Prove: If f is integrable on $[a, b]$ and if for each x in $[a, b] \cap \text{Dom} f$, $f(x) \geq 0$, then $\int_a^b f \geq 0$.

9. Prove: If f is integrable on $[a, b]$, then $|f|$ is integrable on $[a, b]$ and $\left| \int_a^b f \right| \leq \int_a^b |f|$.

10. Prove: If $[a, b] \subseteq \text{Dom} g$, if g and fg are each integrable on $[a, b]$ and if for each x in $[a, b]$, $g(x) \geq 0$, then

$$(\inf f[a, b]) \int_a^b g \leq \int_a^b fg \leq (\sup f[a, b]) \int_a^b g.$$

[Hint: Theorem 8.07.]

11. Prove (The First Mean Value Theorem for Integrals): If f is continuous on $[a, b]$, if g is integrable on $[a, b]$, if $[a, b] \subseteq \text{Dom} g$ and for each x in $[a, b]$, $g(x) \geq 0$, then for some y in $[a, b]$, $\int_a^b fg = f(y) \int_a^b g$. [Hint: If $F(y) = f(y) \int_a^b g$, then F is continuous on $[a, b]$, and hence it must assume all values between its maximum and minimum values.]

8.2 The Fundamental Theorem and Other Results

Having convinced ourselves that the Riemann integral has the properties that make it of use in many applied problems and having established some existence theorems we turn to another problem. As defined, the integral of a given function over a given interval is a number. In order for the theory that we are developing to be of use in certain types of applications we must be able to compute this number. The definition of the Riemann integral is, however, not well suited for this purpose. We would, therefore, hope that from the theory there may come techniques that simplify the computations. This is indeed the case, as we will now show.

Theorem 8.20 (The Fundamental Theorem of the Calculus). *If f is integrable on [a, b] and if g is an antiderivative of f on [a, b], i.e., if for each x in [a, b], $g'(x) = f(x)$, then $\int_a^b f = g(b) - g(a)$.*

Proof. For each subdivision N of $[a, b]$ if $N = \{a_0, \ldots, a_n\}$ then

$$g(b) - g(a) = \sum_{\alpha=1}^{n} [g(a_\alpha) - g(a_{\alpha-1})].$$

Since g is differentiable on $[a_{\alpha-1}, a_\alpha]$ it follows from the Mean Value Theorem that for some x_α in $[a_{\alpha-1}, a_\alpha]$

$$g(a_\alpha) - g(a_{\alpha-1}) = g'(x_\alpha)(a_\alpha - a_{\alpha-1}).$$

But by hypothesis $g'(x_\alpha) = f(x_\alpha)$; therefore

$$g(b) - g(a) = \sum_{\alpha=1}^{n} f(x_\alpha)(a_\alpha - a_{\alpha-1}).$$

Since

$$\inf f[a_{\alpha-1}, a_\alpha] \leq f(x_\alpha) \leq \sup f[a_{\alpha-1}, a_\alpha]$$

it follows that

$$\underline{S}_f(N) \leq g(b) - g(a) \leq \overline{S}_f(N).$$

Therefore $g(b) - g(a)$ is a lower bound for upper sums, $\overline{S}_f(N)$, and hence $g(b) - g(a) \leq \int_a^b f$. But $g(b) - g(a)$ is also an upper bound for lower sums, $\underline{S}_f(N)$, and hence $\int_a^b f \leq g(b) - g(a)$. We, therefore, conclude that

$$\int_a^b f = g(b) - g(a).$$

Q.E.D.

Example. If $f(x) = x^2 + 2x$ and $g(x) = x^3/3 + x^2$, then g is an anti-derivative for f. Therefore

$$\int_0^1 f = g(1) - g(0) = \tfrac{1}{3} + 1 = \tfrac{4}{3}.$$

The Fundamental Theorem requires that the derivative of the restriction of g to $[a, b]$ be equal to f on $[a, b]$. If this equality does not hold at a single point, the conclusion of the theorem is not valid, as the following example shows.

Example. If $f(x) = [\![x]\!]$ then f is monotone on $[1, \frac{5}{2}]$ and hence f is integrable on $[1, \frac{5}{2}]$. We leave as an exercise for the reader the verification that

$$\int_1^{5/2} f = 2.$$

If $g(x) = x$, $x \in [1, 2)$ and $g(x) = 2x$, $x \in (2, \frac{5}{2}]$, then for each x in $[1, \frac{5}{2}]$ with $x \neq 2$ we have that $g'(x) = f(x)$. But $g(\frac{5}{2}) - g(1) = 5 - 1 = 4$.

From this example we see that the requirement that g be an antiderivative for f on $[a, b]$ cannot be weakened to allow even a single exceptional point. Furthermore the existence of an antiderivative for f on $[a, b]$ does not imply that f is integrable on $[a, b]$, as we see from the following example.

Example. If

$$f(x) = x^2 \sin\frac{1}{x^2}, \quad x \neq 0, \quad f(0) = 0,$$

then

$$f'(x) = 2x \sin\frac{1}{x^2} - \frac{2}{x}\cos\frac{1}{x^2}, \quad x \neq 0, \quad f'(0) = 0.$$

Therefore f is an antiderivative for f' on $[0, 1]$ but f' is not integrable on $[0, 1]$ since it is not bounded on $[0, 1]$.

One of the problems in applying the fundamental theorem is that of finding an antiderivative. From the fundamental theorem we deduce the following useful result.

Theorem 8.21 (Substitution Rule). *If f is integrable on $[a, b]$, if g is differentiable on $[c, d]$ and maps $[c, d]$ onto $[a, b]$, if $(f \circ g)g'$ is integrable on $[c, d]$, and if f has an antiderivative on $[a, b]$, then*

1) $\displaystyle\int_a^b f = \int_c^d (f \circ g)g'$ *if* $a = g(c)$ *and* $b = g(d)$.

2) $\displaystyle\int_a^b f = -\int_c^d (f \circ g)g'$ *if* $a = g(d)$ *and* $b = g(c)$.

Proof. If h is an antiderivative for f on $[a, b]$, then

$$\int_a^b f = h(b) - h(a).$$

Since g is differentiable on $[c, d]$ and maps $[c, d]$ onto $[a, b]$, and since h is differentiable on $[a, b]$, we have that $h \circ g$ is differentiable on $[c, d]$ and

$$(h \circ g)'(x) = (h' \circ g)(x)g'(x) = (f \circ g)(x)g'(x).$$

That is, $h \circ g$ is an antiderivative of $(f \circ g)g'$ on $[c, d]$. Therefore

$$\int_c^d (f \circ g)g' = (h \circ g)(d) - (h \circ g)(c).$$

If $a = g(c)$ and $b = g(d)$ then

$$\int_a^b f = \int_c^b (f \circ g)g'$$

and if $a = g(d)$ and $b = g(c)$ then

$$\int_a^b f = -\int_c^d (f \circ g)g'.$$

Q.E.D.

The substitution rule offers the possibility of evaluating an integral with a complicated integrand by "transforming" it into an integral that can be easily evaluated. The rule, however, suffers from the drawback that its conclusion is complicated and difficult to remember. Fortunately this difficulty can be removed by the following definition and an ingenious notational innovation.

Definition 8.22.   1) $\int_a^a f = 0$.

2) If f is integrable on $[a, b]$, then $\int_b^a f = -\int_a^b f$.

We introduce the symbol

$$\int_a^b f(x)\, dx$$

to denote the integral of f on $[a, b]$. If f and g are functions fulfilling the hypotheses of Theorem 8.21 and if $x = g(y)$ then $dx = g'(y)\, dy$. Formally substituting into the integrand of $\int_a^b f(x)\, dx$ we obtain

$$\int_c^d f(g(y))g'(y)\, dy$$

where $g(c) = a$ and $g(d) = b$. But this is our new notation for the integral of $(f \circ g)g'$ on $[c, d]$.

With one additional definition we have a very convenient notation:

Definition 8.23.   If a and b are in Dom g, then $g(x)|_a^b = g(b) - g(a)$.

Example.   Evaluate $\int_0^1 \dfrac{x\, dx}{\sqrt{1 + x}}$.

Solution. If $y = \sqrt{1 + x}$, then $x = y^2 - 1$ and $dx = 2y\,dy$. Since $\sqrt{1 + 0} = 1$ and $\sqrt{1 + 1} = \sqrt{2}$ we obtain, on substitution,

$$\int_0^1 \frac{x\,dx}{\sqrt{1 + x}} = \int_1^{\sqrt{2}} \frac{(y^2 - 1)2y\,dy}{y} = 2\int_1^{\sqrt{2}} (y^2 - 1)\,dy = 2\left(\frac{y^3}{3} - y\right)\Big|_1^{\sqrt{2}}$$
$$= \tfrac{2}{3}(2 - \sqrt{2}).$$

The reader should protest that this example is not valid because we have not verified that the integrand of the given integral has an antiderivative. For the problem at hand this oversight is easily corrected by substituting $\sqrt{1 + x}$ for y in

$$2\left(\frac{y^3}{3} - y\right).$$

That is, if

$$h(x) = 2\left(\frac{(1 + x)^{3/2}}{3} - \sqrt{1 + x}\right),$$

then

$$h'(x) = \sqrt{1 + x} - \frac{1}{\sqrt{1 + x}} = \frac{x}{\sqrt{1 + x}}.$$

This suggests the following question concerning the functions f and g of Theorem 8.21. If $(f \circ g)g'$ has an antiderivative on $[c, d]$, does it follow that f has an antiderivative on $[a, b]$.

Theorem 8.24. *If $[a, b] \subseteq \operatorname{Dom} f$, if g is differentiable on $[c, d]$ and maps $[c, d]$ one-to-one onto $[a, b]$, if $(f \circ g)g'$ has an antiderivative on $[c, d]$, and if $g'(x) \neq 0$, $x \in [c, d]$, then f has an antiderivative on $[a, b]$.*

Proof. From Theorem 7.13 it follows that for each x in $[c, d]$, g^{-1} is differentiable at x and

$$(g' \circ g^{-1})(x) = \frac{1}{(g^{-1})'(x)}.$$

Therefore if h is an antiderivative for $(f \circ g)g'$ on $[c, d]$, then

$$h' = (f \circ g)g'$$

and

$$(h \circ g^{-1})' = (h' \circ g^{-1})(g^{-1})' = (f \circ g \circ g^{-1})(g' \circ g^{-1})(g^{-1})' = f.$$

Q.E.D.

In the next section we will prove a much simpler existence theorem for antiderivatives. We will prove that if f is continuous on $[a, b]$ then f has an antiderivative on $[a, b]$. From this result we can obtain an easily remembered substitution rule for continuous functions. Indeed if f is continuous on $[a, b]$ and if g has a continuous derivative on $[c, d]$ and maps $[c, d]$ onto $[a, b]$, then all of the hypotheses of the substitution rule are fulfilled.

In Definition 8.22 we extended the definition of the integral. We then have an obligation to verify that the basic properties hold for the extended integral. The proofs are rather trivial applications of Definition 8.22 and previously proved results. We therefore leave them as exercises. We remind the reader of the notation '$\langle a, b \rangle$' introduced in Chapter 7 to denote the interval with end points a and b.

E X E R C I S E S

In Exercises 1–3 the functions f and g are integrable on $\langle a, b \rangle$ and $c \in \langle a, b \rangle$.

1. Prove: $\int_a^b (f + g) = \int_a^b f + \int_a^b g$ and $\int_a^b (f - g) = \int_a^b f - \int_a^b g$.

2. Prove: $\int_a^b f = \int_a^c f + \int_c^b f$.

3. Prove: If d is a bound for f on $\langle a, b \rangle$, then $\left| \int_a^b f \right| \le d |b - a|$.

8.3 The Integral as a Function

In an earlier theorem we proved that a function that is integrable on an interval is integrable on every subinterval. Therefore if f is integrable on $[a, b]$ and if

$$F(x) = \int_a^x f(t)\, dt, \quad x \in [a, b],$$

then F is a function whose domain is $[a, b]$. We wish to study the elementary properties of such functions. It is helpful to recall that if f is continuous on $[a, b]$ and has positive values at each point of $[a, b]$, then F gives the area under the curve. (See Figure 8.6.)

Theorem 8.30. *If f is integrable on $[a, b]$ and if*

$$F(x) = \int_a^x f(t)\, dt, \quad x \in [a, b],$$

then F is continuous on $[a, b]$.

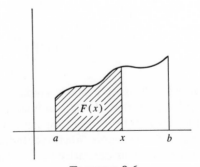

FIGURE 8.6

Proof.   We wish to prove that for each c in $[a, b]$

$$\operatorname*{Lim}_{x \to c} F(x) = F(c).$$

Since f is integrable on $[a, b]$ it follows that f is bounded on $[a, b]$. If d is a bound for f and if $\phi(\epsilon) = \epsilon/d$, then for each x in $N(c, \phi(\epsilon)) \cap [a, b]$

$$|F(x) - F(c)| = \left| \int_a^x f(t) \, dt - \int_a^c f(t) \, dt \right|$$

$$= \left| \int_c^x f(t) \, dt \right| \leq d|x - c| < d \cdot \frac{\epsilon}{d} = \epsilon.$$

Q.E.D.

Theorem 8.31.   *If f is integrable and continuous on $[a, b]$, if*

$$F(x) = \int_a^x f(t) \, dt, \quad x \in [a, b],$$

then F is differentiable on $[a, b]$ and for each c in $[a, b]$ we have that $F'(c) = f(c)$.

Proof.   We wish to prove that

$$\operatorname*{Lim}_{x \to c} \frac{F(x) - F(c)}{x - c} = f(c).$$

Since f is continuous on $[a, b]$, it follows that there exists a convergence test ϕ such that for each x in $N(c, \phi(\epsilon)) \cap [a, b]$

$$|f(x) - f(c)| < \epsilon.$$

Then since

$$F(x) - F(c) = \int_c^x f(t) \, dt \text{ and } (x - c)f(c) = \int_c^x f(c) \, dt$$

we have that

$$\left| \frac{F(x) - F(c)}{x - c} - f(c) \right| = \frac{\left| \int_c^x f(t) \, dt - \int_c^x f(c) \, dt \right|}{|x - c|}$$

$$= \frac{\left| \int_c^x [f(t) - f(c)] \, dt \right|}{|x - c|} < \frac{\epsilon|x - c|}{|x - c|} = \epsilon.$$

Q.E.D.

Theorem 8.31 is a very useful result. It assures us that if f is continuous on $[a, b]$, then f has an antiderivative on $[a, b]$. Furthermore, it provides a method for deducing the basic properties of this antiderivative. Let us illustrate by deducing some of the properties of the antiderivative of the reciprocal function which we call the *natural logarithm function*.

Definition 8.32.

$$\ln x = \int_1^x \frac{dt}{t}, \quad x > 0.$$

In order for the function ln to be of use we must know some of its properties. To begin with, the domain of ln is the set of positive real numbers. It is easily shown that ln is unbounded above:

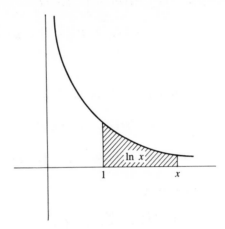

FIGURE 8.7

Recall that

$$\sum_{\alpha=1}^{\infty} \frac{1}{\alpha}$$

is a divergent series. Consequently for each number b there exists an integer n such that

$$b \le \sum_{\alpha=2}^{n} \frac{1}{\alpha}.$$

Furthermore, if $x \in [m, m+1]$, then

$$\frac{1}{m+1} \le \frac{1}{x} \le \frac{1}{m}.$$

Hence

$$\frac{1}{m+1} \le \int_m^{m+1} \frac{dt}{t}, \quad m = 1, 2 \ldots$$

and

$$b \le \sum_{\alpha=1}^{n-1} \frac{1}{\alpha+1} \le \sum_{\alpha=1}^{n-1} \int_\alpha^{\alpha+1} \frac{dt}{t} = \int_1^n \frac{dt}{t} = \ln n.$$

Thus ln is unbounded above. To prove that ln is also unbounded below we need only make a simple application of the Substitution Theorem. Using the notation above we have that

$$b \le \int_1^n \frac{dt}{t}.$$

If $s = 1/t$ then $t = 1/s$, $dt = -ds/s^2$, $dt/t = -ds/s$ and hence

$$\int_1^n \frac{dt}{t} = -\int_1^{1/n} \frac{ds}{s},$$

that is, $\ln n = -\ln (1/n)$. We then have that

$$b \le -\ln \frac{1}{n},$$

$$\ln \frac{1}{n} \le -b.$$

Hence ln is unbounded below.

From Theorems 8.30 and 8.31 we see that for each positive real number x, ln is continuous and differentiable at x and

$$\ln' x = \frac{1}{x}.$$

Since a function that is continuous on a closed interval must assume all values between its maximum and minimum values, since the domain of ln is the set of all positive real numbers, and since ln is unbounded above and below we conclude that Ran ln $= R$. Furthermore if $x > 0$ we have that $\ln' x > 0$; therefore ln is monotone increasing. Also $\ln'' x = -1/x^2$. Therefore $\ln'' x$ is negative and $\ln'$ is decreasing. Finally we note that $\ln 1 = 0$. With this information we can supply a very useful sketch of ln (see Figure 8.8).

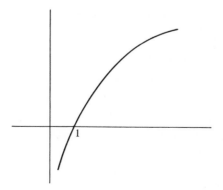

FIGURE 8.8

There are other properties that we expect ln to have. In particular

$$\ln xy = \ln x + \ln y.$$

This is easily proved from the Substitution Theorem:

$$\ln xy = \int_1^{xy} \frac{dt}{t} = \int_1^x \frac{dt}{t} + \int_x^{xy} \frac{dt}{t}.$$

Since $\int_1^x dt/t = \ln x$ we need only prove that $\int_x^{xy} dt/t = \ln y$. This we do in the following way. If $s = t/x$ then $t = sx$ and $dt = x\,ds$. Therefore $dt/t = ds/s$ and

$$\int_x^{xy} \frac{dt}{t} = \int_1^y \frac{ds}{s} = \ln y.$$

Another property which we can prove in a similar manner is

$$\ln \frac{x}{y} = \ln x - \ln y.$$

As before, we have

$$\ln \frac{x}{y} = \int_1^{x/y} \frac{dt}{t} = \int_1^x \frac{dt}{t} + \int_x^{x/y} \frac{dt}{t} = \ln x + \int_x^{x/y} \frac{dt}{t}.$$

Again we need only prove that $\int_x^{x/y} dt/t = -\ln y$. If $s = x/t$, then $t = x/s$ and $dt = -x\,ds/s^2$. Therefore $dt/t = -ds/s$ and

$$\int_x^{x/y} \frac{dt}{t} = -\int_1^y \frac{dt}{t} = -\ln y.$$

Since ln is monotone and differentiable and $\ln' x \neq 0$ it follows by Theorem 7.13 that its inverse, which we call the exponential function, is also monotone and differentiable.

Definition 8.33. $\exp = \ln^{-1}$.

With the assurance that exp is differentiable and since

$$\exp(\ln x) = x,$$

we have from the chain rule that

$$\exp'(\ln x)\ln' x = 1,$$
$$\exp'(\ln x) = x,$$
$$\exp'(x) = \exp x.$$

Thus the exponential function is its own derivative. Furthermore since exp is the inverse of ln and since

$$\ln xy = \ln x + \ln y,$$
$$\ln \frac{x}{y} = \ln x - \ln y,$$

it follows that

$$\exp(x + y) = (\exp x)(\exp y),$$
$$\exp(x - y) = \frac{\exp(x)}{\exp(y)},$$

as we prove in the following way. Since Ran ln $= R$, there exist positive real numbers a and b such that ln $a = x$, ln $b = y$. Then

$$\exp(x + y) = \exp(\ln a + \ln b) = \exp(\ln ab) = ab = (\exp x)(\exp y),$$
$$\exp(x - y) = \exp(\ln a - \ln b) = \exp\left(\ln \frac{a}{b}\right) = \frac{a}{b} = \frac{\exp x}{\exp y}.$$

It is immediate by induction that

$$\exp nx = (\exp x)^n.$$

In particular, if $x = 1$, then

$$\exp n = (\exp 1)^n$$

and if $x = m/n$, $n \neq 0$,

$$\exp m = \left(\exp \frac{m}{n}\right)^n.$$

Therefore for each rational number, m/n, $n \neq 0$, we have that

$$\exp \frac{m}{n} = (\exp 1)^{m/n}.$$

This suggests that exp 1 is a number of special interest, which is indeed the case.

Definition 8.34. $e = \exp 1$.

We then have for all rational numbers m/n, $n \neq 0$, that

$$e^{m/n} = \exp \frac{m}{n}.$$

This suggests that we extend the definition of powers of e to all real numbers in the following way.

Definition 8.35. $e^x = \exp x$.

From this definition we have that

$$e^x \cdot e^y = (\exp x)(\exp y) = \exp(x + y) = e^{x+y}.$$

This basic law of exponents holds for our extended notion of powers. The other basic laws of exponents we leave as exercises for the reader.

It is natural to attempt to extend Definition 8.35 and give meaning to 'a^x'. If $a > 0$, then for some y we have that $a = e^y$ and we would want $a^x = (e^y)^x = e^{yx}$. Hence

Definition 8.36. If $a > 0$ then $a^x = e^{x \ln a}$ and $\log_a x = y$ iff $x = a^y$.

EXERCISES

1. Prove: If $a > 0$ and $b > 0$ then $\log_a b = \dfrac{\ln b}{\ln a}$.

2. Prove: If $a > 0$ then $(\log_e a)(\log_a e) = 1$.

In Exercises 3–6 find $f'(x)$.

3. $f(x) = a^x$, $a > 0$.   **4.** $f(x) = x^a$, $x > 0$.

5. $f(x) = \log_x a$, $a > 0$.   **6.** $f(x) = \log_a x$, $x > 0$.

7. Prove: If f is integrable on $[a, b]$ and if $F(x) = \int_x^b f$, $x \in [a, b]$, then F is continuous on $[a, b]$. If in addition f is continuous on $[a, b]$, then F is differentiable on $[a, b]$.

8. Prove: If $F(x) = \int_0^x \dfrac{dt}{1 + t^2}$, then

     a) F is defined, continuous, and differentiable everywhere.

     b) F is bounded. $\left[\text{Hint: } F(x) \le 1 + \displaystyle\sum_{\alpha=1}^{[x]+1} \dfrac{1}{\alpha^2}.\right]$

     c) F is monotone strictly increasing.

     d) $\text{Lim}_{n \to \infty} F(x)$ exists.

9. Using the information deduced in Exercise 8 discuss the antiderivatives for f if $f(x) = 1/(ax^2 + bx + c)$, $ax^2 + bx + c \ne 0$, for all possible a, b, and c.

10. Prove: If f is integrable on $\langle a, b \rangle$, if $\text{Lim}_{x \to c} g(x) = b$, and for some $N(c, \delta)$ we have that $g(x) \in \langle a, b \rangle$, $x \in N(c, \delta) \cap \text{Dom } g$, then $\text{Lim}_{x \to c} \int_a^{g(x)} f = \int_a^b f$.

11. Prove (The integral test for convergence): If f is monotone decreasing on $[m, \infty)$, if $\text{Lim}_{x \to \infty} f(x) = 0$, if $F(x) = \int_m^x f$, $x \in [m, \infty]$ and if $a_n = f(n)$, $n \ge m$, then $\sum_m^\infty a_\alpha$ converges iff $\text{Lim}_{x \to \infty} F(x)$ exists. [Hint: $a_n \ge \int_n^{n+1} f \ge a_{n+1}$.]

8.4 Arc Length

As in the case of area, work, and displacement our first problem is to decide what we shall mean by length. For the purposes we have in mind we choose to restrict our discussion to simple continuous curves. To each such curve we would like to assign a number that we will call the length of the curve. If the curve is a straight line segment with end points (a_1, b_1)

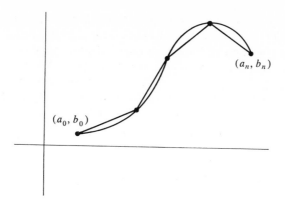

(a_n, b_n)

(a_0, b_0)

FIGURE 8.9

and (a_2, b_2), then its length should be the distance between its end points, as given by the formula

$$\sqrt{(a_2 - a_1)^2 + (b_2 - b_1)^2}.$$

The length of a curve consisting of a finite number of straight line segments should be the sum of the lengths of the segments that compose it. Our intuitive idea of length for other curves is, however, not so easily described.

If $(a_0, b_0), \ldots, (a_n, b_n)$ are points on a simple continuous curve C with (a_0, b_0) and (a_n, b_n) being the end points, and if these points are connected by straight line segments in the order in which they appear on C (see Figure 8.9), we will call the resulting curve an inscribed polygonal path. We have agreed that the length of an inscribed polygonal path is the sum of the lengths of the line segments that compose it. We would surely agree that the length of C should not be less than the length of any inscribed polygonal path. On the other hand, there should exist inscribed polygonal paths whose lengths are as close to the length of C as we please. This suggests that we define the length of C as the supremum of the set of lengths of inscribed polygonal paths. In order to do this we must provide a definition for the 'set of lengths of inscribed polygonal paths' and determine whether or not this set has a supremum.

In our preceding discussion we described an inscribed polygonal path as the curve obtained by connecting points on C by straight line segments, the connection being made in the order in which the points appear on C. To make this clear we must decide what we mean by the order of the points on a curve. We propose the following.

Each simple continuous curve C is the graph of a simple continuous relation. Therefore there exists an interval $[a, b]$ and there exist functions g and f, each continuous on $[a, b]$ for which C is the graph of the relation

$$\{ (g(x), f(x)) \mid x \in [a, b] \}.$$

For each point P on the curve C there is one and only one number x in $[a, b]$ for which P is the graph of $(g(x), f(x))$. Therefore if $P_1, P_2, \ldots, P_n$ are n distinct points on C, then there exist n distinct numbers $x_1, x_2, \ldots, x_n$ in $[a, b]$ such that P_α is the graph of $(g(x_\alpha), f(x_\alpha))$. We then specify that the order of the points $P_1, \ldots, P_n$ on C is determined by the order of $x_1, x_2, \ldots, x_n$ in $[a, b]$. Furthermore each inscribed polygonal path determines a partition of $[a, b]$ and conversely if $\{a_0, \ldots, a_n\}$ is a partition of $[a, b]$, then the points $(g(a_0), f(a_0)), \ldots, (g(a_n), f(a_n))$ determine an inscribed polygonal path whose length is

$$\sum_{\alpha=1}^{n} \sqrt{[g(a_\alpha) - g(a_{\alpha-1})]^2 + [f(a_\alpha) - f(a_{\alpha-1})]^2}.$$

Definition 8.40. If g and f are continuous on $[a, b]$, if $N = \{a_0, a_1, \ldots, a_n\}$, and if N is a subdivision of $[a, b]$, then

$$S_{g,f}(N) = \sum_{\alpha=1}^{n} \sqrt{[g(a_\alpha) - g(a_{\alpha-1})]^2 + [f(a_\alpha) - f(a_{\alpha-1})]^2}.$$

The 'set of lengths of inscribed polygonal paths' for a curve C we then define as

$$\{S_{g,f}(N) \mid N \text{ is a subdivision of } [a, b]\}.$$

If this set is bounded above, then C is said to be *rectifiable* and the length of C is defined as the supremum of this set. For an example of a non-rectifiable curve we refer the reader to Exercise 22, page 208. We now wish to prove that if the parameter functions g and f have continuous derivatives on $[a, b]$, then C is rectifiable and the length of C is given by

$$\int_a^b \sqrt{[g'(x)]^2 + [f'(x)]^2} \, dx.$$

For the proof we need several results that we prove as lemmas. The first result is the triangle inequality, which we prove in two steps.

Lemma 1. $\sqrt{(t + s)^2 + (u + v)^2} \leq \sqrt{t^2 + u^2} + \sqrt{s^2 + v^2}.$

Proof.
$$0 \leq (tv - us)^2$$
$$2stuv \leq t^2v^2 + u^2s^2$$
$$s^2t^2 + 2stuv + u^2v^2 \leq t^2s^2 + t^2v^2 + u^2s^2 + u^2v^2$$
$$(st + uv)^2 \leq (t^2 + u^2)(s^2 + v^2)$$
$$st + uv \leq |st + uv| \leq \sqrt{t^2 + u^2} \sqrt{s^2 + v^2}$$
$$t^2 + 2st + s^2 + u^2 + 2uv + v^2$$
$$\leq t^2 + u^2 + 2\sqrt{t^2 + u^2} \sqrt{s^2 + v^2} + s^2 + v^2$$
$$(t + s)^2 + (u + v)^2 \leq (\sqrt{t^2 + u^2} + \sqrt{s^2 + v^2})^2$$
$$\sqrt{(t + s)^2 + (u + v)^2} \leq \sqrt{t^2 + u^2} + \sqrt{s^2 + v^2}$$

Q.E.D.

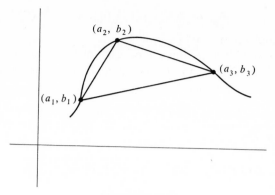

FIGURE 8.10

Lemma 2. $\sqrt{(a_1 - a_2)^2 + (b_1 - b_2)^2} \leq \sqrt{(a_1 - a_3)^2 + (b_1 - b_3)^2}$
$$+ \sqrt{(a_3 - a_2)^2 + (b_3 - b_2)^2}$$

Proof. Lemma 1 with $t = a_1 - a_3$, $s = a_3 - a_2$, $u = b_1 - b_3$, and $v = b_3 - b_2$.

From the triangle inequality, Lemma 2, we can prove by induction that the length of inscribed polygonal paths, $S_{g,f}(N)$, tends to grow with refinement of the subdivision.

Lemma 3. *If f and g are continuous on $[a, b]$, if N_1 is a subdivision of $[a, b]$, and if N is a refinement of N_1, then*

$$S_{g,f}(N_1) \leq S_{g,f}(N).$$

The proof is by induction on the number of points p in N that are not in N_1. We leave the details to the reader.

At this point we pause to prove an important special case of our announced objective. If f is continuous on $[a, b]$, then the graph of f is a simple continuous curve. We will now prove that if f has a continuous derivative on $[a, b]$, then the curve is rectifiable and its length is an integral.

Theorem 8.41. *If f' is continuous on $[a, b]$, then*

$$\{S_{I,f}(N) \mid N \text{ is a subdivision of } [a, b]\}$$

is bounded above, and its supremum is $\int_a^b \sqrt{1 + [f'(x)]^2}\, dx$.

Proof. If $F(x) = \sqrt{1 + [f'(x)]^2}$, $x \in [a, b]$, then since f' is continuous on $[a, b]$ it follows that F is continuous on $[a, b]$ and hence integrable on $[a, b]$. If

$$P_f = \{S_{I,f}(N) \mid N \text{ is a subdivision of } [a, b]\},$$

then we wish to show that P_f is bounded and sup $P_f = \int_a^b \sqrt{1 + [f'(x)]^2}\, dx$.

For each subdivision N of $[a, b]$ if $N = \{a_0, a_1, \ldots, a_n\}$, then since f' is continuous on $[a, b]$ it is continuous on each of the subintervals $[a_{\alpha-1}, a_\alpha]$, $\alpha = 1, \ldots, n$. Therefore by the Mean Value Theorem there exists an x_α in $[a_{\alpha-1}, a_\alpha]$, $\alpha = 1, \ldots, n$ such that

$$f(a_\alpha) - f(a_{\alpha-1}) = f'(x_\alpha)(a_\alpha - a_{\alpha-1}).$$

It then follows that

$$
\begin{aligned}
S_{I,f}(N) &= \sum_{\alpha=1}^{n} \sqrt{(a_\alpha - a_{\alpha-1})^2 + [f(a_\alpha) - f(a_{\alpha-1})]^2} \\
&= \sum_{\alpha=1}^{n} \sqrt{1 + [f'(x_\alpha)]^2}\,(a_\alpha - a_{\alpha-1}).
\end{aligned}
$$

Since

$$\inf F[a_{\alpha-1}, a_\alpha] \le \sqrt{1 + [f'(x_\alpha)]^2} \le \sup F[a_{\alpha-1}, a_\alpha]$$

it follows that

$$\underline{S}_F(N) \le S_{I,f}(N) \le \bar{S}_F(N).$$

For each subdivision N and N' of $[a, b]$ we have that $N \cup N'$ is a refinement of both N and N'. Therefore by Lemma 3

$$S_{I,f}(N) \le S_{I,f}(N \cup N') \le \bar{S}_F(N \cup N') \le \bar{S}_F(N').$$

Thus each upper sum $\bar{S}_F(N)$ is an upper bound for P_f. Therefore

$$\sup P_f \le \int_a^b \sqrt{1 + [f'(x)]^2}\, dx.$$

On the other hand, for each ϵ there exists a subdivision N of $[a, b]$ for which

$$S_{I,f}(N) \ge \underline{S}_F(N) \ge \int_a^b \sqrt{1 + [f'(x)]^2}\, dx - \epsilon.$$

Therefore $\sup P_f = \int_a^b \sqrt{1 + [f'(x)]^2}\, dx$.

Q.E.D.

Example. If $f(x) = x^{2/3}$, then to find the length of the curve between the points $(1, 1)$ and $(8, 4)$ we have that $f'(x) = 2/3x^{1/3}$ and hence

$$\sqrt{1 + [f'(x)]^2} = \sqrt{1 + \frac{4}{9x^{2/3}}} = \frac{\sqrt{9x^{2/3} + 4}}{3x^{1/3}}.$$

From the Fundamental Theorem we see that

$$
\begin{aligned}
\int_1^8 \sqrt{1 + [f'(x)]^2}\, dx &= \tfrac{1}{18} \int_1^8 \sqrt{9x^{2/3} + 4}\, \frac{6\, dx}{x^{1/3}} = \tfrac{1}{18} \cdot \tfrac{2}{3}(9x^{2/3} + 4)^{3/2} \Big|_1^8 \\
&= \tfrac{1}{27}(80\sqrt{10} - 13\sqrt{13}).
\end{aligned}
$$

Theorem 8.41 is adequate for all later arc length problems. The remainder of this section can therefore be omitted without loss of continuity. For the interested reader, however, we press on to the completion of our announced goal—namely, the proof that if f' and g' are continuous on $[a, b]$, then

$$\int_a^b \sqrt{[g'(x)]^2 + [f'(x)]^2}\, dx = \sup\{S_{g,f}(N) \mid N \text{ is a subdivision of } [a, b]\}.$$

The proof proceeds along the same lines as the proof at Theorem 8.41 with one notable exception. If $F(x) = \sqrt{[g'(x)]^2 + [f'(x)]^2}$, $x \in [a, b]$ then F is integrable on $[a, b]$. Furthermore, if $\{a_0, a_1, \ldots, a_n\}$ is a subdivision of $[a, b]$, then there exist numbers x_α and y_α in $[a_{\alpha-1}, a_\alpha]$ such that

$$f(a_\alpha) - f(a_{\alpha-1}) = f'(x_\alpha)(a_\alpha - a_{\alpha-1})$$

and

$$g(a_\alpha) - g(a_{\alpha-1}) = g'(y_\alpha)(a_\alpha - a_{\alpha-1})$$

and hence

$$S_{g,f}(N) = \sum_{\alpha=1}^n \sqrt{[g(a_\alpha) - g(a_{\alpha-1})]^2 + [f(a_\alpha) - f(a_{\alpha-1})]^2}$$
$$= \sum_{\alpha=1}^n \sqrt{[g'(y_\alpha)]^2 + [f'(x_\alpha)]^2}(a_\alpha - a_{\alpha-1}).$$

However, it does not follow from this that $S_{g,f}(N)$ is less than or equal to $\bar{S}_F(N)$. The argument must therefore be modified. The modification we have in mind requires the following lemmas. The proof of the first we leave as an exercise for the reader.

Lemma 4. *If $x > 0$, then for each ϵ, $\sqrt{x + \epsilon^2/2} < \sqrt{x} + \epsilon$.*

Lemma 5. *If f' and g' are continuous on $[a, b]$ and if*

$$F(x) = \sqrt{[g'(x)]^2 + [f'(x)]^2} \quad x \in [a, b],$$

then for each ϵ there exists a δ such that for each subdivision N of $[a, b]$

$$\underline{S}_F(N) - \epsilon < S_{g,f}(N) < \bar{S}_F(N) + \epsilon.$$

if $|N| < \delta$.

Proof. Since f' is continuous on $[a, b]$ it follows that $(f')^2$ is continuous on $[a, b]$ and hence uniformly continuous on $[a, b]$. Therefore there exists a convergence test ϕ such that for each x and y in $[a, b]$

$$\text{if } |x - y| < \phi(\epsilon), \text{ then } |[f'(x)]^2 - [f'(y)]^2| < \epsilon.$$

If

$$\delta = \phi\left(\frac{\epsilon^2}{2(b - a)^2}\right)$$

then for each subdivision N of $[a, b]$ it follows from the continuity of f' and g' that if $|N| < \delta$ and $N = \{a_0, a_1, \ldots, a_n\}$, then there exist numbers x_α and y_α in $[a_{\alpha-1}, a_\alpha]$ for which

$$g(a_\alpha) - g(a_{\alpha-1}) = g'(y_\alpha)(a_\alpha - a_{\alpha-1})$$

and

$$f(a_\alpha) - f(a_{\alpha-1}) = f'(x_\alpha)(a_\alpha - a_{\alpha-1}).$$

Therefore

$$S_{g,f}(N) = \sum_{\alpha=1}^{n} \sqrt{[g(a_\alpha) - g(a_{\alpha-1})]^2 + [f(a_\alpha) - f(a_{\alpha-1})]^2}$$

$$= \sum_{\alpha=1}^{n} \sqrt{[g'(y_\alpha)]^2 + [f'(x_\alpha)]^2}(a_\alpha - a_{\alpha-1}).$$

Since

$$|x_\alpha - y_\alpha| < \phi\left(\frac{\epsilon^2}{2(b-a)^2}\right)$$

it follows that

$$|[f'(x_\alpha)]^2 - [f'(y_\alpha)]^2| < \frac{\epsilon^2}{2(b-a)^2}.$$

Therefore

$$[f'(x_\alpha)]^2 < [f'(y_\alpha)]^2 + \frac{\epsilon^2}{2(b-a)^2}$$

and

$$[f'(y_\alpha)]^2 < [f'(x_\alpha)]^2 + \frac{\epsilon^2}{2(b-a)^2}.$$

Thus

$$\sqrt{[g'(y_\alpha)]^2 + [f'(x_\alpha)]^2} \leq \sqrt{[g'(y_\alpha)]^2 + [f'(y_\alpha)]^2 + \frac{\epsilon^2}{2(b-a)^2}}$$

$$\leq \sqrt{[g'(y_\alpha)]^2 + [f'(y_\alpha)]^2} + \frac{\epsilon}{b-a}$$

$$\sqrt{[g'(y_\alpha)]^2 + [f'(y_\alpha)]^2} \leq \sqrt{[g'(y_\alpha)]^2 + [f'(x_\alpha)]^2 + \frac{\epsilon^2}{2(b-a)^2}}$$

$$\leq \sqrt{[g'(y_\alpha)]^2 + [f'(x_\alpha)]^2} + \frac{\epsilon}{b-a}$$

and

$$\sqrt{[g'(y_\alpha)]^2 + [f'(y_\alpha)]^2} - \frac{\epsilon}{b-a} \leq \sqrt{[g'(y_\alpha)]^2 + [f'(x_\alpha)]^2}$$

$$\leq \sqrt{[g'(y_\alpha)]^2 + [f'(y_\alpha)]^2} + \frac{\epsilon}{b-a}.$$

From this inequality and the fact that

$$S_{g,f}(N) = \sum_{\alpha=1}^{n} \sqrt{[g'(y_\alpha)]^2 + [f'(x_\alpha)]^2}(a_\alpha - a_{\alpha-1})$$

it follows that

$$\underline{S}_F(N) - \epsilon < S_{g,f}(N) < \bar{S}_F(N) + \epsilon.$$

Q.E.D.

Theorem 8.42. *If g' and f' are each continuous on $[a, b]$ then,*

$$\{S_{g,f}(N) \mid N \text{ is a subdivision of } [a, b]\},$$

is bounded above, and its supremum is $\int_a^b \sqrt{[g'(x)]^2 + [f'(x)]^2}\, dx$.

Proof. If $F(x) = \sqrt{[g'(x)]^2 + [f'(x)]^2}$, $x \in [a, b]$, then since g' and f' are each continuous on $[a, b]$, it follows that F is continuous on $[a, b]$ and hence integrable on $[a, b]$. If

$$P_{g,f} = \{S_{g,f}(N) \mid N \text{ is a subdivision of } [a, b]\}$$

then we wish to show that $P_{g,f}$ is bounded and

$$\sup P_{g,f} = \int_a^b \sqrt{[g'(x)]^2 + [f'(x)]^2}\, dx.$$

If N and N' are subdivisions of $[a, b]$, then for each ϵ it follows from Lemma 5 that there exists a refinement M of $N \cup N'$ such that

$$S_{g,f}(N) \le S_{g,f}(M) < \bar{S}_F(M) + \epsilon \le \bar{S}_F(N') + \epsilon.$$

Since this is true for each ϵ we conclude that

$$S_{g,f}(N) \le \bar{S}_F(N').$$

Therefore each upper sum $\bar{S}_F(N)$ is an upper bound for $P_{g,f}$ and hence

$$\sup P_{g,f} \le \int_a^b \sqrt{[g'(x)]^2 + [f'(x)]^2}\, dx.$$

Furthermore for each ϵ there exists a subdivision N such that

$$\underline{S}_F(N) \ge \int_a^b \sqrt{[g'(x)]^2 + [f'(x)]^2}\, dx - \frac{\epsilon}{2}.$$

By Lemma 5 it follows that if N' is a refinement of N with sufficiently small norm, then

$$S_{g,f}(N') \ge \underline{S}_F(N') - \frac{\epsilon}{2} \ge \underline{S}_F(N) - \frac{\epsilon}{2} \ge \int_a^b \sqrt{[g'(x)]^2 + [f'(x)]^2}\, dx - \epsilon.$$

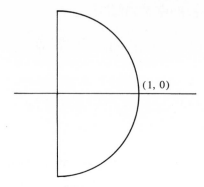

FIGURE 8.11

Therefore

$$\sup P_{g,f} = \int_a^b \sqrt{[g'(x)]^2 + [f'(x)]^2}\, dx.$$

Q.E.D.

8.5 The Trigonometric Functions

We now have the tools necessary for a definition of the trigonometric functions. Basically our problem is to define two functions, which we will denote by 'cos' and 'sin', that provide a "natural" parameterization of the unit circle in that $(1, 0)$ and $(\cos\theta, \sin\theta)$ are the end points of an arc of the unit circle whose length is θ.

Since by definition the unit circle is the graph of the relation

$$\{(x, y) \mid x^2 + y^2 = 1\}$$

and since

$$\{(\sqrt{1 - y^2}, y) \mid y \in [-1, 1]\}$$

gives a parameterization of a semicircle (see Figure 8.11) in terms of parameter functions that have continuous derivatives on $(-1, 1)$, the arc length of the semicircular arc with endpoints $(1, 0)$ and $(\sqrt{1 - y^2}, y)$ is given by

$$\int_0^y \frac{dt}{\sqrt{1 - t^2}}, \quad |y| < 1.$$

We now wish to show that the difficulty at 1 and -1 is not a problem with the arc length but a problem with the integral. We will prove that

$$\lim_{y \to 1} \int_0^y \frac{dt}{\sqrt{1 - t^2}} = 2 \int_0^{\sqrt{2}/2} \frac{dt}{\sqrt{1 - t^2}}.$$

It is, of course, sufficient to prove that

$$\lim_{y \to 1} \int_{\sqrt{2}/2}^{y} \frac{dt}{\sqrt{1 - t^2}} = \int_{0}^{\sqrt{2}/2} \frac{dt}{\sqrt{1 - t^2}}.$$

If $t = \sqrt{1 - s^2}$ then $dt = -s\,ds/\sqrt{1 - s^2}$ and hence

$$\int_{\sqrt{2}/2}^{y} \frac{dt}{\sqrt{1 - t^2}} = -\int_{\sqrt{2}/2}^{\sqrt{1 - y^2}} \frac{ds}{\sqrt{1 - s^2}}.$$

Therefore

$$\lim_{y \to 1} \int_{\sqrt{2}/2}^{y} \frac{dt}{\sqrt{1 - t^2}} = -\lim_{y \to 1} \int_{\sqrt{2}/2}^{\sqrt{1 - y^2}} \frac{ds}{\sqrt{1 - s^2}} = -\int_{\sqrt{2}/2}^{0} \frac{ds}{\sqrt{1 - s^2}}$$

$$= \int_{0}^{\sqrt{2}/2} \frac{ds}{\sqrt{1 - s^2}}.$$

This suggests the following extension of the definition of the integral.

Definition 8.50. 1) If f is integrable on $[a, c - \epsilon]$ for each ϵ, then

$$\int_{a}^{c} f = \lim_{\epsilon \to 0} \int_{a}^{c - \epsilon} f \quad \text{and} \quad \int_{c}^{a} f = -\int_{a}^{c} f,$$

if $\lim_{\epsilon \to 0} \int_{a}^{c - \epsilon} f$ exists,

2) If f is integrable on $[c + \epsilon, b]$ for each ϵ and if $\lim_{\epsilon \to 0} \int_{c + \epsilon}^{b} f$ exists, then

$$\int_{c}^{b} f = \lim_{\epsilon \to 0} \int_{c + \epsilon}^{b} f \quad \text{and} \quad \int_{b}^{c} f = -\int_{b}^{c} f.$$

3) If $\int_{a}^{c} f$ and $\int_{c}^{b} f$ exist, then $\int_{a}^{b} f = \int_{a}^{c} f + \int_{c}^{b} f$ and $\int_{b}^{a} f = -\int_{a}^{b} f$.

From Definition 8.50 and the limit property proved above it follows that

$$\int_{0}^{1} \frac{dt}{\sqrt{1 - t^2}}$$

is the length of one quarter of the circumference of the unit circle.

Definition 8.51. $\pi = 2 \int_{0}^{1} \frac{dt}{\sqrt{1 - t^2}}.$

From this it follows that if

$$F(y) = \int_{0}^{y} \frac{dt}{\sqrt{1 - t^2}}, \quad y \in [-1, 1],$$

then $F:[-1, 1] \xrightarrow[\text{onto}]{1-1} [-\pi/2, \pi/2]$ and $|F(y)|$ is the length of the arc between $(1, 0)$ and (x, y). Since F is one-to-one and continuous it has a continuous inverse, F^{-1}, which maps $[-\pi/2, \pi/2]$ one-to-one onto $[-1, 1]$. Thus for each θ in $[-\pi/2, \pi/2]$, $F^{-1}(\theta)$ is the y-coordinate of a point on the unit circle whose "arc distance" from $(1, 0)$ is θ. Therefore if

$$\sin \theta = F^{-1}(\theta), \qquad \theta \in [-\pi/2, \pi/2],$$
$$\cos \theta = \sqrt{1 - \sin^2 \theta}, \quad \theta \in [-\pi/2, \pi/2],$$

then sin and cos are each continuous on $[-\pi/2, \pi/2]$. Furthermore

$$\sin^2 \theta + \cos^2 \theta = 1, \quad \theta \in [-\pi/2, \pi/2].$$

Since $F(0) = 0$, it follows that $\sin 0 = 0$ and $\cos 0 = 1$. Since $F(1) = \pi/2$ and $F(-1) = -\pi/2$, we have that $\sin \pi/2 = 1$, $\cos \pi/2 = 0$, $\sin(-\pi/2) = -1$, $\cos(-\pi/2) = 0$.

Other properties of sin and cos can be deduced from the properties of F. For example if $s = -t$ then $ds = -dt$, and hence from the substitution rule

$$F(-y) = \int_0^{-y} \frac{dt}{\sqrt{1 - t^2}} = -\int_0^y \frac{ds}{\sqrt{1 - s^2}} = -F(y).$$

Since sin and F are inverses and since for each θ in $[-\pi/2, \pi/2]$ there exists a y in $[-1, 1]$ for which $\theta = F(y)$

$$\sin(-\theta) = \sin(-F(y)) = \sin(F(-y)) = -y = -\sin \theta,$$
$$\cos(-\theta) = \sqrt{1 - \sin^2(-\theta)} = \sqrt{1 - \sin^2 \theta} = \cos \theta.$$

Furthermore since

$$F(y) = \int_0^y \frac{dt}{\sqrt{1 - t^2}}, \quad y \in [-1, 1],$$

it follows that

$$F'(y) = \frac{1}{\sqrt{1 - y^2}}, \quad y \in (-1, 1).$$

From Theorem 7.13 it then follows that

$$\sin' \theta = \frac{1}{F'(\sin \theta)} = \sqrt{1 - \sin^2 \theta} = \cos \theta, \quad \theta \in (-\pi/2, \pi/2).$$

From the fact that sin is differentiable on $(-\pi/2, \pi/2)$ it follows that cos is also differentiable on $(-\pi/2, \pi/2)$. Indeed

$$\cos' \theta = \frac{-2 \sin \theta \cos \theta}{2\sqrt{1 - \sin^2 \theta}} = -\sin \theta, \quad \theta \in (-\pi/2, \pi/2).$$

Furthermore, since $\sin'(0) = 1$

$$\lim_{\theta \to 0} \frac{\sin \theta}{\theta} = 1.$$

We now wish to illustrate how basic trigonometric identities can be deduced from the integral for arc length. We will prove that

$$\sin(\theta + \phi) = \sin \theta \cos \phi + \cos \theta \sin \phi$$

provided $\theta \in [-\pi/2, \pi/2]$, $\phi \in [-\pi/2, \pi/2]$, and $\theta + \phi \in [-\pi/2, \pi/2]$. We first observe that if $a = \sin \theta \cos \phi + \cos \theta \sin \phi$ and if $b = \cos \theta \cos \phi - \sin \theta \sin \phi$, then $a^2 + b^2 = 1$. We leave the details of the computation to the reader. Since $a^2 + b^2 = 1$, it follows that $a \in [-1, 1]$. Since F is one-to-one we need only prove that

$$\int_0^{\sin(\theta + \phi)} \frac{dt}{\sqrt{1 - t^2}} = \int_0^{d} \frac{dt}{\sqrt{1 - t^2}}.$$

From the definition of F

$$\theta = \int_0^{\sin \theta} \frac{dt}{\sqrt{1 - t^2}},$$

$$\phi = \int_0^{\sin \phi} \frac{dt}{\sqrt{1 - t^2}}.$$

Therefore

$$\int_0^{\sin(\theta + \phi)} \frac{dt}{\sqrt{1 - t^2}} = \theta + \phi = \int_0^{\sin \theta} \frac{dt}{\sqrt{1 - t^2}} + \int_0^{\sin \phi} \frac{dt}{\sqrt{1 - t^2}}.$$

If in the last integral we make the substitution $t = u \cos \theta + \sin \theta \sqrt{1 - u^2}$, then

$$dt = \frac{\cos \theta \sqrt{1 - u^2} - u \sin \theta}{\sqrt{1 - u^2}} \, du, \qquad \frac{1}{\sqrt{1 - t^2}} = \frac{1}{\cos \theta \sqrt{1 - u^2} - u \sin \theta}.$$

Therefore

$$\int_0^{\sin \phi} \frac{dt}{\sqrt{1 - t^2}} = \int_{\sin \theta}^{a} \frac{du}{\sqrt{1 - u^2}},$$

and hence

$$\int_0^{\sin(\theta + \phi)} \frac{dt}{\sqrt{1 - t^2}} = \int_0^{a} \frac{dt}{\sqrt{1 - t^2}}.$$

Since F is one-to-one, it follows from this that

$$\sin(\theta + \phi) = a = \sin \theta \cos \phi + \cos \theta \sin \phi.$$

From this formula in turn we have that

$$\sin(\theta - \phi) = \sin \theta \cos \phi - \cos \theta \sin \phi$$

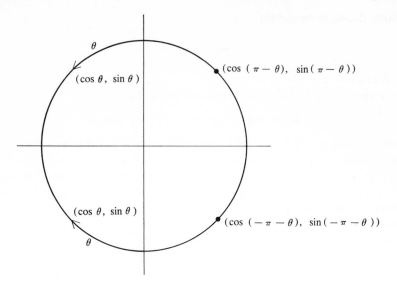

FIGURE 8.12

and hence

$$\sin (\theta + \phi) - \sin (\theta - \phi) = 2 \cos \theta \sin \phi.$$

If $\theta = (x + \pi/2)/2$ and $\phi = (x - \pi/2)/2$, then

$$\sin x - \sin \frac{\pi}{2} = 2 \cos \frac{x + \pi/2}{2} \sin \frac{x - \pi/2}{2}$$

and

$$\mathrm{Lim}_{x \to \frac{\pi}{2}^-} \frac{\sin x - \sin \pi/2}{x - \pi/2} = \mathrm{Lim}_{x \to \frac{2}{\pi}^-} \cos \frac{x + \pi/2}{2} \mathrm{Lim}_{x \to \frac{\pi}{2}^-} \frac{\sin \dfrac{x - \pi/2}{2}}{\dfrac{x - \pi/2}{2}}$$

$$= \cos \frac{\pi}{2} = 0.$$

Therefore sin has a left derivative at $\pi/2$. In a similar manner we can prove that it has a right derivative at $-\pi/2$ which is also 0. With these examples to serve as guides we leave the remaining properties of interest to the reader and turn to the problem of extending the definition of sin and cos.

From symmetry considerations (see Figure 8.12) we can extend the definition of sin and cos to $[-\pi, \pi]$ by defining

$$\begin{array}{ll}
\sin \theta = \sin (\pi - \theta) & \theta \in (\pi/2, \pi] \\
\cos \theta = -\cos (\pi - \theta) & \theta \in (\pi/2, \pi] \\
\sin \theta = \sin (-\pi - \theta) & \theta \in [-\pi, -\pi/2) \\
\cos \theta = -\cos (-\pi - \theta) & \theta \in [-\pi, -\pi/2).
\end{array}$$

From this it follows that if $\theta \in [-\pi, \pi]$, then

$$\sin (-\theta) = -\sin \theta$$
$$\cos (-\theta) = \cos \theta$$
$$\sin^2 \theta + \cos^2 \theta = 1$$
$$\sin' \theta = \cos \theta$$
$$\cos' \theta = -\sin \theta$$
$$\sin \pi = 0$$
$$\cos \pi = -1.$$

Furthermore, if $\theta \in [-\pi, \pi]$, $\phi \in [-\pi, \pi]$, and $\theta + \phi \in [-\pi, \pi]$ then

$$\sin (\theta + \phi) = \sin \theta \cos \phi + \cos \theta \sin \phi.$$

We leave the proofs to the reader.

Finally we can extend the definition of sin and cos to the set of all real numbers by the periodicity condition that

$$\sin (x + 2\pi) = \sin x, \qquad \cos (x + 2\pi) = \cos x.$$

We then complete the definition of the trigonometric functions by defining

$$\tan x = \frac{\sin x}{\cos x} \quad \cos x \neq 0, \qquad \cot x = \frac{\cos x}{\sin x}, \qquad \sin x \neq 0,$$

$$\sec x = \frac{1}{\cos x}, \quad \cos x \neq 0, \qquad \csc x = \frac{1}{\sin x}, \qquad \sin x \neq 0.$$

Again we leave the proofs of the basic formulas as exercises.

8.6 Integration by Parts

Integration by parts is a very useful method for evaluating certain types of integrals. The method depends upon the following theorem.

Theorem 8.60. *If g is differentiable on $[a, b]$ and if f' is continuous on $[a, b]$ then F defined by*

$$F(x) = f(x)g(x) - \int_a^x f'(t)g(t)\, dt$$

is an antiderivative for fg' on $[a, b]$.

Proof. Since g is differentiable on $[a, b]$ and since f' is continuous on $[a, b]$, we have that $f'g$ is continuous on $[a, b]$. Then by Theorem 8.31

$$F'(x) = f'(x)g(x) + f(x)g'(x) - f'(x)g(x) = f(x)g'(x).$$

Q.E.D.

Remark. From Theorem 8.60 and the Fundamental Theorem it follows that if $\int_a^b f(t)g'(t)\, dt$ exists, then

$$\int_a^b f(t)g'(t)\, dt = f(b)g(b) - f(a)g(a) - \int_a^b f'(t)g(t)\, dt.$$

The value of this equality is that it enables us to reduce the problem of evaluating a given integral to that of evaluating one that may be in some sense simpler. Let us illustrate.

Example. $\int_0^1 xe^x\, dx.$

If we make the identification

$$f(x) = x \qquad g'(x) = e^x$$

we then have

$$f'(x) = 1 \qquad g(x) = e^x$$

and hence

$$\int_0^1 xe^x\, dx = xe^x\Big|_0^1 - \int_0^1 e^x\, dx = (e - 0) - e^x\Big|_0^1 = 1.$$

In this example it should be noted that g is not uniquely determined by the fact that $g'(x) = e^x$. Indeed g' has many antiderivatives, any one of which will serve our purpose.

Example. $\int_0^1 x^3\sqrt{1 - x^2}\, dx.$

If $f(x) = x^2$ and $g'(x) = x\sqrt{1 - x^2}$, we then have that $f'(x) = 2x$ and $g(x) = -\frac{1}{3}(1 - x^2)^{3/2}$. Therefore

$$\int_0^1 x^3\sqrt{1 - x^2}\, dx = -\frac{1}{3}x^2(1 - x^2)^{3/2}\Big|_0^1 + \frac{2}{3}\int_0^1 x(1 - x^2)^{3/2}\, dx$$

$$= -\frac{2}{15}(1 - x^2)^{5/2}\Big|_0^1 = \frac{2}{15}.$$

The following is a very interesting application of integration by parts.

Example. $\int_0^{\pi/2} e^x \sin x\, dx.$

If $f(x) = \sin x$ and $g'(x) = e^x$ then $f'(x) = \cos x$ and $g(x) = e^x$, hence

$$\int_0^{\pi/2} e^x \sin x\, dx = e^x \sin x\Big|_0^{\pi/2} - \int_0^{\pi/2} e^x \cos x\, dx.$$

Another application of parts integration to the new integral with $f(x) = \cos x$ and $g'(x) = e^x$, hence $f'(x) = -\sin x$ and $g(x) = e^x$, gives

$$\int_0^{\pi/2} e^x \sin x\, dx = e^x \sin x\Big|_0^{\pi/2} - \left(e^x \cos x\Big|_0^{\pi/2} + \int_0^{\pi/2} e^x \sin x\, dx\right)\cdot$$

Solving for the integral we have

$$\int_0^{\pi/2} e^x \sin x \, dx = \tfrac{1}{2}[e^x \sin x - e^x \cos x]\Big|_0^{\pi/2} = \tfrac{1}{2}[e^{\pi/2} - 1].$$

Example. $\int_a^b \cos^n \theta \, d\theta$, $n \geq 1$.

If $n > 2$ then by parts integration

$$f(\theta) = \cos^{n-1} \theta \qquad\qquad g'(\theta) = \cos \theta$$
$$f'(\theta) = -(n-1) \cos^{n-2} \theta \sin \theta \qquad g(\theta) = \sin \theta.$$

Therefore

$$\int_a^b \cos^n \theta \, d\theta = [\cos^{n-1} \theta \sin \theta]\Big|_a^b + (n-1) \int_a^b \cos^{n-2} \theta \sin^2 \theta \, d\theta.$$

Since $\sin^2 \theta = 1 - \cos^2 \theta$ we have on substitution that

$$\int_a^b \cos^n \theta \, d\theta = [\cos^{n-1} \theta \sin \theta]\Big|_a^b$$
$$+ (n-1) \int_a^b \cos^{n-2} \theta \, d\theta - (n-1) \int_a^b \cos^n \theta \, d\theta.$$

Hence, solving for $\int_a^b \cos^n \theta \, d\theta$,

$$\int_a^b \cos^n \theta \, d\theta = \frac{1}{n} [\cos^{n-1} \theta \sin \theta]\Big|_a^b + \frac{n-1}{n} \int_a^b \cos^{n-2} \theta \, d\theta.$$

This formula reduces the problem of integrating an nth power of cos to the problem of integrating an $(n-2)$th power of cos. By repeated application we would finally arrive at the problem of evaluating

$$\int_a^b \cos \theta \, d\theta \quad \text{or} \quad \int_a^b \cos^2 \theta \, d\theta.$$

Since $\cos^2 \theta = (1 + \cos 2\theta)/2$

$$\int_a^b \cos^2 \theta \, d\theta = \int_a^b \frac{1 + \cos 2\theta}{2} \, d\theta = \left[\frac{\theta}{2} + \frac{1}{4} \sin 2\theta\right]\Big|_a^b.$$
$$\int_a^b \cos \theta \, d\theta = \sin \theta \Big|_a^b.$$

The last example is a particularly interesting one. With this and previously proved results we have a method for integrating rational functions, the method of partial fraction decomposition.

It can be proved that for each rational function f there exist numbers $c_1, c_2, \cdots, c_n$ and functions $f_1, f_2, \ldots, f_n$ such that

$$f = \sum_{\alpha=1}^n c_\alpha f_\alpha$$

and each f_α is a function of one of the following four types.

Type 1. $f_\alpha(x) = \sum\limits_{\beta=0}^{m} a_\beta x^\beta$,   i.e., f is a polynomial function.

Type 2. $f_\alpha(x) = \dfrac{a}{(ax + b)^m}$, $m \geq 1$, $ax + b \neq 0$, $a \neq 0$.

Type 3. $f_\alpha(x) = \dfrac{2ax + b}{(ax^2 + bx + c)^m}$, $m \geq 1$, $ax^2 + bx + c \neq 0$,

$$b^2 - 4ac < 0.$$

Type 4. $f_\alpha(x) = \dfrac{1}{[1 + (x - a)^2]^m}$, $m \geq 1$.

Functions of Types 1, 2, and 3 have simple antiderivatives defined respectively by

1) $g_\alpha(x) = \sum\limits_{\beta=0}^{m} \dfrac{a_\beta x^{\beta+1}}{\beta + 1}$.

2) $g_\alpha(x) = \ln|ax + b|$ if $m = 1$.

$\quad g_\alpha(x) = \dfrac{-1}{(m - 1)(ax + b)^{m-1}}$ if $m > 1$.

3) $g_\alpha(x) = \ln|ax^2 + bx + c|$ if $m = 1$.

$\quad g_\alpha(x) = \dfrac{-1}{(m - 1)(ax^2 + bx + c)^{m-1}}$ if $m > 1$.

Therefore integrals of functions of Types 1, 2, and 3 can be evaluated by the Fundamental Theorem.

Example. $\displaystyle\int_0^1 \dfrac{x^3\,dx}{x + 1} = \int_0^1 \left(x^2 - x + 1 - \dfrac{1}{x + 1}\right) dx$

$$= \left.\left(\dfrac{x^3}{3} - \dfrac{x^2}{2} + x - \ln|x + 1|\right)\right|_0^1.$$

Example. $\displaystyle\int_0^{-1} \dfrac{2x\,dx}{(2x - 1)^2} = \int_0^{-1} \dfrac{1}{2}\left(\dfrac{2}{2x - 1} + \dfrac{2}{(2x - 1)^2}\right) dx$

$$= \left.\left(\dfrac{1}{2}\ln|2x - 1| + \dfrac{1}{2}\dfrac{1}{2x - 1}\right)\right|_0^{-1}.$$

The integrals of functions of Type 4 can be evaluated by the substitution rule. If $x - a = \tan\theta$ then $dx = \sec^2\theta\,d\theta$. Therefore on substitution into

$$\frac{dx}{[1 + (x - a)^2]^m}$$

we obtain

$$(\cos^{2m-2}\theta)\,d\theta.$$

Example.

$$\int_1^2 \frac{(2x^2 + x + 1)\,dx}{x(x^2 + 1)} = \int_1^2 \left(\frac{1}{x} + \frac{1}{2}\frac{2x}{x^2 + 1} + \frac{1}{1 + x^2}\right)dx$$

$$= (\ln |x| + \tfrac{1}{2} \ln |x^2 + 1|)\Big|_1^2 + \int_1^2 \frac{dx}{1 + x^2}.$$

If $x = \tan \theta$ then

$$\int_1^2 \frac{dx}{1 + x^2} = \int_{\pi/4}^{\text{Arc tan } 2} d\theta = \text{Arc tan } 2 - \pi/4$$

where Arc tan is the inverse of tan restricted to $(-\pi/2, \pi/2)$.

EXERCISES

Evaluate the following integrals.

1. $\displaystyle\int_0^1 x^2 \sin x \, dx.$ **2.** $\displaystyle\int_0^1 x \ln x \, dx.$

3. $\displaystyle\int_0^1 \sin^2 x \cos^2 x \, dx.$ **4.** $\displaystyle\int_0^1 \frac{dx}{x^2 + x + 1}.$

5. $\displaystyle\int_1^2 \frac{dx}{x(x^2 + x + 1)}.$ **6.** $\displaystyle\int_1^2 \frac{dx}{x^2(x + 1)^2}.$

7. $\displaystyle\int_0^1 \frac{x^3 \, dx}{(x^2 - 3x - 2)}.$ **8.** $\displaystyle\int_0^1 \frac{x^3 \, dx}{(x^2 - 3x - 2)^2}.$

9. $\displaystyle\int_0^1 \frac{(x^2 + 2x + 4)\,dx}{(x^2 + 2x + 3)^2}.$

*8.7 A Necessary and Sufficient Condition for the Existence of Integrals

We have proved that in order for f to be integrable on $[a, b]$ it is sufficient for f to be continuous on $[a, b]$ or for f to be monotone on $[a, b]$. These conditions, however, are not necessary. For example, any bounded function that is continuous on $[a, b]$, except possibly at a single point, is integrable on $[a, b]$.

Theorem 8.70. *If $c \in [a, b]$, if f is bounded on $[a, b]$, and continuous on $[a, b]$ except possibly at c, then f is integrable on $[a, b]$.*

Proof Procedure. It is sufficient to prove that for each ϵ there exists a subdivision N for which

$$\bar{S}_f(N) - \underline{S}_f(N) < \epsilon.$$

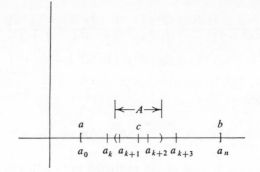

FIGURE 8.13

To establish that such a subdivision does exist we note that if $N = \{a_0, a_1, \ldots, a_n\}$, then

$$\overline{S}_f(N) - \underline{S}_f(N) = \sum_{\alpha=1}^{n} (\sup f[a_{\alpha-1}, a_\alpha] - \inf f[a_{\alpha-1}, a_\alpha])(a_\alpha - a_{\alpha-1}).$$

The basis of our proof is the following. If A is an open interval that contains c, then f is continuous on the closed and bounded set $[a, b] - A$. Therefore f is uniformly continuous on $[a, b] - A$. We then divide the terms of $\overline{S}_f(N) - \underline{S}_f(N)$ into two classes, 1) those terms for which $[a_{\alpha-1}, a_\alpha] \subseteq [a, b] - A$ and 2) those terms for which $[a_{\alpha-1}, a_\alpha] \nsubseteq [a, b] - A$. For terms of the first type it follows, because of the uniform continuity of f on $[a, b] - A$, that if the norm of N is sufficiently small then

$$(\sup f[a_{\alpha-1}, a_\alpha] - \inf f[a_{\alpha-1}, a_\alpha])(a_\alpha - a_{\alpha-1}) < \frac{\epsilon}{2(b-a)}(a_\alpha - a_{\alpha-1})$$

and hence the sum of all such terms does not exceed $\frac{\epsilon}{2}$.

For terms of the second type it follows, since f is bounded, that

$$(\sup f[a_{\alpha-1}, a_\alpha] - \inf f[a_{\alpha-1}, a_\alpha])(a_\alpha - a_{\alpha-1}) < 2d(a_\alpha - a_{\alpha-1})$$

where d is a bound for f. Since with at most two exceptions any Type 2 interval lies entirely within A, the total length of all such intervals does not exceed the length of A plus twice the norm of N (see Figure 8.13). Therefore the sum of all Type 2 terms can be made smaller than $\epsilon/2$ by choosing the length of A and the norm of N sufficiently small.

In summary $\overline{S}_f(N) - \underline{S}_f(N)$ can be divided into two parts, a sum of terms that can be made small because of uniform continuity, and a sum of terms that can be made small because the function is bounded and the total lengths of the intervals can be made small.

In the proof to follow and in the material ahead we will use the symbol '$\sum_A$' to indicate the sum of those terms of $\overline{S}_f(N) - \underline{S}_f(N)$ that involve subintervals that have a point in common with A, and '$\sum_{\sim A}$' to indicate the sum of those terms that involve subintervals that have no points in common with A.

Proof. If d is a bound for f on $[a, b]$, then for each ϵ there exists an open interval A with length not greater than $\epsilon/8d$ which contains c as an interior point. We then have that f is continuous on the closed and bounded set $[a, b] - A$, hence it is uniformly continuous on $[a, b] - A$. Thus there exists a δ_1 such that for each x and y in $[a, b] - A$

$$\text{if } |x - y| < \delta_1 \text{ then } |f(x) - f(y)| < \frac{\epsilon}{2(b - a)}.$$

If $\delta = \min \{\delta_1, \epsilon/16d\}$, then there exists a subdivision N of $[a, b]$ with norm less than δ. If $N = \{a_0, \ldots, a_n\}$ and if $[a_{\alpha-1}, a_\alpha] \subset [a, b] - A$, then there exist numbers x_α and y_α in $[a_{\alpha-1}, a_\alpha]$ for which

$$\sup f[a_{\alpha-1}, a_\alpha] = f(x_\alpha), \qquad \inf f[a_{\alpha-1}, a_\alpha] = f(y_\alpha),$$

$$\sup f[a_{\alpha-1}, a_\alpha] - \inf f[a_{\alpha-1}, a_\alpha] = f(x_\alpha) - f(y_\alpha) < \frac{\epsilon}{2(b - a)},$$

and hence

$$\sum_{\sim A} (\sup f[a_{\alpha-1}, a_\alpha] - \inf f[a_{\alpha-1}, a_\alpha])(a_\alpha - a_{\alpha-1})$$

$$\leq \sum_{\sim A} \frac{\epsilon}{2(b - a)} (a_\alpha - a_{\alpha-1}) \leq \sum_{\alpha=1}^{n} \frac{\epsilon}{2(b - a)} (a_\alpha - a_{\alpha-1}) = \frac{\epsilon}{2}.$$

Furthermore since d is a bound for f

$$-d \leq \inf f[a_{\alpha-1}, a_\alpha] \leq \sup f[a_{\alpha-1}, a_\alpha] \leq d;$$

hence

$$\sup f[a_{\alpha-1}, a_\alpha] - \inf f[a_{\alpha-1}, a_\alpha] \leq 2d$$

and

$$\sum_{A} (\sup f[a_{\alpha-1}, a_\alpha] - \inf f[a_{\alpha-1}, a_\alpha])(a_\alpha - a_{\alpha-1})$$

$$\leq \sum_{A} 2d(a_\alpha - a_{\alpha-1}) \leq 2d \left(\frac{\epsilon}{8d} + 2 \cdot \frac{\epsilon}{16d} \right) = \frac{\epsilon}{2}.$$

Then

$$\bar{S}_f(N) - \underline{S}_f(N) = \sum_{\sim A} (\sup f[a_{\alpha-1}, a_\alpha] - \inf f[a_{\alpha-1}, a_\alpha])(a_\alpha - a_{\alpha-1})$$

$$+ \sum_{A} (\sup f[a_{\alpha-1}, a_\alpha] - \inf f[a_{\alpha-1}, a_\alpha])(a_\alpha - a_{\alpha-1})$$

$$< \frac{\epsilon}{2} + \frac{\epsilon}{2} = \epsilon,$$

and hence f is integrable on $[a, b]$.

Q.E.D.

From Theorem 8.70 it is easily proved by induction that if f is bounded and continuous on $[a, b]$, except possibly at a finite number of points, then f is integrable on $[a, b]$. For reasons that will be made clear later, we now wish to prove this result by a modification of the argument used above.

Theorem 8.71. *If f is bounded on $[a, b]$ and continuous on $[a, b]$ except possibly at the points c_β, $\beta = 1, 2, \ldots, n$, then f is integrable on $[a, b]$.*

Proof. If d is a bound for f on $[a, b]$ then for each ϵ there exist open intervals A_β, $\beta = 1, \ldots, n$, such that $c_\beta \in A_\beta$ and the length of A_β is less than $\epsilon/8dn$. Thus if

$$A = \bigcup_{\beta=1}^{n} A_\beta$$

then A is an open set, consisting of n open intervals whose total length is not greater than $\epsilon/8d$. Since A is open and contains the points $c_1, \ldots, c_n$, the function f is continuous on the closed and bounded set $[a, b] - A$ and hence is uniformly continuous there. Thus there exists a number δ_1 such that for each x and y in $[a, b] - A$

$$\text{if } |x - y| < \delta_1 \text{ then } |f(x) - f(y)| < \frac{\epsilon}{2(b - a)}.$$

Thus if $\delta = \min\{\delta_1, \epsilon/16dn\}$ then there exists a subdivision N of $[a, b]$ with norm less than δ. If $N = \{a_0, a_1, \ldots, a_n\}$ and if $[a_{\alpha-1}, a_\alpha] \subset [a, b] - A$, then there exist numbers x_α and y_α in $[a_{\alpha-1}, a_\alpha]$ such that

$$\sup f[a_{\alpha-1}, a_\alpha] = f(x_\alpha), \quad \inf f[a_{\alpha-1}, a_\alpha] = f(y_\alpha),$$

$$\sup f[a_{\alpha-1}, a_\alpha] - \inf f[a_{\alpha-1}, a_\alpha] = f(x_\alpha) - f(y_\alpha) < \frac{\epsilon}{2(b - a)}$$

and hence

$$\sum_{\sim A} (\sup f[a_{\alpha-1}, a_\alpha] - \inf f[a_{\alpha-1}, a_\alpha])(a_\alpha - a_{\alpha-1})$$

$$< \sum_{\sim A} \frac{\epsilon}{2(b - a)} (a_\alpha - a_{\alpha-1}) \leq \sum_{\alpha=1}^{n} \frac{\epsilon}{2(b - a)} (a_\alpha - a_{\alpha-1}) = \frac{\epsilon}{2}.$$

Furthermore since d is a bound for f

$$-d \leq \inf f[a_{\alpha-1}, a_\alpha] \leq \sup f[a_{\alpha-1}, a_\alpha] \leq d;$$

hence

$$\sup f[a_{\alpha-1}, a_\alpha] - \inf f[a_{\alpha-1}, a_\alpha] \leq 2d$$

and

$$\sum_{A} (\sup f[a_{\alpha-1}, a_\alpha] - \inf f[a_{\alpha-1}, a_\alpha])(a_\alpha - a_{\alpha-1})$$

$$\leq \sum_{A} 2d(a_\alpha - a_{\alpha-1}) \leq 2d\left(\frac{\epsilon}{8d} + 2n \cdot \frac{\epsilon}{16dn}\right) = \frac{\epsilon}{2}.$$

Then

$$\bar{S}_f(N) - \underline{S}_f(N) = \sum_{\sim A} (\sup f[a_{\alpha-1}, a_\alpha] - \inf f[a_{\alpha-1}, a_\alpha])(a_\alpha - a_{\alpha-1})$$
$$+ \sum_{A} (\sup f[a_{\alpha-1}, a_\alpha] - \inf f[a_{\alpha-1}, a_\alpha])(a_\alpha - a_{\alpha-1})$$
$$< \frac{\epsilon}{2} + \frac{\epsilon}{2} = \epsilon.$$

Therefore f is integrable on $[a, b]$.

Q.E.D.

Note that the foregoing argument does not depend upon there being a finite number of points of discontinuity but rather upon the existence of a finite number of intervals that contain all of the points of discontinuity. This suggests that a bounded function with infinitely many discontinuities might be integrable provided the points of discontinuity can be contained in a finite number of open intervals whose total length is as small as we please.

Example. If f is defined on $[0, 1]$ by

$$f(x) = 1 \qquad x \in [0, 1] \text{ and } x \neq \frac{1}{n}$$
$$f(x) = 0 \qquad x = \frac{1}{n}, \quad n > 0$$

then for each ϵ there exists an open interval A_0 of length $\epsilon/16$ that contains 0. Furthermore since 0 is the only accumulation point of $\{1/n \mid n > 0\}$ we have that there are only a finite number, m, of points in $\{1/n \mid n > 0\}$ that are in $[0, 1] - A_0$. Then there are open intervals A_α, $\alpha = 1, \ldots, m$ such that A_α has length $\epsilon/16m$ and $1/\alpha \in A_\alpha$. If

$$A = \bigcup_{\alpha=0}^{m} A_\alpha$$

then A contains all of the points of discontinuity of f, and A is an open set consisting of a finite number of intervals of total length $\epsilon/8$. From this point the argument proceeds as before. Details are left to the reader.

This example suggests an obvious generalization of Theorem 8.71 for which we introduce

Definition 8.72. S has *exterior Jordan content zero* (or simply Jordan content zero) iff for each ϵ there exist open intervals A_α, $\alpha = 1, \ldots, n$, whose total length does not exceed ϵ and $S \subseteq \bigcup_{\alpha=1}^{n} A_\alpha$.

Theorem 8.73. *If f is bounded on $[a, b]$ and if the set of points of discontinuity of f on $[a, b]$ has exterior Jordan content zero, then f is integrable on $[a, b]$.*

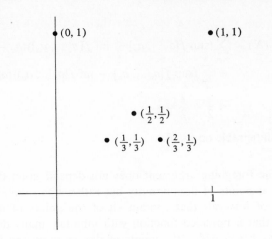

FIGURE 8.14

The proof we leave to the reader.

At this point it appears that we have squeezed this method for all that it is worth. We have established that if f is bounded on $[a, b]$ and if the set of discontinuities of f on $[a, b]$ has Jordan content zero, then f is integrable on $[a, b]$. If we have truly gotten all from this method of proof that seems possible, it is then time to ask: Is this condition necessary? Does there exist a function f that is bounded on an interval $[a, b]$ whose discontinuities on $[a, b]$ form a set whose Jordan content is not zero but for which f is integrable on $[a, b]$? The answer is "yes," as we see from the following:

Example. If Dom $f = [0, 1]$ and if
$$f(x) = 0, \quad x \text{ irrational},$$
$$f(x) = \frac{1}{n}, \quad x = \frac{m}{n}, \quad n > 0, \text{ and } m \text{ and } n \text{ relatively prime},$$

then f is continuous at the irrationals and discontinuous at the rationals (see Exercise 11, page 208). Furthermore it is intuitively clear that a finite collection of open intervals whose total length is less than 1 cannot cover up all of the rational points in $[0, 1]$. A proof is required, but we beg the question in order to consider the problem of the existence of the integral.

Note that f has been so defined that if $x \in [0, 1]$ then
$$0 \le f(x) \le 1.$$

Thus f is bounded. Furthermore $f(x) = 1$ only if $x = 0$ or $x = 1$; indeed
$$\text{if } x \ne 0 \text{ and } x \ne 1, \text{ then } 0 \le f(x) \le \tfrac{1}{2}.$$

But $f(x) = \frac{1}{2}$ only if $x = \frac{1}{2}$. Thus
$$0 \le f(x) \le \tfrac{1}{3} \text{ if } x \ne 0, \ x \ne \tfrac{1}{2}, \text{ and } x \ne 1.$$

These observations suggest that for each ϵ there are only a finite number of points in $[0, 1]$ at which

$$\epsilon \leq f(x).$$

In particular there are only a finite number, n, of points in $[0, 1]$ at which

$$\frac{\epsilon}{b - a} \leq f(x).$$

If each of those n points is then covered by an open interval A_α and if

$$A = \bigcup_{\alpha = 1}^{n} A_\alpha$$

then for each x in $[0, 1] - A$

$$0 \leq f(x) \leq \frac{\epsilon}{b - a}.$$

If N is a subdivision of $[a, b]$ and $N = \{a_0, a_1, \ldots, a_n\}$, then

$$\sup f[a_{\alpha - 1}, a_\alpha] - \inf f[a_{\alpha - 1}, a_\alpha] < \frac{\epsilon}{b - a} \text{ if } [a_{\alpha - 1}, a_\alpha] \subseteq [0, 1] - A$$

and

$$\sup f[a_{\alpha - 1}, a_\alpha] - \inf f[a_{\alpha - 1}, a_\alpha] \leq 1, \text{ if } [a_{\alpha - 1}, a_\alpha] \nsubseteq [0, 1] - A.$$

Again the terms of $\bar{S}_f(N) - \underline{S}_f(N)$ are of two types. The sum of the terms of the first type can be made small because

$$f(x) < \frac{\epsilon}{b - a}.$$

The sum of the terms of the second type can be made small because the total length of the intervals forming A can be chosen small.

We leave the details of this argument to the reader and continue the discussion of existence theorems employing the new kind of argument we have illustrated. We need the following definition.

Definition 8.74. If $a \in \text{Dom} f$ or if a is an accumulation point of $\text{Dom} f$ and if for some δ_1 the function f is bounded in $N(a, \delta_1)$, then

$$s(f, a) = \inf \{\sup f[N(a, \delta)] - \inf f[N(a, \delta)] \mid \delta \leq \delta_1\}.$$

'$s(f, a)$' is read the *saltus of f at a*.

The boundedness of f in $N(a, \delta_1)$ is, of course, sufficient to insure the existence of $s(f, a)$. That $s(f, a)$ is not dependent upon δ_1 we leave as an exercise for the reader. As the word 'saltus' suggests,[1] the saltus of f at a is a measure of the 'jump' of f at a.

[1] The same Latin root occurs in the word 'somersault', whose etymological meaning is 'an over jump'.

Example.   If $f(x) = [\![x]\!]$, then $s(f, n) = 1$ for each integer n.

Example.   If $f(x) = x$, then $s(f, x) = 0$ for each x.

For the theorems ahead we will need the following properties of the saltus.

Lemma 1.   *If $a \in \mathrm{Dom}\, f$ or if a is an accumulation point of $\mathrm{Dom}\, f$ and if for some δ_1 we have that for each x and y in $N(a, \delta_1) \cap \mathrm{Dom}\, f$*

$$|f(x) - f(y)| < \epsilon$$

then $s(f, a) \le \epsilon$.

Proof.   From the given hypotheses it follows that f is bounded in $N(a, \delta_1)$ and hence

$$s(f, a) = \inf\{\sup f[N(a, \delta)] - \inf f[N(a, \delta)] \mid \delta \le \delta_1\}.$$

If $s(f, a) > \epsilon$ it would then follow that if $\delta \le \delta_1$, then

$$\sup f[N(a, \delta)] - \inf f[N(a, \delta)] > \epsilon.$$

If $\epsilon_1 = \sup f[N(a, \delta)] - \inf f[N(a, \delta)] - \epsilon$, then there exist x and y in $N(a, \delta) \cap \mathrm{Dom}\, f$ such that

$$f(x) > \sup f[N(a, \delta)] - \frac{\epsilon_1}{2} \text{ and } f(y) < \inf f[N(a, \delta)] + \frac{\epsilon_1}{2}.$$

Therefore

$$f(x) - f(y) > \sup f[N(a, \delta)] - \frac{\epsilon_1}{2} - \inf f[N(a, \delta)] - \frac{\epsilon_1}{2} = \epsilon.$$

This is a contradiction that forces us to conclude that $s(f, a) \le \epsilon$.

Q.E.D.

Lemma 2.   *If $s(f, a) < \epsilon$ then there exists a δ such that for each x and y in $N(a, \delta) \cap \mathrm{Dom}\, f$*

$$|f(x) - f(y)| < \epsilon.$$

Proof.   The existence of $s(f, a)$ means that $a \in \mathrm{Dom}\, f$ or a is an accumulation point of $\mathrm{Dom}\, f$, that for some δ_1 the function f is bounded on $N(a, \delta_1)$, and that

$$s(f, a) = \inf\{\sup f[N(a, \delta)] - \inf f[N(a, \delta)] \mid \delta \le \delta_1\}.$$

Therefore if $s(f, a) < \epsilon$, then for some δ we have that

$$\sup f[N(a, \delta)] - \inf f[N(a, \delta)] < \epsilon.$$

It then follows that for each x and y in $N(a, \delta) \cap \operatorname{Dom} f$

$$|f(x) - f(y)| \leq \sup f[N(a, \delta)] - \inf f[N(a, \delta)] < \epsilon.$$

(Why?)

Q.E.D.

Recall that in the proof of the last existence theorem our approach was to divide $\bar{S}_f(N) - \underline{S}_f(N)$ into two parts consisting of a sum of terms which could be made small because of uniform continuity and a sum of terms that could be made small because the total length of a certain collection of open intervals could be made small.

Uniform continuity was used to establish, for each ϵ, that

$$|f(x) - f(y)| < \epsilon$$

provided x and y are sufficiently close together. While uniform continuity is sufficient to establish this property, it is not necessary, as we now prove. For our proof we require Theorem 5.82, which assures us that if $\mathscr{C}$ is an open covering of a closed and bounded set S, then there exists a δ with the property that for each x in S there is a set A in $\mathscr{C}$ for which

$$N(x, \delta) \subseteq A.$$

Theorem 8.75. *If f is bounded on the closed and bounded set S, if g is the restriction of f to S, and if for some ϵ and each x in S, $s(g, x) < \epsilon$, then there exists a δ such that for each x and y in $S \cap \operatorname{Dom} f$*

$$|f(x) - f(y)| < \epsilon \text{ if } |x - y| < \delta.$$

Proof. If $\mathscr{C} = \{N(c, \delta) \mid c \in S \text{ and for each } x \text{ and } y \text{ in } N(c, \delta) \cap \operatorname{Dom} f,$ $|f(x) - f(y)| < \epsilon\}$, then by Lemma 2 it follows that $\mathscr{C}$ is an open covering for the closed and bounded set S. By Theorem 5.82 there exists a δ such that for each x and y in $S \cap \operatorname{Dom} f$, if $|x - y| < \delta$, then there exists a neighborhood in $\mathscr{C}$ that contains both x and y and hence

$$|f(x) - f(y)| < \epsilon.$$

Q.E.D.

The next few theorems deal with functions f that are bounded on a closed and bounded interval $[a, b]$. We will be interested in the set of points in $[a, b]$ at which the restriction of f to $[a, b]$ has saltus greater than or equal to ϵ and also in the set of points in $[a, b]$ at which the restriction has positive saltus. We introduce the following notation for these sets.

Definition 8.76. *If f is bounded on $[a, b]$ and if g is the restriction of f to $[a, b]$, then*

$$S_\epsilon(f, a, b) = \{x \in [a, b] \mid s(g, x) \geq \epsilon\},$$
$$S_0(f, a, b) = \{x \in [a, b] \mid s(g, x) > 0\}.$$

We are now prepared for

Theorem 8.77. *If f is bounded on $[a, b]$, then f is integrable on $[a, b]$ iff for each ϵ the set $S_\epsilon(f, a, b)$ has Jordan content zero.*

Proof. If for each ϵ the set $S_\epsilon(f, a, b)$ has Jordan content zero, and if $\epsilon_1 = \epsilon/2(b - a)$ then for each ϵ the set $S_{\epsilon_1}(f, a, b)$ has Jordan content zero. Thus there exists a collection of open intervals A_α, $\alpha = 1, \ldots, n$ which covers $S_{\epsilon_1}(f, a, b)$ and such that the length of each A_α is not greater than $\epsilon/8dn$, where d is a bound for f on $[a, b]$. If

$$A = \bigcup_{\alpha=1}^{n} A_\alpha$$

then A is an open set consisting of the union of a finite number of open intervals whose total length is not greater than $\epsilon/8d$. Then $[a, b] - A$ is a closed and bounded set. Furthermore by Theorem 8.75 there exists a δ_1 such that for each x and y in $([a, b] - A) \cap \operatorname{Dom} f$

$$|f(x) - f(y)| < \frac{\epsilon}{2(b - a)} \text{ if } |x - y| < \delta_1.$$

(Why?) Therefore if $\delta = \min\{\delta_1, \epsilon/16dn\}$ then there exists a subdivision N of $[a, b]$ with norm less than δ. If $N = \{a_0, a_1, \ldots, a_n\}$, then

$$\sum_{\sim A} (\sup f[a_{\alpha-1}, a_\alpha] - \inf f[a_{\alpha-1}, a_\alpha])(a_\alpha - a_{\alpha-1})$$

$$\leq \sum_{\sim A} \frac{\epsilon}{2(b - a)}(a_\alpha - a_{\alpha-1}) \leq \frac{\epsilon}{2}$$

$$\sum_{A} (\sup f[a_{\alpha-1}, a_\alpha] - \inf f[a_{\alpha-1}, a_\alpha])(a_\alpha - a_{\alpha-1})$$

$$\leq \sum_{A} 2d(a_\alpha - a_{\alpha-1}) \leq 2d\left(\frac{\epsilon}{8d} + 2n\frac{\epsilon}{16dn}\right) = \frac{\epsilon}{2}.$$

Hence

$$\bar{S}_f(N) - \underline{S}_f(N) \leq \frac{\epsilon}{2} + \frac{\epsilon}{2} = \epsilon.$$

Therefore f is integrable on $[a, b]$.

Conversely, if for some ϵ the set $S_\epsilon(f, a, b)$ does not have Jordan content zero, then there exists a δ for which every finite collection of open intervals that cover $S_\epsilon(f, a, b)$ has total length greater than δ. If $N = \{a_0, \ldots, a_n\}$, if N is a subdivision of $[a, b]$, and if N has k points in common with $S_\epsilon(f, a, b)$, then those k points can be covered by k open intervals whose total length is exactly $\delta/2$. It then follows that the total length of all of the intervals $[a_{\alpha-1}, a_\alpha]$ which contain points of $S_\epsilon(f, a, b)$ as interior points must exceed $\delta/2$. (Why?) Since for any such interval

$$\sup f[a_{\alpha-1}, a_\alpha] - \inf f[a_{\alpha-1}, a_\alpha] \geq \epsilon$$

it follows that

$$\bar{S}_f(N) - \underline{S}_f(N) \geq \frac{\epsilon\delta}{2}.$$

Consequently, f is not integrable on $[a, b]$.

Q.E.D.

While the condition in Theorem 8.76 is both necessary and sufficient we can hope for a simpler one. Our feeling, in view of the existence theorems proved thus far, is that functions that are bounded on a closed and bounded interval are integrable provided the set of discontinuities is not too large. Thus if f is bounded on $[a, b]$, then f should be integrable on $[a, b]$ provided that

$$\{x \in [a, b] \mid s(f, x) > 0\}$$

is not large in some sense. We will next show that it must be small in the sense of

Definition 8.78. S has *exterior Lebesque measure zero* (or simply measure zero) iff for each ϵ there exists a sequence of open intervals $\{A_n\}_1$ such that $S \subseteq \bigcup_{\alpha=1}^{\infty} A_\alpha$ and if l_n is the length of A_n, $n \geq 1$, then $\sum_1^\infty l_\alpha \leq \epsilon$.

Note that the basic difference between Jordan constant zero and Lebesque measure zero is that for Jordan content we only permit the set to be covered by a finite number of open intervals, while for measure zero we permit an infinite covering. Thus every set of Jordan content zero is also a set of measure zero. (Why?) To prove our last existence theorem we need

Lemma 3. *If f is bounded on $[a, b]$, then for each ϵ the set $S_\epsilon(f, a, b)$ is closed.*

Proof. If c is an accumulation point of $S_\epsilon(f, a, b)$ and if g is the restriction of f to $[a, b]$, then $s(g, c) \geq \epsilon$ or $s(g, c) < \epsilon$. If $s(g, c) < \epsilon$ and if $\epsilon_1 = \epsilon - s(g, c)$, then $s(g, c) < \epsilon - (\epsilon_1/2)$. From Lemma 2 it then follows that for some δ and for each x and y in $N(c, \delta) \cap \text{Dom } g$

$$|g(x) - g(y)| < \epsilon - \frac{\epsilon_1}{2}$$

But since c is an accumulation point of $S_\epsilon(f, a, b)$ there exists a number d in $S_\epsilon(f, a, b) \cap N(c, \delta)$. Furthermore there exists a δ_1 such that $N(d, s_1) \subseteq N(c, \delta)$. Therefore for each x and y in $N(d, \delta_1) \cap \text{Dom } g$

$$|g(x) - g(y)| < \epsilon - \frac{\epsilon_1}{2}.$$

From Lemma 1 it then follows that $s(g, d) \leq \epsilon - (\epsilon_1/2) < \epsilon$. But this is a contradiction. Therefore $s(g, c) \geq \epsilon$; hence $c \in S_\epsilon(f, a, b)$ and hence $S_\epsilon(f, a, b)$ is closed.

Q.E.D.

Theorem 8.79 (Lebesque). *If f is bounded on $[a, b]$, then f is integrable on $[a, b]$ iff $S_0(f, a, b)$ has Lebesque measure zero.*

Proof. Since $S_\epsilon(f, a, b) \subseteq S_0(f, a, b)$, for each ϵ, we have for each ϵ that every open covering of $S_0(f, a, b)$ is an open covering for $S_\epsilon(f, a, b)$. But by Lemma 3 the set $S_\epsilon(f, a, b)$ is closed, and hence every open covering of $S_\epsilon(f, a, b)$ contains a finite subcovering of $S_\epsilon(f, a, b)$. From this it follows that if $S_0(f, a, b)$ has Lebesque measure zero, then for each ϵ the set $S_\epsilon(f, a, b)$ has Jordan content zero. Hence by Theorem 8.77 the function f is integrable on $[a, b]$.

Conversely, if f is integrable on $[a, b]$, then for each ϵ the set $S_\epsilon(f, a, b)$ has Jordan content zero. In particular, if $n > 0$, then $S_{1/n}(f, a, b)$ has Jordan content zero. Therefore, for each ϵ there exists a finite set of open intervals $\mathscr{C}_n$ which is a covering for $S_{1/n}(f, a, b)$ and for which the total of the lengths of the intervals in $\mathscr{C}_n$ does not exceed ϵ/n^2.

Therefore, if

$$\mathscr{C} = \bigcup_{n=1}^{\infty} \mathscr{C}_n$$

then $\mathscr{C}$ is a countable collection of open intervals. The total length of all the intervals in $\mathscr{C}$ does not exceed

$$\sum_{\alpha=1}^{\infty} \frac{\epsilon}{2^n}$$

and $S_0(f, a, b) \subseteq \mathscr{C}$. Since

$$\sum_{\alpha=1}^{\infty} \frac{\epsilon}{2^n} = \epsilon$$

it follows that $S_0(f, a, b)$ has measure zero.

Q.E.D.

EXERCISES

1. Prove: Every finite set has Jordan content zero.
2. Prove: Every countable set has measure zero.
3. Prove: Every subset of a set of measure zero has measure zero.
4. Prove: If A and B each have measure zero, then $A \cup B$ and $A \cap B$ each have measure zero.
5. Prove: The set of rationals in $[0, 1]$ has measure zero but does not have Jordan content zero.

6. Prove: If $a \in \text{Dom} f$, then f is continuous at a iff $s(f, a) = 0$.

7. Use Theorem 8.79 to prove that if f and g are integrable on $[a, b]$, then $f + g$, $f - g$, fg, and $f \circ g$ are integrable on $[a, b]$.

8. Find the error in the following argument.

Lemon. If $[a, b] \subseteq \text{Dom} f$, and if $A = \{x \in [a, b] \mid f \text{ is not continuous at } x\}$, then A is closed.

Spoof. If c is an accumulation point of A, then since $A \subseteq [a, b]$, it follows that $c \in [a, b]$. Therefore, f is continuous at c, or f is not continuous at c. If f is continuous at c, then there exists a convergence test ϕ with the property that

$$(\forall \epsilon) \, \forall x \in N(c, \phi(\epsilon/2)), \; |f(x) - f(c)| < \frac{\epsilon}{2}.$$

Since c is an accumulation point of A there exists a number d in $N(c, \frac{1}{2}\phi(\epsilon/2)) \cap A$. Since $N(d, \frac{1}{2}\phi(\epsilon/2)) \subseteq N(c, \phi(\epsilon/2))$ we have that if $x \in N(d, \frac{1}{2}\phi(\epsilon/2))$, then

$$|f(x) - f(d)| = |f(x) - f(c) + f(c) - f(d)| \leq |f(x) - f(c)|$$
$$+ |f(d) - f(c)| < \frac{\epsilon}{2} + \frac{\epsilon}{2} = \epsilon.$$

Thus if $\psi(\epsilon) = \frac{1}{2}\phi(\epsilon/2)$, then

$$(\forall \epsilon) \, \forall x \in N(d, \psi(\epsilon)), \; |f(x) - f(d)| < \epsilon,$$

that is, f is continuous at d. But $d \in A$. This is a contradiction that forces us to conclude that f is not continuous at c; hence $c \in A$; hence A is closed.

CHAPTER **9**

Sequences of Functions

9.0 Introduction

In an earlier chapter we studied sequences of real numbers and found them to be an interesting and useful source of information about the real numbers and functions defined on the real numbers. In this chapter we will consider sequences of functions and will demonstrate their usefulness in extending our knowledge of real analysis.

If $\{f_n\}_k$ is a sequence of functions each of which has domain S, then for each x in S it follows that $\{f_n(x)\}_k$ is a sequence of real numbers. If each of these sequences of real numbers converges, then we can define a function f by

$$f(x) = \operatorname*{Lim}_{n \to \infty} f_n(x), \quad x \in S.$$

Such a function f we will call the pointwise[1] limit of $\{f_n\}_k$.

Definition 9.00. If $\{f_n\}_k$ is a sequence of functions each of which is defined on the set S and if $S \subseteq \operatorname{Dom} f$, then

$$\operatorname*{Lim}_{n \to \infty} f_n = f \text{ on } S \text{ iff } \operatorname*{Lim}_{n \to \infty} f_n(x) = f(x), \quad x \in S.$$

Without supplying the formal definitions we will carry over the language of sequences and series of real numbers to functions of real numbers.

Let us now consider an example.

Example. If $S = [0, 1]$ and if for each positive integer n and each x in $[0, 1]$

$$f_n(x) = 2nx, \qquad 0 \le x \le \frac{1}{2n}$$

$$= -2n\left(x - \frac{1}{n}\right), \qquad \frac{1}{2n} < x \le \frac{1}{n}$$

$$= 0 \qquad \frac{1}{n} < x \le 1$$

---

[1] The adjective is used to distinguish this type of limit from others that can be defined.

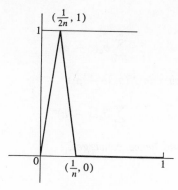

$\left(\frac{1}{2n}, 1\right)$

$\left(\frac{1}{n}, 0\right)$

FIGURE 9.1

(see Figure 9.1) then

$$\operatorname*{Lim}_{n \to \infty} f_n(x) = 0, \qquad x \in [0, 1].$$

Therefore,

$$\operatorname*{Lim}_{n \to \infty} f_n = f$$

where $f(x) = 0$, $x \in [0, 1]$.

Of special interest are those functions that are defined by *power series*. Consider a sequence of polynomial functions defined by the form

$$b_n(x - a)^n.$$

The partial sums of such a sequence are polynomial functions f_n defined by

$$f_n(x) = \sum_{\alpha = 0}^{n} b_\alpha(x - a)^\alpha.$$

The limit of $\{f_n\}_0$ is therefore a function f whose domain is the set of all x for which

$$\sum_{\alpha = 0}^{\infty} b_\alpha(x - a)^\alpha$$

converges. For all such x

$$f(x) = \sum_{\alpha = 0}^{\infty} b_\alpha(x - a)^\alpha.$$

To determine the domain of f we note that if $x = a$, then clearly the series converges. Indeed it converges to b_0. Therefore, $a \in \operatorname{Dom} f$ and $f(a) = b_0$. One interesting property of power series is that if $\sum_0^\infty b_\alpha(c - a)^\alpha$ converges, then $\sum_0^\infty b_\alpha(x - a)^\alpha$ converges if $x \in N(a, |c - a|)$; that is, if $c \in \operatorname{Dom} f$, then $N(a, |c - a|) \subseteq \operatorname{Dom} f$.

Theorem 9.01. *If*

$$\sum_{\alpha=0}^{\infty} b_{\alpha}(c - a)^{\alpha}$$

converges, then for each x in $N(a, |c - a|)$

$$\sum_{\alpha=0}^{\infty} b_{\alpha}(x - a)^{\alpha}$$

converges absolutely and hence converges.

Proof. Since

$$\sum_{\alpha=0}^{\infty} b_{\alpha}(c - a)^{\alpha}$$

converges, its terms are bounded; that is, for some d

$$|b_n(c - a)^n| < d, \quad n \geq 0.$$

For each x if x is in $N(a, |c - a|)$, then $c \neq a$ and

$$\left|\frac{x - a}{c - a}\right| < 1.$$

Therefore,

$$\sum_{\alpha=0}^{\infty} d \left|\frac{x - a}{c - a}\right|^{\alpha}$$

converges. But

$$|b_n(x - a)^n| = \left|b_n(c - a)^n \frac{(x - a)^n}{(c - a)^n}\right|$$
$$= |b_n(c - a)^n| \left|\frac{x - a}{c - a}\right|^n < d\left|\frac{x - a}{c - a}\right|^n.$$

Thus by the comparison test

$$\sum_{\alpha=0}^{\infty} |b_{\alpha}(x - a)^{\alpha}|$$

converges; hence

$$\sum_{\alpha=0}^{\infty} b_{\alpha}(x - a)^{\alpha}$$

converges.

Q.E.D.

Theorem 9.02. *If*

$$\sum_{\alpha=0}^{\infty} b_{\alpha}(x - a)^{\alpha}$$

does not converge everywhere, then there exists a nonnegative number r such that

$$\sum_{\alpha=0}^{\infty} b_\alpha (x - a)^\alpha$$

converges if $x \in N(a, r)$ and diverges if $x \notin \overline{N(a, r)}$.

Proof.   If

$$\sum_{\alpha=0}^{\infty} b_\alpha (x - a)^\alpha$$

does not converge everywhere, then there exists a number c such that

$$\sum_{\alpha=0}^{\infty} b_\alpha (c - a)^\alpha$$

diverges. By Theorem 9.01 it follows that if $|x - a| > |c - a|$, then

$$\sum_{\alpha=0}^{\infty} b_\alpha (x - a)^\alpha$$

must also diverge. Therefore $|c - a|$ is an upper bound for

$$\left\{ x - a \mid \sum_{\alpha=0}^{\infty} b_\alpha (x - a)^\alpha \text{ converges} \right\}.$$

Since this set is nonempty and bounded above, it has a supremum r. From Theorem 9.01 it follows that

$$\sum_{\alpha=0}^{\infty} b_\alpha (x - a)^\alpha$$

converges if $x \in N(a, r)$ and diverges if $x \notin \overline{N(a, r)}$. (Why?)

Q.E.D.

From Theorem 9.02 we see that a power series $\sum_{0}^{\infty} b_\alpha (x - a)^\alpha$ either converges at each point of the open interval $(-\infty, \infty)$ or for some nonnegative number r it converges at each point of the open interval $N(a, r)$ and diverges at each point of $R - \overline{N(a, r)}$. In each case we refer to the open intervals, $(-\infty, \infty)$ and $N(a, r)$, respectively, as the *interval of convergence* of the series. The number r is called the *radius of convergence*. Series that converge everywhere are said to have *infinite* radius of convergence.

The theorem on power series gives no information about the behavior of the series at the end points of its interval of convergence. Several interesting questions come immediately to mind. Does a power series converge or diverge at the end points of its interval of convergence? Are there power series having a specified radius of convergence? Are there power series with zero radius of convergence? Are there power series with infinite radius of convergence? We resolve these questions in the following examples.

Example. The series $\sum_0^\infty (x^\alpha/\alpha!)$ converges for each x, as we can verify by testing for absolute convergence using the ratio test.

$$\frac{|x^{n+1}/(n+1)!|}{|x^n/n!|} = |x| \frac{n!}{(n+1)!} = \frac{|x|}{n+1}$$

and

$$\operatorname*{Lim}_{n\to\infty} \frac{|x|}{n+1} = 0.$$

Therefore the series has an infinite radius of convergence.

Example. The series $\sum_0^\infty (\alpha! x^\alpha)$ converges only at 0.

$$\frac{|(n+1)! x^{n+1}|}{|n! x^n|} = \frac{(n+1)!}{n!} |x| = (n+1)|x|.$$

Since the sequence $\{(n+1)|x|\}_0$ converges to 0 if $x = 0$ and diverges to infinity if $x \neq 0$, we have that the series has radius of convergence 0.

Example. For each positive r the series $\sum_0^\infty (x^\alpha/r^\alpha)$ has radius of convergence r, since

$$\left| \frac{x^{n+1}}{r^{n+1}} \frac{r^n}{x^n} \right| = \frac{|x|}{r},$$

and for convergence, we must have

$$\frac{|x|}{r} < 1 \text{ or } |x| < r.$$

Example. $\sum_1^\infty (x^\alpha/\alpha^2)$ has radius of convergence 1 and converges at both end points.

$\sum_1^\infty (x^\alpha/\alpha)$ has radius of convergence 1, converges at -1, and diverges at 1.

$\sum_0^\infty x^\alpha$ has radius of convergence 1 and diverges at both end points.

EXERCISES

In Exercises 1–3 find $\operatorname{Lim}_{n\to\infty} f_n$ on S.

1. $S = [0, 1]$ and

$$f_n(x) = 4n^2 x \qquad\qquad 0 \leq x \leq \frac{1}{2n}$$

$$= -4n^2\left(x - \frac{1}{n}\right) \qquad \frac{1}{2n} < x \leq \frac{1}{n}$$

$$= 0 \qquad\qquad\qquad \frac{1}{n} < x \leq 1$$

2. $S = [0, 1]$ and

$$f_n(x) = \frac{1}{1 + x^n} \text{ for } x \in [0, 1].$$

3. For each x in S, $f_n(x) = a_n$ and $\text{Lim}_{n \to \infty} a_n = a$.

4. Prove: If $\{a_n\}_0$ is bounded, then $\sum_0^\infty a_\alpha x^\alpha$ has a radius of convergence that is equal to or greater than 1.

5. Prove: If $\{a_n\}_0$ is a sequence of nonzero real numbers and if

$$\underset{n \to \infty}{\text{Lim}} \left| \frac{a_n}{a_{n+1}} \right| = r,$$ then $\sum_0^\infty a_\alpha x^\alpha$ has radius of convergence r.

In Exercises 6–9 find the radius of convergence.

6. $\sum\limits_{\alpha=0}^\infty \alpha x^\alpha.$

7. $\sum\limits_{\alpha=0}^\infty \alpha^\alpha x^\alpha.$

8. $\sum\limits_{\alpha=0}^\infty \alpha x^\alpha/(\alpha + 1).$

9. $\sum\limits_{\alpha=0}^\infty \frac{1}{2}\alpha(\alpha + 1)x^\alpha.$

10. Prove: If $f_n(x) = \sqrt[2^n]{x}$, $x > 0$ and $n \geq 1$ then for each positive x
  1) $\{f_n(x)\}_1$ is a monotone sequence.
  2) $\{f_n(x)\}_1$ converges.
  3) $\underset{n \to \infty}{\text{Lim}}\, f_n(x) = 1$. [Hint: $(\sqrt[2^{n+1}]{x})^2 = \sqrt[2^n]{x}$.]

11. Prove: If $f_n(x) = 2^n(\sqrt[2^n]{x} - 1)$, $x > 0$ and $n \geq 1$, then for each positive x

  1) $\{f_n(x)\}_1$ is a monotone sequence. [Hint: If $\sqrt[2^n]{x} > 1$, then
  $2(\sqrt[2^n]{x} - 1) < (\sqrt[2^n]{x} + 1)(\sqrt[2^n]{x} - 1) = \sqrt[2^{n-1}]{x} - 1$.]

  2) $\{f_n(x)\}_1$ converges.
  $$\left[\text{Hint: } 2^n(\sqrt[2^n]{x} - 1) = -2^n\left(\sqrt[2^n]{\frac{1}{x}} - 1\right)\sqrt[2^n]{x}.\right]$$

9.1 Sequences and Continuity

Our belief that continuous functions are interesting and important prompts us to ask if we can learn anything new and interesting about continuous functions from our knowledge of convergence of sequences of functions.

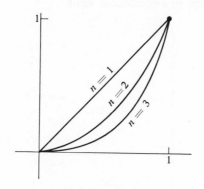

FIGURE 9.2

For example if $\{f_n\}_k$ converges to f on a set S and if each f_n is continuous on S, does it follow that f is continuous on S? From Exercise 2, page 328, we see that the limit function of a sequence of continuous functions need not be continuous. This fact is further illustrated by the following.

Example. If $S = [0, 1]$ and if

$$f_n(x) = x^n$$

then $\underset{n\to\infty}{\text{Lim }} x^n = 0$ if $0 \le x < 1$ and $\underset{n\to\infty}{\text{Lim }} 1^n = 1$. That is,

$$\underset{n\to\infty}{\text{Lim }} f_n = f$$

where

$$f(x) = 0, \ x \in [0, 1) \text{ and } f(1) = 1.$$

Thus each f_n is continuous on $[0, 1]$ but the limit function f is discontinuous at 1.

Suppose that each f_n is discontinuous on S, does it follow that f is discontinuous?

Example. If $S = [0, 1]$ and

$$f_n(x) = \frac{[\![x]\!]}{n}$$

then since $[\![x]\!] = 0$, $x \in [0, 1)$ and $[\![1]\!] = 1$, it follows that $f_n(x) = 0$, $x \in [0, 1)$ and $f_n(1) = 1/n$. Consequently, for each x in $[0, 1]$

$$\underset{n\to\infty}{\text{Lim }} f_n(x) = 0,$$

that is,

$$\underset{x\to\infty}{\text{Lim }} f_n = f$$

where $f(x) = 0$ for each x in $[0, 1]$. Thus a sequence of discontinuous functions can converge to a continuous limit.

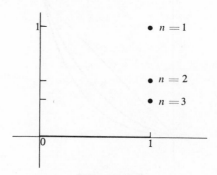

FIGURE 9.3

Since a sequence of continuous functions can converge to a discontinuous function and a sequence of discontinuous functions can converge to a continuous limit, it is reasonable to ask what conditions will assure that the limit function be continuous. One such condition is *uniform convergence*, which we define thus:

Definition 9.10. $\{f_n\}_k$ *converges uniformly* to f *on* S iff there exists a convergence test ϕ with the property that for each ϵ and each x in S

$$\text{if } n > \phi(\epsilon), \text{ then } |f_n(x) - f(x)| < \epsilon.$$

We are now prepared to prove that a uniformly convergent sequence of continuous functions converges to a continuous limit.

Theorem 9.11. *If* $\{f_n\}_k$ *is a sequence of functions that converges uniformly to* f *on* S, *then* f *is continuous on* S, *if each* f_n, $n \geq k$, *is continuous on* S.

Proof. From Definition 9.10 there exists a convergence test ϕ_1 with the property that for each x in S and for each ϵ

$$\text{if } n > \phi_1(\epsilon), \text{ then } |f_n(x) - f(x)| < \epsilon.$$

By the Archimedean order property there exists an integer n such that $n > \phi_1(\epsilon/3)$. It then follows that for each x in S

$$|f_n(x) - f(x)| < \frac{\epsilon}{3}.$$

Since by hypothesis, f_n is continuous on S, it follows that for each a in S there exists a ϕ_n with the property that

$$\text{if } x \in N(a, \phi_n(\epsilon)) \cap S, \text{ then } |f_n(x) - f_n(a)| < \epsilon.$$

Therefore, if $\phi(\epsilon) = \phi_n(\epsilon/3)$, then for each x in $N(a, \phi(\epsilon)) \cap S$

$$\begin{aligned}
|f(x) - f(a)| &= |f(x) - f_n(x) + f_n(x) - f_n(a) + f_n(a) - f(a)| \\
&\leq |f(x) - f_n(x)| + |f_n(x) - f_n(a)| + |f_n(a) - f(a)| \\
&< \frac{\epsilon}{3} + \frac{\epsilon}{3} + \frac{\epsilon}{3} = \epsilon.
\end{aligned}$$

Thus f is continuous at a.

$$\text{Q.E.D.}$$

Example. If $f_n(x) = 2^n(\sqrt[2^n]{x} - 1)$, $x > 0$, and $n \geq 1$, then $\{f_n(x)\}_1$ converges for each positive x. (See Exercise 11, page 329.) If

$$f(x) = \operatorname*{Lim}_{n \to \infty} f_n(x), \quad x > 0,$$

then f is continuous at each positive real number because if

$$F(x) = f_n(x) - f_m(x), \quad m \neq n, \quad x > 0,$$

then

$$F'(x) = x^{(1/2^n)-1} - x^{(1/2^m)-1}.$$

Therefore, $F'(x) = 0$ if and only if $x = 1$. Thus if $b > 1$, it follows that F cannot have a local maximum or a local minimum on $(1, b)$. Since $F(1) = 0$, we then have that for each x in $[1, b]$

$$|F(x)| = |f_n(x) - f_m(x)| \leq |f_n(b) - f_m(b)|.$$

By the Cauchy criterion there exists a convergence test ϕ such that

$$\text{if } n > \phi(\epsilon) \text{ and } m > \phi(\epsilon), \text{ then } |f_n(b) - f_m(b)| < \epsilon.$$

Consequently, $\{f_n\}_1$ is uniformly convergent on $[1, b]$, and hence f is continuous on $[1, b]$.

If $0 < b < 1$, it can be proved by a similar argument that f is continuous on $[b, 1]$. Therefore, f is continuous at each positive x.

Theorem 9.11 provides useful information about functions defined by power series. Suppose that $\sum_0^\infty b_\alpha(x - a)^\alpha$ has interval of convergence A and that

$$f(x) = \sum_{\alpha = 0}^\infty b_\alpha(x - a)^\alpha, \quad x \in A.$$

Is f continuous on A?

Since f is the limit of a sequence of polynomial functions, which are continuous everywhere, it follows that f will be continuous on any subset of A on which the convergence is uniform. We will prove that the convergence is uniform on every closed subinterval of A. The proof is a simple application of the following very useful test for uniform convergence for series. By the uniform convergence of a series we, of course, mean the uniform convergence of its sequence of partial sums.

Theorem 9.12 (The Weierstrass M-Test). $\sum_k^\infty f_\alpha$ converges uniformly on S if there exists a convergent series of positive numbers $\sum_k^\infty M_\alpha$ with the droperty that for each x in S

$$|f_n(x)| \leq M_n, \quad n \geq k.$$

Proof. Since $\sum_k^\infty M_\alpha$ is convergent, it follows that it has a convergence test ϕ with the property that

$$\text{if } m > \phi(\epsilon) \text{ and } n > \phi(\epsilon), \text{ then } \left| \sum_{\alpha = m}^n M_\alpha \right| < \epsilon.$$

Therefore, for each x in S

$$\text{if } n \geq m > \phi(\epsilon), \text{ then } \left| \sum_{\alpha = m}^n f_\alpha(x) \right| \leq \sum_{\alpha = m}^n |f_\alpha(x)| \leq \sum_{\alpha = m}^n M_\alpha < \epsilon.$$

Thus, $\sum_k^\infty f_\alpha$ converges uniformly on S.

Q.E.D.

Applying the Weierstrass M-Test to power series, we have

Theorem 9.13. *If $c > 0$ and $\overline{N(a, c)}$ is a subset of the interval of convergence of*

$$\sum_{\alpha = 0}^{\infty} b_\alpha(x - a)^\alpha,$$

then

$$\sum_{\alpha = 0}^{\infty} b_\alpha(x - a)^\alpha$$

converges uniformly on $\overline{N(a, c)}$.

Proof. Since $\overline{N(a, c)}$ is a subset of the interval of convergence of

$$\sum_{\alpha = 0}^{\infty} b_\alpha(x - a)^\alpha,$$

it follows that

$$\sum_{\alpha = 0}^{\infty} b_\alpha c^\alpha$$

converges absolutely. (Why?) Since for each x in $N(a, c)$ we have that

$$|b_\alpha(x - a)^\alpha| \leq |b_\alpha c^\alpha|,$$

it follows by the Weierstrass M-Test that

$$\sum_{\alpha = 0}^{\infty} b_\alpha(x - a)^\alpha$$

is uniformly convergent on $\overline{N(a, c)}$.

Q.E.D.

Corollary 9.14. $\sum_0^\infty b_\alpha(x - a)^\alpha$ *converges uniformly on every closed and bounded subinterval of its interval of convergence.*

The proof is left to the reader.

Corollary 9.15. *If $\sum_0^\infty b_\alpha(x - a)^\alpha$ has interval of convergence A and if*

$$f(x) = \sum_{\alpha = 0}^{\infty} b_\alpha(x - a)^\alpha, \quad x \in A,$$

then f is continuous on A.

The proof is left to the reader.

The remaining theorems of this section are not required for any of the results that follow and may be omitted without loss of continuity. Their purpose is to call to the attention of the reader the interesting fact that the proof of Theorem 9.11 does not require that the functions of the sequence

$\{f_n\}_k$ be continuous on S. From the proof it is apparent that if the saltus of f_n at x tends to zero as n tends to infinity we can still establish the continuity of f at x.

Theorem 9.16. *If $\{f_n\}_k$ converges uniformly to f on S, and if for each x in S*

$$\operatorname*{Lim}_{n \to \infty} s(f_n, x) = 0$$

then f is continuous at x.

The proof is very similar to that of Theorem 9.11 and is left to the reader.

It is interesting to note that the requirement of uniform convergence and the restriction on the saltus can be combined to produce a condition that is both necessary and sufficient for a sequence to converge to a continuous function.

Definition 9.17. If $\{f_n\}_k$ is a sequence of functions each defined on S, then $\{f_n\}_k$ is *continuously convergent* on S iff for each a in S there exist convergence tests ϕ and ψ such that for each ϵ and each x in $N(a, \phi(\epsilon)) \cap S$

if $m > \psi(\epsilon)$ and $n > \psi(\epsilon)$, then $|f_m(x) - f_n(a)| < \epsilon$.

Theorem 9.18. *$\{f_n\}_k$ converges to a continuous function on S iff $\{f_n\}_k$ is continuously convergent on S.*

Proof. If $\{f_n\}_k$ is continuously convergent on S, then by the Cauchy criterion it is convergent. If

$$\operatorname*{Lim}_{n \to \infty} f_n = f,$$

then for each x in S

$$\operatorname*{Lim}_{n \to \infty} f_n(x) = f(x);$$

that is, there exists a convergence test ϕ_x with the property that

if $n > \phi_x(\epsilon)$, then $|f_n(x) - f(x)| < \epsilon$.

Also for each a in S there exist mappings ϕ and ψ as in Definition 9.17. Thus if $\eta(\epsilon) = \phi(\epsilon/3)$, then for each x in $N(a, \eta(\epsilon)) \cap S$ there exists an integer n such that $n > \psi(\epsilon/3)$, $n > \phi_x(\epsilon/3)$, and $n > \phi_a(\epsilon/3)$. Therefore,

$$
\begin{aligned}
|f(x) - f(a)| &= |f(x) - f_n(x) + f_n(x) - f_n(a) + f_n(a) - f(a)| \\
&\leq |f(x) - f_n(x)| + |f_n(x) - f_n(a)| + |f_n(a) - f(a)| \\
&\leq \frac{\epsilon}{3} + \frac{\epsilon}{3} + \frac{\epsilon}{3} = \epsilon
\end{aligned}
$$

and hence f is continuous at a.

Conversely, if $\{f_n\}_k$ converges to f, a continuous function on S, then $\{f_n\}_k$ must be continuously convergent on S, for otherwise there would exist an a in S at which f is continuous, but for some ϵ, for each δ, and for each M there exist x, m, and n such that

$$x \in N(a, \delta) \cap S, \ m > M, \ n > M, \ \text{but} \ |f_m(x) - f_n(a)| \geq \epsilon.$$

In particular, if $\delta = 1/p$, p a positive integer, there is an a_p in $N(a, 1/p) \cap S$ with the property that for each M there exist m and n such that

$$m > M, \ n > M, \ \text{and} \ |f_m(a_p) - f_n(a)| \geq \epsilon.$$

Furthermore, $\{a_p\}_1$ converges to a (why?), and hence $\{f(a_p)\}_1$ converges to $f(a)$ (why?). Consequently, there is a convergence test η such that

$$\text{if } p > \eta\left(\frac{\epsilon}{3}\right), \text{ then } |f(a_p) - f(a)| < \frac{\epsilon}{3}$$

and for each a_p there is a mapping ϕ_p such that for each n

$$\text{if } n > \phi_p\left(\frac{\epsilon}{3}\right), \text{ then } |f_n(a_p) - f(a_p)| < \frac{\epsilon}{3}.$$

Finally, there is a mapping ϕ_a such that for each n

$$\text{if } n > \phi_a\left(\frac{\epsilon}{3}\right), \text{ then } |f_n(a) - f(a)| < \frac{\epsilon}{3}.$$

Thus, if $M = \max\{\phi_p(\epsilon/3), \phi_a(\epsilon/3)\}$, then for each m and n if $m > M$ and $n > M$, then

$$\begin{aligned}|f_m(a_p) - f_n(a)| &= |f_m(a_p) - f(a_p) + f(a_p) - f(a) + f(a) - f_n(a)| \\ &\leq |f_m(a_p) - f(a_p)| + |f(a_p) - f(a)| + |f(a) - f_n(a)| \\ &< \frac{\epsilon}{3} + \frac{\epsilon}{3} + \frac{\epsilon}{3} = \epsilon.\end{aligned}$$

This contradicts the defining properties of $\{a_p\}_1$. We, therefore, conclude that $\{f_n\}_k$ is continuously convergent on S.

$$\text{Q.E.D.}$$

Corollary 9.19. *If $\{f_n\}_k$ is a sequence of functions continuous on S and uniformly convergent on S, then $\{f_n\}_k$ is continuously convergent on S.*

The proof is left to the reader.

EXERCISES

1. Prove: If $f_n(x) = 1/(1 + x^n)$, then $\{f_n\}_1$ does not converge uniformly on $[0, 1]$.

2. Prove: If $\sum_0^\infty a_\alpha$ converges absolutely and if

$$f(x) = \sum_{\alpha=0}^{\infty} a_\alpha \sin \alpha x,$$

then f is continuous everywhere.

9.2 Sequences and Integration

Suppose that each function of $\{f_n\}_k$ is integrable on $[a, b]$ and that the limit function f of this sequence is also integrable on $[a, b]$. Is it true that

$$\int_a^b f(x)\,dx = \lim_{n\to\infty} \int_a^b f_n(x)\,dx\,?$$

Since

$$f(x) = \lim_{n\to\infty} f_n(x)$$

we are asking if

$$\int_a^b \lim_{n\to\infty} f_n(x)\,dx = \lim_{n\to\infty} \int_a^b f_n(x)\,dx.$$

Example.   If as in Exercise 1 on page 328

$$f_n(x) = 4n^2 x,\quad 0 \le x \le \frac{1}{2n}$$

$$= -4n^2\left(x - \frac{1}{n}\right),\quad \frac{1}{2n} < x \le \frac{1}{n}$$

$$= 0,\quad \frac{1}{n} < x \le 1$$

then $\lim\limits_{n\to\infty} f_n = f$ where $f(x) = 0$, $x \in [0, 1]$. We then have that

$$\int_0^1 f_n(x)\,dx = 1;$$

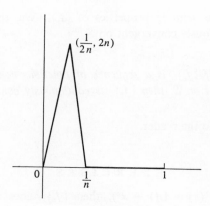

FIGURE 9.4

hence

$$\lim_{n \to \infty} \int_0^1 f_n(x)\, dx = 1.$$

However,

$$\int_0^1 f(x)\, dx = 0.$$

Thus

$$\int_0^1 \lim_{n \to \infty} f_n(x)\, dx \neq \lim_{n \to \infty} \int_0^1 f_n(x)\, dx.$$

From this example we see that care must be used when dealing with integrals of limits of sequences. Fortunately, however, we can establish the desired equality if the convergence is uniform.

Theorem 9.20. *If $\{f_n\}_k$ converges uniformly to f on $[a, b]$, if f is integrable on $[a, b]$, and if f_n is integrable on $[a, b]$, $n \geq k$, then*

$$\lim_{n \to \infty} \int_a^b f_n(x)\, dx = \int_a^b f(x)\, dx.$$

Proof. Since $\{f_n\}_k$ converges uniformly to f on $[a, b]$ there exists a convergence test ϕ with the property that if $n > \phi(\epsilon)$ and $x \in [a, b]$ then

$$|f_n(x) - f(x)| < \epsilon.$$

Therefore,

$$\left| \int_a^b f_n(x)\, dx - \int_a^b f(x)\, dx \right| = \left| \int_a^b [f_n(x) - f(x)]\, dx \right|$$

$$\leq \int_a^b |f_n(x) - f(x)|\, dx < \epsilon(b - a).$$

Consequently,

$$\lim_{n \to \infty} \int_a^b f_n(x)\, dx = \int_a^b f(x)\, dx.$$

$$\text{Q.E.D.}$$

From Theorem 9.20 it follows that power series can be integrated term for term.

Corollary 9.21. *If $\sum_0^\infty c_\alpha x^\alpha$ converges at each point of $[a, b]$, then*

$$\int_a^b \left(\sum_{\alpha=0}^\infty c_\alpha x^\alpha \right) dx = \sum_{\alpha=0}^\infty c_\alpha \frac{b^{\alpha+1} - a^{\alpha+1}}{\alpha + 1}.$$

The proof is left to the reader.

If we now raise the question of term for term differentiation, the reader will hardly be surprised to find that the derivative of the limit function is

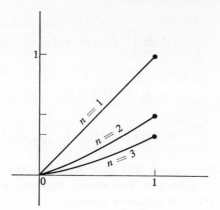

FIGURE 9.5

not necessarily the limit of the sequence of derivatives. That this is the case is illustrated by the following.

Example.   If $S = [0, 1]$ and if for each positive n

$$f_n(x) = \frac{x^n}{n}$$

(see Figure 9.5), then

$$\operatorname*{Lim}_{n \to \infty} f_n(x) = 0, \quad x \in [0, 1],$$

that is,

$$\operatorname*{Lim}_{n \to \infty} f_n = f$$

where $f(x) = 0$ for each x in $[0, 1]$. Therefore, $f'(x) = 0$ for each x in $[0, 1]$. However, for each n

$$f'_n(x) = x^{n-1}$$

and

$$\operatorname*{Lim}_{n \to \infty} f'_n(1) = \operatorname*{Lim}_{n \to \infty} 1^{n-1} \neq f'(0).$$

Thus

$$f' \neq \operatorname*{Lim}_{n \to \infty} f'_n.$$

Note furthermore that not only does $\{f_n\}_k$ converge to f on $[0, 1]$ but the convergence is uniform. The secret is to require uniform convergence of the sequence of derivatives.

Theorem 9.22.   *If $\{f_n\}_k$ converges to f on $[a, b]$ and if $\{f'_n\}_k$ converges uniformly to g on $[a, b]$, if g is continuous on $[a, b]$ and if f'_n is integrable on $[a, b]$, $n \geq k$, then f is differentiable on $[a, b]$ and*

$$f'(x) = g(x), \quad x \in [a, b].$$

Proof. Since f_n' is integrable on $[a, b]$ and has f_n as antiderivative, it follows from the Fundamental Theorem that

$$f_n(x) - f_n(a) = \int_a^x f_n'(t)\, dt.$$

Since $\{f_n'\}_k$ converges uniformly to g, which is continuous and hence integrable on $[a, b]$, it follows that

$$\lim_{n \to \infty} \int_a^x f_n'(t)\, dt = \int_a^x g(t)\, dt.$$

Therefore, since

$$\lim_{n \to \infty} [f_n(x) - f_n(a)] = f(x) - f(a)$$

we have that

$$f(x) - f(a) = \int_a^x g(t)\, dt$$

from which it follows that f is differentiable on $[a, b]$ and

$$f'(x) = g(x).$$

$$\text{Q.E.D.}$$

Example. If $f_n(x) = 2^n(\sqrt[2^n]{x} - 1)$, $x > 0$, and $n \geq 1$, then $\{f_n(x)\}_1$ converges for each positive x (see Exercise 11, page 329). Furthermore,

$$f_n'(x) = x^{(1/2^n)-1}$$

and

$$\lim_{n \to \infty} f_n'(x) = \frac{1}{x}.$$

If $g(x) = 1/x$, $x > 0$, then g is integrable on every interval $[a, b]$ for which $0 < a < b$ and $\{f_n'\}_1$ converges uniformly to g on $[a, b]$. (Why?) Therefore, if

$$f(x) = \lim_{n \to \infty} f_n(x), \quad x > 0,$$

then

$$f'(x) = \frac{1}{x}, \quad x > 0.$$

But

$$\ln' x = \frac{1}{x}, \quad x > 0.$$

Therefore, if

$$F(x) = \ln x - f(x), \quad x > 0,$$

then $F'(x) = 0$, and hence for some number c we must have that

$$F(x) = \ln x - f(x) = c, \quad x > 0.$$

But $\ln 1 = 0$ and $f(1) = 0$. Therefore, $c = 0$ and hence $f(x) = \ln x$, i.e.,

$$\ln x = \operatorname*{Lim}_{n \to \infty} 2^n(\sqrt[2^n]{x} - 1), \quad x > 0.$$

For power series, Theorem 9.22 assures us that term-for-term differentiation is proper so long as the point at which we are differentiating lies within the interval of convergence of the series of derivatives. Thus if

$$f(x) = \sum_{\alpha=0}^{\infty} a_\alpha x^\alpha,$$

then f is differentiable on the interior of the interval of convergence of

$$\sum_{\alpha=1}^{\infty} \alpha a_\alpha x^{\alpha-1}$$

and for each such x we have that

$$f'(x) = \sum_{\alpha=1}^{\infty} \alpha a_\alpha x^{\alpha-1}.$$

The beauty of this result is enhanced by the fact that the two series have the same radius of convergence.

Theorem 9.23. $\sum_{\alpha=0}^{\infty} b_\alpha(x - a)^\alpha$ *and* $\sum_{\alpha=1}^{\infty} \alpha b_\alpha(x - a)^{\alpha-1}$ *have the same interval of convergence.*

Proof. If A and A' are the intervals of convergence of

$$\sum_{\alpha=0}^{\infty} b_\alpha(x - a)^\alpha \text{ and } \sum_{\alpha=1}^{\infty} \alpha b_\alpha(x - a)^{\alpha-1},$$

respectively, then $A \subseteq A'$ or $A' \subseteq A$.

If $A \subset A'$, then there exist numbers x and y in $A' - A$ such that $a < x < y$ and

$$\sum_{\alpha=0}^{\infty} b_\alpha(x - a)^\alpha$$

diverges. Since $y \in A'$, it follows that

$$\sum_{\alpha=1}^{\infty} \alpha b_\alpha(y - a)^{\alpha-1}$$

converges. Consequently, by the nth term test the sequence $\{nb_n(y - a)^{n-1}\}_1$ converges and hence is bounded. That is, there exists a number d such that

$$|nb_n(y - a)^{n-1}| \le d, \quad n \ge 1.$$

It then follows that if $n \geq 1$

$$|b_n(x - a)^n| = |b_n(y - a)^n| \left|\frac{x - a}{y - a}\right|^n < |nb_n(y - a)^{n-1}| |y - a| \left|\frac{x - a}{y - a}\right|^n$$
$$< d|y - a| \left|\frac{x - a}{y - a}\right|^n.$$

Since $a < x < y$,

$$\left|\frac{x - a}{y - a}\right| < 1.$$

Therefore,

$$d|y - a| \left|\frac{x - a}{y - a}\right|^n$$

is the nth term of a convergent geometric series. From the comparison test it then follows that

$$\sum_{\alpha = 0}^{\infty} b_\alpha(x - a)^\alpha$$

converges. This is a contradiction that forces us to conclude that $A' \subseteq A$.

If $A' \subset A$ then there are numbers x and y in $A - A'$ such that $a < y < x$ and

$$\sum_{\alpha = 0}^{\infty} \alpha b_\alpha(y - a)^{\alpha - 1}$$

diverges. Since $x \in A$

$$\sum_{\alpha = 0}^{\infty} b_\alpha(x - a)^\alpha$$

converges and hence $\{b_n(x - a)^n\}_0$ converges. Therefore, there exists a number d such that

$$|b_n(x - a)^n| \leq d, \quad n \geq 0.$$

Thus if $n \geq 1$, then

$$|nb_n(y - a)^{n-1}| = \frac{n}{|y - a|} |b_n(x - a)^n| \left|\frac{y - a}{x - a}\right|^n \leq \frac{d}{|y - a|} \left(n \left|\frac{y - a}{x - a}\right|^n\right).$$

Since

$$\left|\frac{y - a}{x - a}\right| < 1$$

it follows from the ratio test that

$$\frac{d}{|y - a|} \left(n \left|\frac{y - a}{x - a}\right|^n\right)$$

is the nth term of a convergent series and hence by the comparison test

$$\sum_{\alpha=1}^{\infty} \alpha b_{\alpha}(y - a)^{\alpha-1}$$

converges. This is a contradiction that forces us to conclude that $A = A'$.

Q.E.D.

Corollary 9.24.   *If* $\sum\limits_{\alpha=0}^{\infty} b_{\alpha}(x - a)^{\alpha}$ *has interval of convergence* A *and if*

$$f(x) = \sum_{\alpha=0}^{\infty} b_{\alpha}(x - a)^{\alpha}, \quad x \in A,$$

then f is differentiable on A and

$$f'(x) = \sum_{\alpha=0}^{\infty} \alpha b_{\alpha}(x - a)^{\alpha-1}, \quad x \in A.$$

The proof is left to the reader.

From Corollary 9.24 we can deduce the following useful information.

Corollary 9.25.   *If* $\sum\limits_{\alpha=0}^{\infty} b_{\alpha}(x - a)^{\alpha}$ *has interval of convergence* A *and if*

$$f(x) = \sum_{\alpha=0}^{\infty} b_{\alpha}(x - a)^{\alpha}, \quad x \in A,$$

then $b_n = \dfrac{f^{(n)}(a)}{n!}$, $n \geq 0$.

Proof.   From Corollary 9.24 it follows by induction that

$$f^{(n)}(x) = \sum_{\alpha=r}^{\infty} \alpha(\alpha - 1) \cdots (\alpha - n + 1) b_{\alpha}(x - a)^{\alpha-n}, \quad x \in A.$$

Therefore $f^{(n)}(a) = n! b_n$.

Q.E.D.

Corollary 9.25 shows that the requirement that a function be defined by a power series is a very stringent restriction, for even though the power series may have an infinite radius of convergence the value that the function assumes at any given point is completely determined by the value that the function and each of its derivatives assume at the origin.

In summary we see that if $\sum_{0}^{\infty} b_{\alpha}(x - a)^{\alpha}$ has a nonzero radius of convergence and if

$$f(x) = \sum_{\alpha=0}^{\infty} b_{\alpha}(x - a)^{\alpha},$$

then f has derivatives of all orders at a and $f^{(n)}(a) = n!b_n$. Suppose, however, that we consider the converse of this statement. That is, suppose that we are given a function f that has derivatives of all orders at a. Will

$$\sum_{\alpha=0}^{\infty} \frac{f^{(\alpha)}(a)}{\alpha!} (x - a)^{\alpha}$$

have a nonzero radius of convergence? If so, will it be true for each x in the interval of convergence that

$$f(x) = \sum_{\alpha=0}^{\infty} \frac{f^{(\alpha)}(a)}{\alpha!} (x - a)^{\alpha} ?$$

Functions exist for which this is not the case, as we see from the following:

Example. If

$$f(0) = 0,$$
$$f(x) = e^{-1/x^2}, \quad x \neq 0,$$

then we will prove that f has derivatives of all orders at 0, that

$$\sum_{\alpha=0}^{\infty} \frac{f^{(\alpha)}(0)}{\alpha!} x^{\alpha}$$

converges everywhere; yet if $x \neq 0$,

$$f(x) \neq \sum_{\alpha=0}^{\infty} \frac{f^{(\alpha)}(0)}{\alpha!} x^{\alpha}.$$

In order to prove this we will show that if $n \geq 0$ there exists a polynomial function p_n such that

$$f^{(n)}(0) = 0,$$
$$f^{(n)}(x) = p_n\left(\frac{1}{x}\right) e^{-1/x^2}, \quad x \neq 0.$$

The proof is by induction.

For $n = 0$ the assertion is true with $p_0(x) = 1$. Assume that for $n = k$ there exists a polynomial function p_k such that

$$f^{(k)}(0) = 0,$$
$$f^{(k)}(x) = p_k\left(\frac{1}{x}\right) e^{-1/x^2}, \quad x \neq 0.$$

If $x \neq 0$, it then follows that

$$f^{(k+1)}(x) = p_k\left(\frac{1}{x}\right) e^{-1/x^2}\left(\frac{3}{x^3}\right) - \frac{1}{x^2} p_k'\left(\frac{1}{x}\right) e^{-1/x^2}.$$

Therefore, if

$$p_{k+1}(x) = 3x^3 p_k(x) - x^2 p_k'(x),$$

then

$$f^{(k+1)}(x) = p_{k+1}\left(\frac{1}{x}\right)e^{-1/x^2}.$$

If $x = 0$, then

$$f^{(k+1)}(0) = \lim_{x \to 0} \frac{f^{(k)}(x) - f^{(k)}(0)}{x - 0} = \lim_{x \to 0} \frac{1}{x} p_k\left(\frac{1}{x}\right)e^{-1/x^2}.$$

If $p_k(x) = \sum_0^\infty a_\alpha x^\alpha$, we then have that

$$f^{(k+1)}(0) = \lim_{x \to 0} \frac{1}{x} \sum_{\alpha=0}^n a_\alpha \frac{1}{x^\alpha} e^{-1/x^2} = \sum_{\alpha=0}^n a_\alpha \lim_{x \to 0} \frac{1}{x^{\alpha+1}e^{1/x^2}}.$$

It is sufficient to prove that if $n \geq 1$, then

$$\lim_{x \to 0} \frac{1}{x^n e^{1/x^2}} = 0, \quad n \geq 1.$$

This follows from l'Hospital's Rule and is left to the reader.

Having established that f has derivatives of all orders at the origin, and indeed that $f^{(n)}(0) = 0$, it follows that for each x

$$\sum_{\alpha=0}^\infty \frac{f^{(\alpha)}(0)}{\alpha!} x^\alpha$$

converges to zero. However, $f(x) = 0$ only if $x = 0$; thus if $x \neq 0$

$$f(x) \neq \sum_{\alpha=0}^\infty \frac{f^{(\alpha)}(0)}{\alpha!} x^\alpha.$$

The explanation of this peculiar behavior is supplied by Taylor's formula with remainder. Given any function f which has derivatives of all orders at a, if

$$\sum_{\alpha=0}^\infty \frac{f^{(\alpha)}(a)}{\alpha!} (x - a)^\alpha$$

has interval of convergence A, then for each x in A and for each non-negative n there exists a number y_n such that

$$f(x) = \sum_{\alpha=0}^n \frac{f^{(n)}(a)}{\alpha!} (x - a)^\alpha + \frac{f^{(n+1)}(y_n)(x - a)^{n+1}}{(n + 1)!}.$$

Therefore, in order that

$$f(x) = \sum_{\alpha=0}^\infty \frac{f^{(n)}(a)}{\alpha!} (x - a)^\alpha$$

it is necessary and sufficient that

$$\lim_{n \to \infty} \frac{f^{(n+1)}(y_n)(x - a)^{n+1}}{(n + 1)!} = 0.$$

One simple condition that assures this is that the derivatives have a common bound.

Theorem 9.26. *If f has derivatives of all orders at a, if*

$$\sum_{\alpha=0}^{\infty} \frac{f^{(\alpha)}(a)}{\alpha!} (x - a)^{\alpha}$$

has interval of convergence A, and if there exists a bound d such that

$$\forall x \in A, \quad |f^{(n)}(x)| < d, \quad n \geq 0,$$

then for each x in A

$$f(x) = \sum_{\alpha=0}^{\infty} \frac{f^{(\alpha)}(a)}{\alpha!} (x - a)^{\alpha}.$$

The proof is left to the reader.

Example. If $f(x) = \sin x$ then $f^{(n)}(x) = \sin x$ if $n = 4m$
$$= \cos x \text{ if } n = 4m + 1$$
$$= -\sin x \text{ if } n = 4m + 2$$
$$= -\cos x \text{ if } n = 4m + 3.$$

Therefore, $f^{(n)}(0) = 0$ if $n = 4m$
$$= 1 \text{ if } n = 4m + 1$$
$$= 0 \text{ if } n = 4m + 2$$
$$= -1 \text{ if } n = 4m + 3.$$

and

$$\sum_{\alpha=0}^{\infty} \frac{f^{(n)}(0)}{\alpha!} x^{\alpha} = \sum_{\alpha=0}^{\infty} \frac{(-1)^{\alpha} x^{2\alpha+1}}{(2\alpha + 1)!}.$$

Since $|f^{(n)}(x)| \leq 1$, it follows that

$$\sin x = \sum_{\alpha=0}^{\infty} \frac{(-1)^{\alpha} x^{2\alpha+1}}{(2\alpha + 1)!}.$$

EXERCISES

1. Find the power series representation for cos.
2. Find the power series representation for exp.
3. Find the interval of convergence of the series representation for sin, cos, and exp.

*9.3 An Everywhere-Continuous Nowhere-Differentiable Function

In the chapter on differentiation it was established that there exist functions that are continuous at a certain point but are not differentiable at that

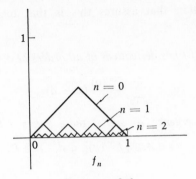

FIGURE 9.6

point. This is hardly surprising. However in the nineteenth century Weierstrass discovered that there exist functions that have this property at every point. This we will prove by a sequence of lemmas using an example from van der Waerden.

Definition 9.30. $\{x\} = \min\{[\![x]\!] + 1 - x, \ x - [\![x]\!]\}.$

As defined, $\{x\}$ is simply the distance from x to the nearest integer. The reader can prove the following lemmas.

Lemma 1. $(\forall x),\ 0 \le \{x\} \le \frac{1}{2}.$

Lemma 2. *If* $x - y \in Z$ *then* $\{x\} = \{y\}.$

The next step is to define a sequence of functions which we will prove to be continuous and uniformly convergent on the set of all real numbers.

Lemma 3. *If*

$$f_n(x) = \frac{\{4^n x\}}{4^n}, \quad n \ge 0,$$

then f_n *is continuous everywhere and* $0 \le f_n(x) < (1/4^n)$.

Again we leave the proof to the reader.

From Lemma 3 it follows, by the comparison test, that for each x

$$\sum_{\alpha=0}^{\infty} f_n(x)$$

converges. Indeed by the Weierstrass M-Test the convergence is uniform. Since the convergence is uniform and since f_n is continuous for each n, we have proved

Lemma 4. *If* $F(x) = \sum_{\alpha=0}^{\infty} f_n(x)$, *then* F *is continuous everywhere.*

We now wish to prove that F is not differentiable anywhere. To do this we will prove that for each a there exists a sequence $\{a_n\}_k$ such that

$$\lim_{n \to \infty} a_n = a$$

but

$$\lim_{n \to \infty} \frac{F(a_n) - F(a)}{a_n - a}$$

does not exist. From this it will follow by the Stoltz criterion that $F'(a)$ does not exist.

Lemma 5. $(\forall a)$ *if*

$$a_n = a + 4^{-n}, \quad \llbracket 4^n a \rrbracket \ even$$
$$= a - 4^{-n}, \quad \llbracket 4^n a \rrbracket \ odd$$

then $\lim_{n \to \infty} a_n = a.$

Proof. We have for each n that $0 \le |a_n - a| < 4^{-n}$. Since

$$\lim_{n \to \infty} \frac{1}{4^n} = 0,$$

it follows that

$$\lim_{n \to \infty} |a_n - a| = 0;$$

hence

$$\lim_{n \to \infty} (a_n - a) = 0;$$

hence

$$\lim_{n \to \infty} a_n = a.$$

Q.E.D.

Lemma 6. *If* $n < m$ *and if* $b = \llbracket 2^{2n+1} a \rrbracket$ *then*

$$2^{-2n-1} b \le a_m < 2^{-2n-1}(b + 1).$$

Proof. Since $b = \llbracket 2^{2n+1} a \rrbracket$, it follows that

$$b \le 2^{2n+1} a < b + 1,$$
$$2^{-2n-1} b \le a < 2^{-2n-1}(b + 1).$$

If $n < m$, then either

$$2^{-2n-1} b \le a < 2^{-2n-1} b + 4^{-m}$$

or

$$2^{-2n-1} b + 4^{-m} \le a < 2^{-2n-1}(b + 1) - 4^{-m}$$

or
$$2^{-2n-1}(b + 1) - 4^{-m} \le a < 2^{-2n-1}(b + 1).$$

If $2^{-2n-1}b \le a < 2^{-2n-1}b + 4^{-m}$, then
$$2^{2m-2n-1}b \le 4^m a < 2^{2m-2n-1} + 1.$$

Therefore, $[\![4^m a]\!] = 2^{2m-2n-1}b$; hence $[\![4^m a]\!]$ is even and
$$a_m = a + 4^{-m}.$$

Consequently,
$$2^{-2n-1}b \le a < a_m = a + 4^{-m} < 2^{-2n-1}b + 2 \cdot 4^{-m} \le 2^{-2n-1}(b + 1).$$

If $2^{-2n-1}b + 4^{-m} \le a < 2^{-2n-1}(b + 1) - 4^{-m}$, then since $a - 4^{-m} \le a_m \le a + 4^{-m}$ it follows that
$$2^{-2n-1}b \le a_m < 2^{-2n-1}(b + 1).$$

If $2^{-2n-1}(b + 1) - 4^{-m} \le a < 2^{-2n-1}(b + 1)$, then
$$2^{2m-2n-1}(b + 1) - 1 \le 4^m a < 2^{2m-2n-1}(b + 1).$$

Therefore, $[\![4^m a]\!] = 2^{2m-2n-1}(b + 1) - 1$; that is, $[\![4^m a]\!]$ is odd, and hence
$$a_m = a - 4^{-m}.$$

Thus
$$2^{-2n-1}b < 2^{-2n-1}(b + 1) - 2 \cdot 4^{-m} < a - 4^{-m} = a_m < a < 2^{-2n-1}(b + 1).$$
$$\text{Q.E.D.}$$

Lemma 7. *If $n < m$, then $|f_n(a_m) - f_n(a)| = |a_m - a|$.*

Proof. If $b = [\![2^{2n+1}a]\!]$, then
$$\frac{b}{2} \le 4^n a < \frac{b + 1}{2},$$

and from Lemma 6
$$\frac{b}{2} \le 4^n a_m < \frac{b + 1}{2}.$$

Therefore if b is even, then $b/2$ is an integer and both $4^n a_m$ and $4^n a$ lie between $b/2$ and $(b/2) + (1/2)$. Consequently,
$$\{4^n a\} = 4^n a - \frac{b}{2},$$
$$\{4^n a_m\} = 4^n a_m - \frac{b}{2}.$$

Hence
$$f_n(a) = a - \frac{b}{2 \cdot 4^n},$$
$$f_n(a_m) = a_m - \frac{b}{2 \cdot 4^n},$$

and
$$f_n(a_m) - f_n(a) = a_m - a.$$

If b is odd then $(b + 1)/2$ is an integer, both $4^n a_m$ and $4^n a$ lie between $[(b + 1)/2] - (1/2)$ and $(b + 1)/2$; hence

$$\{4^n a_m\} = \frac{b + 1}{2} - 4^n a_m$$

$$\{4^n a\} = \frac{b + 1}{2} - 4^n a.$$

Therefore,

$$f_n(\dot{a}_m) - f_n(a) = a - a_m.$$

Q.E.D.

Lemma 8.

$$\sum_{\alpha = 0}^{m-1} \frac{f_\alpha(a_m) - f_\alpha(a)}{a_m - a}$$

is even or odd according as m is even or odd.

The proof is immediate from Lemma 7 by induction.

Theorem 9.31. *There exists an everywhere-continuous nowhere-differentiable function.*

Proof. If

$$F(x) = \sum_{\alpha = 0}^{\infty} \frac{\{4^\alpha x\}}{4^\alpha},$$

then by Lemma 4 we have that F is continuous everywhere. Furthermore, for each a if

$$a_n = a + 4^{-n}, \quad [\![4^n a]\!] \text{ even},$$
$$= a - 4^{-n}, \quad [\![4^n a]\!] \text{ odd},$$

then by Lemma 5 we have that $\underset{n \to \infty}{\text{Lim }} a_n = a$. Since

$$|4^n a_m - 4^n a| = 4^{n-m}$$

it follows from Lemma 2 that if $n \geq m$,

$$\{4^n a_m\} = \{4^n a\}$$

and hence

$$f_n(a_m) = f_n(a).$$

Therefore, if $n \geq m$,

$$\sum_{\alpha = 0}^{n} f_\alpha(a_m) - \sum_{\alpha = 0}^{n} f_\alpha(a) = \sum_{\alpha = 0}^{m-1} [f_\alpha(a_m) - f_\alpha(a)].$$

Hence

$$F(a_m) - F(a) = \sum_{\alpha=0}^{m-1} [f_\alpha(a_m) - f_\alpha(a)]$$

and, by Lemma 8,

$$\left| \frac{F(a_{m+1}) - F(a)}{a_{m+1} - a} - \frac{F(a_m) - F(a)}{a_m - a} \right|$$

$$= \left| \sum_{\alpha=0}^{m} \frac{f_\alpha(a_{m+1}) - f_\alpha(a)}{a_{m+1} - a} - \sum_{\alpha=0}^{m-1} \frac{f_\alpha(a_m) - f_\alpha(a)}{a_m - a} \right| \geq 1.$$

Therefore, by the Cauchy criterion

$$\operatorname*{Lim}_{n \to \infty} \frac{F(a_n) - F(a)}{a_n - a}$$

does not exist. Since $\operatorname*{Lim}_{n \to \infty} a_n = a$, it then follows from the Stoltz criterion that

$$\operatorname*{Lim}_{x \to a} \frac{F(x) - F(a)}{x - a}$$

does not exist. That is, F is not differentiable at a.

Q.E.D.

Part II References

BARTLE, ROBERT G. *The Elements of Real Analysis*. New York: John Wiley and Sons, 1964.

BATES, G. E., and F. L. KIOKEMEISTER. *The Real Number System*. Boston: Allyn and Bacon, Inc., 1960.

GELBAUM, B. R., and J. M. H. OLMSTED. *Counterexamples in Analysis*. San Francisco: Holden Day, 1964.

HARDY, G. H. *A Course of Pure Mathematics*. Cambridge: Cambridge University Press, 1952.

LANDAU, E. *Differential and Integral Calculus*. New York: Chelsea Publishing Company, 1951.

LANDAU, E. *Foundations of Analysis*. New York: Chelsea Publishing Company, 1951.

OLMSTED, J. M. H. *Advanced Calculus*. New York: Appleton-Century-Crofts, 1961.

OLMSTED, J. M. H. *The Real Number System*. New York: Appleton-Century-Crofts, 1962.

OLMSTED, J. M. H. *Real Variables*. New York: Appleton-Century-Crofts, 1959.

SOMINSKII, I. S. *The Method of Mathematical Induction*. New York: Blaisdell Publishing Co., 1961.

TAYLOR, A. S. *Advanced Calculus*. New York: Ginn and Company, 1955.

List of Symbols

References are to pages on which the symbol is introduced.

Index